Earth's Changing Surface: Teacher's Edition

W9-CSW-592

Contents in Brief

Teacher's Edition

See Program Component List on page ii

Student Edition

Prentice Hall Science Explorer

Series Tables of Contents

Teacher's Edition

Earth's Changing Surface

PRENTICE HALL Science Explorer

PEARSON
Prentice Hall

Boston, Massachusetts
Upper Saddle River, New Jersey

Pearson Prentice Hall™ is a trademark of Pearson Education, Inc.
Pearson® is a registered trademark of Pearson plc.
Prentice Hall® is a registered trademark of Pearson Education, Inc.
Lab zone™ is a trademark of Pearson Education, Inc.

Planet Diary® is a registered trademark of Addison Wesley Longman, Inc.

Discovery Channel School® is a registered trademark of Discovery Communications, Inc., used under license.
The Discovery Channel logo is a trademark of Discovery Communications, Inc.

SciLinks® is a trademark of the National Science Teachers Association. The SciLinks® service includes copyrighted materials and is owned and provided by the National Science Teachers Association. All rights reserved.

Science News® is a registered trademark of Science Services, Inc.

ISBN 0-13-201168-9   1 2 3 4 5 6 7 8 9 10   10 09 08 07 06

Pacing Options

SCIENCE EXPLORER offers many aids to help you plan your instruction time, whether regular class periods or block scheduling. Section-by-section lesson plans for each chapter include suggested times for Student Edition activities. TeacherExpress™ and the Lab zone™ Easy Planner CD-ROM will help you manage your time electronically.

PRENTICE HALL
TeacherEXPRESS™
Plan • Teach • Assess

Lab zone™

Pacing Chart

	PERIODS	BLOCKS		PERIODS	BLOCKS
Careers: Fossils Reveal Dinosaur Diet	1	$^1/_2$			
Chapter 1 Mapping Earth's Surface			**Chapter 4 A Trip Through Geologic Time**		
Chapter 1 Project: *Getting on the Map*	Ongoing	Ongoing	Chapter 4 Project: *A Journey Back in Time*	Ongoing	Ongoing
1 Exploring Earth's Surface	1–2	$^1/_2$–1	**1** Fossils	2–3	1–1$^1/_2$
2 Models of Earth	2–3	1–1$^1/_2$	**2** The Relative Age of Rocks	1–2	$^1/_2$–1
3 Tech & Design: Maps and Computers	1–2	$^1/_2$–1	**3** Radioactive Dating	1–2	$^1/_2$–1
4 Topographic Maps	1–2	$^1/_2$–1	**4** The Geologic Time Scale	1–2	$^1/_2$–1
Chapter 1 Review and Assessment	1	$^1/_2$	**5** Early Earth	1	$^1/_2$
Chapter 2 Weathering and Soil Formation			**6** Eras of Earth's History	3–4	1$^1/_2$–2
Chapter 2 Project: *Soils for Seeds*	Ongoing	Ongoing	Chapter 4 Review and Assessment	1	$^1/_2$
1 Rocks and Weathering	2–3	1–1$^1/_2$	Interdisciplinary Exploration: The Gift of the Nile	2–3	1–2
2 How Soil Forms	2–3	1–1$^1/_2$			
3 Soil Conservation	1	$^1/_2$			
Chapter 2 Review and Assessment	1	$^1/_2$			
Chapter 3 Erosion and Deposition					
Chapter 3 Project: *Design and Build a Dam*	Ongoing	Ongoing			
1 Changing Earth's Surface	2–3	1–1$^1/_2$			
2 Water Erosion	4–5	2–2$^1/_2$			
3 Integrating Physics: The Force of Moving Water	1–2	$^1/_2$–1			
4 Glaciers	1–2	$^1/_2$–1			
5 Waves	1	$^1/_2$			
6 Wind	1	$^1/_2$			
Chapter 3 Review and Assessment	1	$^1/_2$			

Research-Based and Proven to Work

As the originator of the small book concept in middle school science, and as the nation's number one science publisher, Prentice Hall takes pride in the fact that we've always listened closely to teachers. In doing so, we've developed programs that effectively meet the needs of your classroom.

As we continue to listen, we realize that raising the achievement level of all students is the number one challenge facing teachers today. To assist you in meeting this latest challenge, Prentice Hall has combined the very best author team with solid research to create a program that meets your high standards and will ensure that no child is left behind.

With Prentice Hall, you can be confident that your students will not only be motivated, inspired, and excited to learn science, but that they will also achieve the success needed in today's environment of the No Child Left Behind (NCLB) legislation and testing reform.

On the following pages, you will read about the key elements found throughout *Science Explorer* that truly set this program apart and ensure success for you and your students.

> As we continue to listen, we realize that raising the achievement level of all students is the number one challenge facing teachers today.

A Science Program Backed by Research

In developing Prentice Hall *Science Explorer*, we used research studies as a central, guiding element. Research on *Science Explorer* indicated key elements of a textbook program that ensure students' success: support for reading and mathematics in science, consistent opportunities for inquiry, and an ongoing assessment strand. This research was conducted in phases and continues today.

1. Exploratory: Needs Assessment

Along with periodic surveys concerning state and national standards as well as curriculum issues and challenges, we conducted specific product development research, which included discussions with teachers and advisory panels, focus groups, and quantitative surveys. We explored the specific needs of teachers, students, and other educators regarding each book we developed in Prentice Hall *Science Explorer*.

2. Formative: Prototype Development and Field-Testing

During this phase of research, we worked to develop prototype materials. Then we tested the materials by field-testing with students and teachers and by performing qualitative and quantitative surveys. In our early prototype testing, we received feedback about our lesson structure. Results were channeled back into the program development for improvement.

3. Summative: Validation Research

Finally, we conducted and continue to conduct long-term research based on scientific, experimental designs under actual classroom conditions. This research identifies what works and what can be improved in the next revision of Prentice Hall *Science Explorer*. We also continue to monitor the program in the market. We talk to our users about what works, and then we begin the cycle over again. The next section contains highlights of this research.

A Science Program With Proven Results

In a year-long study in 2000–2001, students in six states using Prentice Hall *Science Explorer* outscored students using other science programs on a nationally normed standardized test.

The study investigated the effects of science textbook programs at the eighth-grade level. Twelve eighth-grade science classes with a total of 223 students participated in the study. The selected classes were of similar student ability levels.

Each class was tested at the beginning of the school year using the TerraNova CTBS Basic Battery Plus, and then retested at the end of the school year. The final results, shown in the graph, show a significant improvement in test scores from the pre-test to the post-test evaluation.

• All tests were scored by CTB/McGraw-Hill, the publisher of the TerraNova exam. Statistical analyses and conclusions were performed by an independent firm, Pulse Analytics, Inc.

In Japan, Lesson Study Research has been employed for a number of years as a tool for teachers to improve their curriculum. In April 2003, Prentice Hall adapted this methodology to focus on a lesson from this edition. Our goal was to test the effectiveness of lesson pedagogy and improve it while in the program development stage. In all three classrooms tested, student learning increased an average of 10 points from the pre- to the post-assessment.

• Detailed results of these studies can be obtained at **www.PHSchool.com/research.**

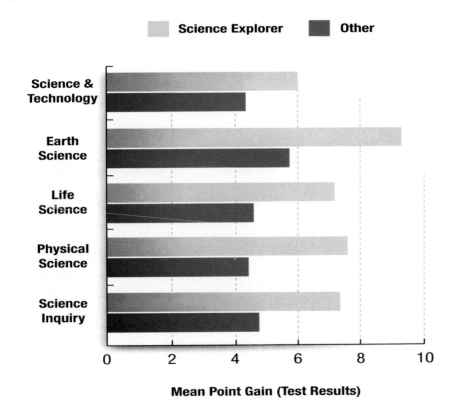

Foundational Research:
Inquiry in the Science Classroom

"How do I know if my students are inquiring?" "If students are busy doing lots of hands-on activities, are they using inquiry?" "What is inquiry, anyway?" If you're confused, you are not alone. Inquiry is the heart and soul of science education, with most of us in continuous pursuit of achieving it with our students!

Defining Science Inquiry

What is it? Simply put, inquiry is the intellectual side of science. It is thinking like a scientist—being inquisitive, asking why, and searching for answers. The National Science Education Content Standards define inquiry as the process in which students begin with a question, design an investigation, gather evidence, formulate an answer to the original question, and communicate the investigative process and results. Since it is often difficult to accomplish all this in one class period, the standards also acknowledge that at times students need to practice only one or two inquiry components.

Understanding Inquiry

The National Research Council in Inquiry and the National Science Education Standards (2000) identified several "essential features" of classroom inquiry. We have modified these essential features into questions to guide you in your quest for enhanced and more thoughtful student inquiry.

1. *Who asks the question?* In most curricula, these focusing questions are an element given in the materials. As a teacher you can look for labs that, at least on a periodic basis, allow students to pursue their own questions.

2. *Who designs the procedures?* To gain experience with the logic underlying experimentation, students need continuous practice with designing procedures. Some labs in which the primary target is content acquisition designate procedures. But others should ask students to do so.

3. *Who decides what data to collect?* Students need practice in determining the data to collect.

4. *Who formulates explanations based upon the data?* Students should be challenged to think—to analyze and draw conclusions based on their data, not just copy answers from the text materials.

5. *Who communicates and justifies the results?* Activities should push students not only to communicate but also to justify their answers. Activities also should be thoughtfully designed and interesting so that students want to share their results and argue about conclusions.

Making Time for Inquiry

One last question—Must each and every activity have students do all of this? The answer is an obvious and emphatic "No". You will find a great variety of activities in *Science Explorer*. Some activities focus on content acquisition, and thus they specify the question and most of the procedures. But many others stress in-depth inquiry from start to finish. Because inquiry is an intellectual pursuit, it cannot merely be characterized by keeping students busy and active. Too many students have a knack for being physically but not intellectually engaged in science. It is our job to help them engage intellectually.

Michael J. Padilla, Ph.D.
Program Author of *Science Explorer*
Professor of Science Education
University of Georgia
Athens, Georgia

"Because inquiry is an intellectual pursuit, it cannot merely be characterized by keeping students busy and active."

Evaluator's Checklist

Does your science program promote inquiry by—

✔ Enabling students to pursue their own questions

✔ Allowing students to design their own procedures

✔ Letting students determine what data are best to collect

✔ Challenging students to think critically

✔ Pushing students to justify their answers

Inquiry in *Science Explorer*

Science Explorer offers the most opportunities to get students to think like a scientist. By providing inquiry opportunities throughout the program, *Science Explorer* enables students to enhance their understanding by participating in the discovery.

Student Edition Inquiry

Six lab and activity options are included in every chapter, structured from directed to open-ended—providing you the flexibility to address all types of learners and accommodate your class time and equipment requirements. As Michael Padilla notes, some activities focus on content acquisition, and thus the question and most of the procedures are specified. But many others stress in-depth inquiry from start to finish. The graph below shows how, in general, inquiry levels are addressed in the Student Edition.

Science Explorer encourages students to develop inquiry skills across the spectrum from teacher-guided to open-ended. Even more opportunities for real-life applications of inquiry are included in Science & Society, Technology & Society, Careers in Science, and Interdisciplinary Exploration features.

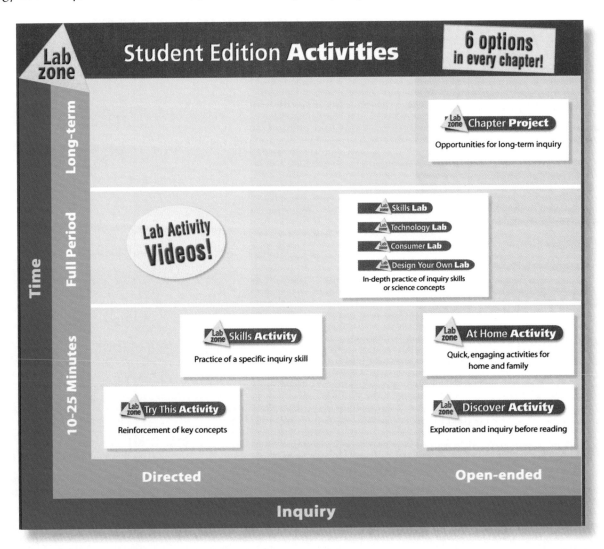

Inquiry Skills Chart

SCIENCE EXPLORER provides comprehensive teaching, practice, and assessment of science skills, with an emphasis on the process skills necessary for inquiry. This chart lists the skills covered in the program and cites the page numbers where each skill is covered.

Basic Process SKILLS

	Student Text: Projects and Labs	Student Text: Activities	Student Text: Caption and Review Questions	Teacher's Edition: Extensions
Observing	20, 55, 82, 83, 122	11, 56, 69, 101, 113	77, 93	11, 16, 28, 50, 56, 101, 113
Inferring	20, 55, 122	44, 86, 91, 110, 117	30, 34, 39, 45, 50, 69, 88, 100, 106, 116, 121, 126, 145, 150	86, 91, 110, 115, 117
Predicting	31, 70, 71	21, 43, 72, 87, 89, 123, 125	8, 34, 42, 43, 45, 54, 59, 62, 67, 69, 73, 74, 81, 87, 90, 98, 133, 136	21, 43, 72, 123
Classifying	20	9	45, 62, 79, 94, 111, 112	9, 98
Making Models	5, 31, 65, 82, 83, 109, 146, 147	26, 67, 103, 119, 127, 130	81	14, 26, 45, 67, 68, 80, 94, 112, 113, 119, 120, 124, 127, 130
Communicating	20, 47, 55, 71, 83, 109, 122, 147	116	10, 61, 100, 145	7, 10, 25, 27, 30, 43, 49, 53, 54, 57, 90, 97, 100, 140
Measuring	5, 70, 146, 147			13, 150
Calculating	46, 47, 146, 147	12, 99, 125, 132	10, 30, 34, 124	99, 132
Creating Data Tables				16, 128, 139, 141
Graphing	71		106	129

Advanced Process SKILLS

	Student Text: Projects and Labs	Student Text: Activities	Student Text: Caption and Review Questions	Teacher's Edition: Extensions
Posing Questions		96, 134	62	88, 96, 125, 134, 142
Developing Hypotheses	47, 55, 70, 71	66, 87, 89	62, 106, 145	48, 58, 66, 70
Designing Experiments	37, 47, 55, 65, 71, 83		62	47, 55, 71, 87

Advanced Process SKILLS (continued)

	Student Text: Projects and Labs	Student Text: Activities	Student Text: Caption and Review Questions	Teacher's Edition: Extensions
Controlling Variables	37, 83			
Forming Operational Definitions		6, 48		6, 48
Interpreting Data	47, 70, 71, 122	29, 89		78, 89, 144
Drawing Conclusions	46, 47, 71, 83, 122	38, 44, 51, 74		18, 51, 52, 69, 74, 114

Critical Thinking SKILLS

Comparing and Contrasting		81	10, 18, 19, 27, 30, 45, 62, 95, 102, 106, 116, 121, 132, 142	6, 9, 17, 23, 41, 79, 81, 112, 119, 136
Applying Concepts	31		34, 57, 106, 118, 121, 126, 150	
Interpreting Diagrams, Graphs, Photographs, and Maps	20, 31, 46	23, 29, 44, 89, 137, 144	7, 10, 12, 13, 17, 19, 29, 34, 49, 51, 54, 73, 90, 121, 128, 129, 150	7, 11, 13, 15, 16, 18, 23, 26, 27, 29, 30, 44
Relating Cause and Effect	122	137	45, 52, 59, 69, 81, 90, 95, 97, 100, 106, 116, 133, 145, 150	18, 38, 89, 120
Making Generalizations			116	69
Making Judgments			68, 106, 126, 150	17, 34
Problem Solving			30, 34, 59, 103, 106, 150	25, 85

Informational Organizational SKILLS

Concept Maps			33, 149	32, 60, 97, 104, 148
Compare/Contrast Tables				6, 9, 45, 81, 95, 111
Venn Diagrams				
Flowcharts			61, 105	51, 77, 101, 105, 111
Cycle Diagrams				

The *Science Explorer* program provides additional teaching, reinforcement, and assessment of skills in the *Inquiry Skills Activities Book* and the *Integrated Science Laboratory Manual*.

A National Look at Science Education

Project 2061 was established by the American Association for the Advancement of Science (AAAS) as a long-term project to improve science education nationwide. A primary goal of Project 2061 is to define a "common core of learning"—the knowledge and skills we want all students to achieve. Project 2061 published *Science for All Americans* in 1989 and followed this with Benchmarks for Science Literacy in 1993. Benchmarks recommends what students should know and be able to do by the end of grades 2, 5, 8, and 12. Project 2061 clearly states that *Benchmarks* is not a curriculum but a tool for designing successful curricula.

The National Research Council (NRC) used *Science for All Americans* and *Benchmarks* to develop the National Science Education Standards (NSES), which were published in 1996. The NSES are organized into six categories (Content, Teaching, Assessment, Professional Development, Program, and System) to help schools establish the conditions necessary to achieve scientific literacy for all students.

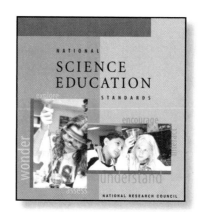

Michael Padilla, the program author of *Science Explorer,* guided one of six teams of teachers whose work led to the publication of *Benchmarks.* He also was a contributing writer of the National Science Education Standards. Under his guidance, *Science Explorer* has implemented these standards through its inquiry approach, a focus on student learning of important concepts and skills, and teacher support aligned with the NSES teaching standards.

Neither *Benchmarks* nor the NSES requires a single, uniform national curriculum, and in fact there is a great diversity nationwide in science curricula. The correlations that follow are designed to help you use the *Science Explorer* program to meet your particular curriculum needs.

Meeting the National Science Education Standards

MAPPING EARTH'S SURFACE

Science as Inquiry (Content Standard A)
● **Use appropriate tools and techniques to gather, analyze, and interpret data** Students create a scale map of a small area. *(Chapter Project)*
● **Develop descriptions, explanations, predictions, and models using evidence** Students study maps to infer which state borders were determined by lines of latitude and longitude. Students make a topographic map of a model landform. *(Skills Lab, Skills Lab)*

Science and Technology (Content Standard E)
● **Understanding about science and technology** Maps and globes are drawn to scale and use symbols to represent topography and other features on Earth's surface. Satellites and computers have revolutionized mapmaking. Topographic maps provide highly accurate information on the elevation, relief, and slope of the group surface. *(Models of Earth, Maps and Computers, Topographic Maps, Skills Lab)*

Science in Personal and Social Perspectives (Content Standard F)
● **Science and Technology in Society** The GPS has influenced the way engineers, surveyors, and ordinary people pinpoint their location. *(Technology and Society)*

History and the Nature of Science (Content Standard G)
● **History of Science** Centuries ago, people invented instruments and techniques to show Earth's surface accurately. *(Models of Earth, Science and History)*

WEATHERING AND SOIL FORMATION

Science as Inquiry (Content Standard A)
● **Design and conduct a scientific investigation** Students investigate how soil composition affects plant growth. Students compare the rates of weathering that take place under different conditions. *(Chapter Project, Skills Lab)*
● **Develop descriptions, explanations, predictions, and models using evidence** Students observe a sample of soil to determine its characteristics. *(Consumer Lab)*

A National Look at Science Education (continued)

Life Science (Content Standard C)
● **Populations and ecosystems** Some soil organisms mix the soil and make spaces in it for air and water; others make humus. *(How Soil Forms)*

Earth and Space Science (Content Standard D)
● **Structure of the Earth system** Weathering is the process that breaks down rock and other materials at Earth's surface. Soil forms as rock is broken down by weathering and mixes with other materials. Soil is one of Earth's most valuable resources. *(Rocks and Weathering, How Soil Forms, Soil Conservation, Chapter Project, Skills Lab, Consumer Lab)*

Science in Personal and Social Perspectives (Content Standard F)
● **Science and technology in society** Students examine the issue of preserving stone monuments. *(Science and Society)*

EROSION AND DEPOSITION

Science as Inquiry (Content Standard A)
● **Develop descriptions, explanations, predictions, and models using evidence** Students make models to show how erosion and deposition can change a landscape. Students investigate the relationship between the height and width of a hill. Students use a stream table to model how rivers erode the land. *(Chapter Project, Skills Lab)*

Physical Science (Content Standard B)
● **Transfer of energy** As gravity pulls water down a slope, the water's potential energy changes to kinetic energy. The energy in waves comes from wind that blows across the water's surface. *(The Force of Moving Water, Waves)*

Earth and Space Science (Content Standard D)
● **Structure of the Earth system** Weathering, erosion, and deposition act together in a cycle that wears down and builds up Earth's surface. The forces that cause erosion and deposition are gravity, running water, glaciers, waves, and wind. *(Chapter Project, Skills Lab)*

Science in Personal and Social Perspectives (Content Standard F)
● **Risks and benefits** Students examine the issue of protecting homes in flood plains. *(Science and Society)*

A TRIP THROUGH GEOLOGIC TIME

Science as Inquiry (Content Standard A)
● **Develop descriptions, explanations, predictions, and models using evidence** Students interpret relative ages of rock layers and make a model of geologic time. *(Skills Lab)*
● **Communicate scientific procedures and explanations** Students make travel brochures and a timeline and use them to present a geologic time period. *(Chapter Project)*

Physical Science (Content Standard B)
● **Properties and changes of properties in matter** During radioactive decay, the atoms of one element break down to form atoms of another element. *(Radioactive Dating)*

Life Science (Content Standard C)
● **Diversity and adaptations of organisms** The fossil record provides evidence that many different organisms have existed at different times and that organisms have changed over time. *(Fossils, Early Earth, Skills Lab)*

Earth and Space Science (Content Standard F)
● **Earth's history** Fossils help scientists infer how Earth's surface has changed. Rock layers provide a record of Earth's geologic history. *(Chapter Project, Skills Lab)*

Note: To see how the benchmarks are supported by *SCIENCE EXPLORER,* go to **PHSchool.com.**

Reading

Reading Comprehension in the Science Classroom

Q&A

Q: Why are science texts often difficult for students to read and comprehend?

A: In general, science texts make complex literacy and knowledge demands on learners. They have a more technical vocabulary and a more demanding syntax, and place a greater emphasis on inferential reasoning.

Q: What does research say about facilitating comprehension?

A: Studies comparing novices and experts show that the conceptual organization of experts' knowledge is very different from that of novices. For example, experts emphasize core concepts when organizing knowledge, while novices focus on superficial details. To facilitate comprehension, effective teaching strategies should support and scaffold students as they build an understanding of the key concepts and concept relationships within a text unit.

Q: What strategies can teachers use to facilitate comprehension?

A: Three complementary strategies are very important in facilitating student comprehension of science texts. First, guide student interaction with the text using the built-in strategies. Second, organize the curriculum in terms of core concepts (e.g., the **Key Concepts** in each section). Third, develop visual representations of the relationships among the key concepts and vocabulary that can be referred to during instruction.

Nancy Romance, Ph.D.
Professor of Science Education
Florida Atlantic University
Fort Lauderdale, Florida

"Effective teaching strategies should support and scaffold students as they build an understanding of the key concepts and concept relationships within a text unit."

Reading Support in *Science Explorer*

The latest research emphasizes the importance of activating learners' prior knowledge and teaching them to distinguish core concepts from less important information. These skills are now more important than ever, because success in science requires students to read, understand, and connect complex terms and concepts.

Before students read—
Reading Preview introduces students to the key concepts and key terms they'll find in each section. The **Target Reading Skill** is identified and applied with a graphic organizer.

During the section—
Boldface Sentences identify each key concept and encourage students to focus on the big ideas of science.

Reading Checkpoints reinforce students' understanding by slowing them down to review after every concept is discussed.

Caption Questions draw students into the art and photos, helping them connect the content to the images.

After students read—
Section Assessment revisits the **Target Reading Skill** and encourages students to use the graphic organizer.

Each review question is scaffolded and models the way students think, by first easing them into a review and then challenging them with increasingly more difficult questions.

Evaluator's Checklist

Does your science program promote reading comprehension with—

✔ Text structured in an outline format and key concepts highlighted in boldface type

✔ Real-world applications to activate prior knowledge

✔ Key concepts, critical vocabulary, and a reading skill for every section

✔ Sample graphic organizers for each section

✔ Relevant photos and carefully constructed graphics with questions

✔ Reading checkpoints that appear in each section

✔ Scaffolded questions in section assessments

Math in the Science Classroom

Why should students concern themselves with mathematics in your science class?

Good science requires good data from which to draw conclusions. Technology enhances the ability to measure in a variety of ways. Often the scientist must measure large amounts of data, and thus an aim of analysis is to reduce the data to a summary that makes sense and is consistent with established norms of communication—i.e., mathematics.

Calculating measures of central tendency (e.g., mean, median, or mode), variability (e.g., range), and shape (graphic representations) can effectively reduce 500 data points to 3 without losing the essential characteristics of the data. Scientists understand that a trade-off exists between precision and richness as data are folded into categories, and so margins of error can be quantified in mathematical terms and factored into all scientific findings.

Mathematics is the language used by scientists to model change in the world. Understanding change is a vital part of the inquiry process. Mathematics serves as a common language to communicate across the sciences. Fields of scientific research that originated as separate disciplines are now integrated, such as happened with bioengineering. What do the sciences have in common? Each uses the language of mathematics to communicate about data and the process of data analysis. Recognizing this need, *Science Explorer* integrates mathematics practice throughout the program and gives students ample opportunity to hone their math skills.

Clearly, mathematics plays an important role in your science classroom!

William Tate, Ph.D.
Professor of Education and
Applied Statistics and
Computation
Washington University
St. Louis, Missouri

"Mathematics is the language used by scientists to model change in the world."

Integrated Math Support

In the Student Edition

The math instruction is based on principles derived from Prentice Hall's research-based mathematics program.

Sample Problems, Math Practice, Analyzing Data, and a Math Skills Handbook all help to provide practice at point of use, encouraging students to Read and Understand, Plan and Solve, and then Look Back and Check.

Color-coded variables aid student navigation and help reinforce their comprehension.

In the Teacher's Edition

Math teaching notes enable the science teacher to support math instruction and math objectives on high-stakes tests.

In the Guided Reading and Study Workbook

These unique worksheets help students master reading and enhance their study and math skills. Students can create a record of their work for study and review.

Evaluator's Checklist

Does your science program promote math skills by—

✔ Giving students opportunities to collect data

✔ Providing students opportunities to analyze data

✔ Enabling students to practice math skills

✔ Helping students solve equations by using color-coded variables

✔ Using sample problems to apply science concepts

Technology and Design

Technology and Design in the Science Classroom

Much of the world we live in is designed and made by humans. The buildings in which we live, the cars we drive, the medicines we take, and often the food we eat are products of technology. The knowledge and skills needed to understand the processes used to create these products should be a component of every student's basic literacy.

Some schools offer hands-on instruction on how technology development works through industrial arts curricula. Even then, there is a disconnect among science (understanding how nature works), mathematics (understanding data-driven models), and technology (understanding the human-made world). The link among these fields of study is the engineering design process—that process by which one identifies a human need and uses science knowledge and human ingenuity to create a technology to satisfy the need. Engineering gives students the problem-solving and design skills they will need to succeed in our sophisticated, three-dimensional, technological world.

As a complement to "science as inquiry," the National Science Education Standards (NRC, 1996) call for students at all age levels to develop the abilities related to "technology as design," including the ability to identify and frame a problem and then to design, implement, and evaluate a solution. At the 5–8 grade level, the standards call for students to be engaged in complex problem-solving and to learn more about how science and technology complement each other. It's also important for students to understand that there are often constraints involved in design as well as trade-offs and unintended consequences of technological solutions to problems.

As the *Standards for Technological Literacy* (ITEA, 2000) state, "Science and technology are like conjoined twins. While they have separate identities they must remain inextricably connected." Both sets of standards emphasize how progress in science leads to new developments in technology, while technological innovation in turn drives advances in science.

Ioannis Miaoulis, Ph.D.
President
Museum of Science
Boston, Massachusetts

"Engineering gives students the problem-solving and design skills they will need to succeed in our sophisticated, three-dimensional, technological world."

Evaluator's Checklist

Does your science program promote technology and design by—

✔ Incorporating technology and design concepts and skills into the science curriculum

✔ Giving students opportunities to identify and solve technological design problems

✔ Providing students opportunities to analyze the impact of technology on society

✔ Enabling students to practice technology and design skills

Technology and Design

Technology and Design in *Science Explorer*

How often do you hear your students ask: "Why do I need to learn this?" Connecting them to the world of technology and design in their everyday life is one way to help answer this question. It is also why so many state science curricula are now emphasizing technology and design concepts and skills.

Science Explorer makes a special effort to include a technology and design strand that encourages students to not only identify a need but to take what they learned in science and apply it to design a possible solution, build a prototype, test and evaluate the design, and/or troubleshoot the design. This strand also provides definitions of technology and engineering and discusses the similarities and differences between these endeavors and science. Students will learn to analyze the risks and benefits of a new technology and to consider the tradeoffs, such as safety, costs, efficiency, and appearance.

In the Student Edition

Integrated Technology & Design Sections

Sections throughout *Science Explorer* specifically integrate technology and design with the content of the text. For example, students not only learn how seismographs work but also learn what role seismographs play in society and how people use the data that are gathered.

Technology Labs

These labs help students gain experience in designing and building a device or product that meets a particular need or solves a problem. Students follow a design process of Research and Investigate, Design and Build, and Evaluate and Redesign.

Chapter Projects

Chapter Projects work hand-in-hand with the chapter content. Students design, build, and test based on real-world situations. They have the opportunity to apply the knowledge and skills learned to building a product.

Special Features

This technology and design strand is also reflected in Technology & Society and Science & Society features as well as Scuence & History timelines and Technology & Design in History timelines. These highly visual features introduce a technology and its impact on society. For example, students learn how a hybrid car differs from a traditional car.

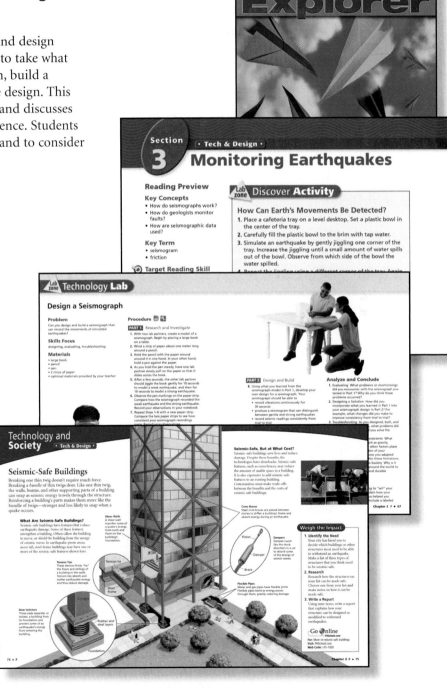

Assessment in the Science Curriculum

No Child Left Behind clearly challenges school districts across the nation to raise expectations for all students with testing of student achievement in science beginning in 2007–2008.

A primary goal of NCLB is to provide classroom teachers with better data from scientifically valid assessments in order to inform instructional planning and to identify students who are at risk and require intervention. It has been a common practice to teach a science lesson, administer a test, grade it, and move on. This practice is a thing of the past. With the spotlight now on improving student performance, it is essential to use assessment results as a way to identify student strengths and challenges. Providing student feedback and obtaining student input is a valuable, essential part of the assessment process.

Assessment is a never-ending cycle, as is shown in the following diagram. Although you may begin at any point in the assessment cycle, the basic process is the same.

An important assessment strategy is to ensure that students have ample opportunities to check their understanding of skills and concepts before moving on to the next topic. Checking for understanding also includes asking appropriate, probing questions with each example presented. This enables students and teachers to know whether the skills or concepts being introduced are actually understood.

Eileen Depka
Supervisor of Standards
and Assessment
Waukesha, Wisconsin

"Meeting the NCLB challenge will necessitate an integrated approach to assessment with a variety of assessment tools."

Use a variety of assessment tools to gain information and strengthen student understanding.

Implement the plan with a focus on gathering and using assessment information throughout.

Analyze assessment results to create a picture of student strengths and challenges.

IMPLEMENT **ASSESS** **ANALYZE** **STRATEGIZE** **TARGET**

Identify strategies to achieve the target, create a plan for implementation, and choose assessments tools.

Choose a target to create a focused path on which to proceed.

Evaluator's Checklist

Does your science program include assessments that—

✔ Are embedded before, during, and after lesson instruction
✔ Align to standards and to the instructional program
✔ Assess both skill acquisition and understanding
✔ Include meaningful rubrics to guide students
✔ Mirror the various formats of standardized tests

Assessment in *Science Explorer*

Science Explorer's remarkable range of strategies for checking progress will help teachers find the right opportunity for reaching all their students.

The assessment strategies in *Science Explorer* will help both students and teachers alike ensure student success in content mastery as well as high-stakes test performance. A wealth of opportunities built into the Student Edition helps students monitor their own progress. Teachers are supported with ongoing assessment opportunities in the Teacher's Edition and an easy-to-use, editable test generator linked to content objectives. These integrated, ongoing assessment tools assure success.

Especially to support state and national testing objectives, Prentice Hall has developed test preparation materials that model the NCLB approach.

- **Diagnostic Assessment** tools provide in-depth analysis of strengths and weaknesses, areas of difficulty, and probable underlying causes that can help teachers make instructional decisions and plan intervention strategies.

- **Progress Monitoring** tools aligned with content objectives and state tests provide ongoing, longitudinal records of student achievement detailing individual student progress toward meeting end-of-year and end-of-schooling grade level, district, or state standards.

- **Outcomes** tools that mimic state and national tests show whether individual students have met the expected standards and can help a school system judge whether it has made adequate progress in improving its performance year by year.

Caption Questions enhance critical thinking skills.

Reading Checkpoints reinforce students' understanding.

Scaffolded Section Assessment Questions model the way students think.

Comprehensive Chapter Reviews and Assessments provide opportunities for students to check their own understanding and practice valuable high-stakes test-taking skills.

ExamView® **Computer Test Bank CD-ROM** provides teachers access to thousands of modifiable test questions in English and Spanish.

Test Preparation Blackline Masters and Student Workbook include diagnostic and prescription tools, progress-monitoring aids, and practice tests that help teachers focus on improving test scores.

Section 3 Assessment

Target Reading Skill Sequencing Refer to your flowchart about seismographs as you answer Question 1.

Reviewing Key Concepts

1. a. **Defining** What is a seismogram?
   b. **Explaining** How can geologists tell apart the different types of seismic waves on a seismogram?
   c. **Comparing and Contrasting** Two identical seismographs are located 1,000 km and 1,200 km from an earthquake's epicenter. How would the two seismograms for the earthquake compare?

2. a. **Reviewing** What changes are measured by the instruments used to monitor faults?
   b. **Describing** How are satellites used to measure movements along a fault?
   c. **Inferring** A satellite that monitors a fault detects an increasing tilt in the land surface along the fault. What could this change in the land surface indicate?

3. a. **Listing** What are three ways in which geologists use seismographic data?
   b. **Explaining** How do geologists use seismographic data to make maps of faults?
   c. **Making Generalizations** Why is it difficult to predict earthquakes?

Writing in Science

Dialogue Geologists in Alaska have just detected an earthquake and located the earthquake's epicenter. Write a dialogue in which the geologists notify a disaster response team that will help people in the earthquake area.

Chapter 2 F ◆ 65

Standardized Test Prep

Test-Taking Tip
When answering questions about diagrams, read all parts of the diagram carefully, including title, captions, and labels. Make sure that you understand the meaning of arrows and other symbols. Determine exactly what the question asks. Then eliminate those answer choices that are not supported by the diagram.

Practice answering this question.
The diagram shows how stress affects a mass of rock in a process called
   A compression.
   B tension.
   C squeezing.
   D shearing.
The correct answer is **D** because the arrows show rock being pulled in opposite directions.

Choose the letter that best answers the question or completes the statement.

1. In a strike-slip fault, rock masses along the fault move
   A in the same direction.
   B down only.
   C together.
   D sideways past each other.

2. Stress will build until an earthquake occurs if friction along a fault is
   F decreasing.   G high.
   H low.   J changed to heat.

Use the information below and your knowledge of science to answer Questions 3 and 4.

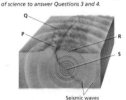

Seismic waves

3. When an earthquake occurs, seismic waves travel
   A from P in all directions.
   B from R to S.
   C from S in all directions.
   D from Q to P.

4. At point R, seismic waves from an earthquake would be
   F weaker than at P.
   G likely to cause little damage.
   H weaker than at Q.
   J likely to cause the most damage.

5. To estimate the total energy released by an earthquake, a geologist should use the
   A Mercalli scale.   B Richter scale.
   C epicenter scale.   D moment magnitude scale.

Constructed Response

6. A geologist discovers a large fault beneath a major city. Why would this information be helpful in determining earthquake risk in the area? What three safety steps should the geologist recommend?

Chapter 2 F ◆ 79

Master Materials List

SCIENCE EXPLORER offers an abundance of activity options in the Student Edition so that you can pick and choose those that suit your needs. Prentice Hall has worked with Neo/SCI Corporation to develop Consumable Kits and Nonconsumable Kits that precisely match the needs of the SCIENCE EXPLORER labs. Use this Master Materials List or the Materials Ordering CD-ROM to help order your supplies. For more information on materials kits for this program, contact your local Prentice Hall sales representative or Neo/SCI Corporation at 1-800-526-6689 or **www.neosci.com**.

Consumable Materials

Description	Textbook Section(s)	Quantity per class	Description	Textbook Section(s)	Quantity per class
Alka Seltzer, tablet	2-1 (DIS)	10	Pebbles, bag, 2.75 lb.	3-1 (SA), 3-3 (DIS)	1
Cardboard, piece, 32 × 32 cm	1-4 (DIS)	40	*Pen, felt-tip	2-1 (DIS)	5
Cloth, muslin, 12 × 36"	2-1 (Lab)	1	*Pencil	2-1 (Lab), 2-3 (DIS), 3-1 (Lab)	15
Cornmeal, bag, 454 g	3-6 (DIS)	1	*Pencils, colored, pkg/4	1-2 (Lab), 1-3 (DIS)	1
Cup, plastic foam, with plastic lid, 6 oz.	3-2 (Lab)	10	*Pencil, marking	1-4 (Lab)	5
Detergent, liquid, 18 oz.	3-2 (Lab)	1	Petri dish, plastic, pkg/20	2-2 (Lab), 3-2 (TT)	3
Diatomaceous earth, bag, 1 lb.	3-2 (Lab)	1	*Plastic, clear, hard sheet	1-4 (Lab)	5
Dropper, plastic, pkg/10	2-2 (Lab), 3-2 (TT)	1	*Sand, beach, sample	3-5 (DIS)	10
Food coloring, any color	1-4 (Lab)	1	Sand, coarse, 5 lb.	3-3 (DIS)	1
Food coloring, blue, 30 mL	3-2 (Lab)	1	Sand, white, fine, 3 lb.	3-1 (Lab), 3-1 (SA), 3-3 (DIS), 3-4 (DIS)	1
Iron filings, 8 oz.	4-5 (DIS)	1	Sandpaper, piece, 9" × 11"	3-1 (DIS)	5
Knife, plastic	2-1 (DIS), 4-2 (DIS), 4-3 (DIS)	10	*Sandwich	4-2 (TT)	5
Limestone, chips, 100 g	2-1 (Lab)	1	Seeds, bean, 1.5 oz.	2-1 (CP)	1
Measuring cup, plastic	3-2 (TT)	5	Skewer, wooden	3-1 (Lab)	5
Modeling clay, any color, 1 lb.	1-4 (Lab), 4-3 (DIS)	1	Soap, bar, small	3-2 (DIS), 3-4 (DIS)	15
Modeling clay, blue, 1 lb.	4-2 (DIS)	1	Soil, potting, bag, 8 qt.	2-2 (Lab)	1
Modeling clay, green, 1 lb.	4-2 (DIS)	1	Spoon, plastic	2-2 (Lab), 3-1 (Lab), 3-5 (DIS)	5
Modeling clay, red, 1 lb.	4-2 (DIS)	1	Steel wool, piece	2-1 (TT)	10
Modeling clay, white, 1 lb.	2-3 (DIS), 3-3 (DIS), 4-1 (TT), 4-2 (DIS)	1	Stick, craft	2-3 (DIS)	50
Modeling clay, yellow, 1 lb.	4-2 (DIS)	1	Stirrer, plastic	3-2 (Lab)	125
*Newspaper	3-2 (TT)	1	Straw, drinking	3-6 (DIS), 4-5 (DIS)	10
*Noodle, uncooked, round, hollow	4-2 (TT)	5	String, ball	2-2 (TT)	1
*Orange	1-2 (DIS)	5	Sugar, cube, bag	4-1 (TT)	1
Pan, aluminum, 9"	2-3 (DIS), 3-6 (DIS)	10	Tape, masking, roll	2-1 (Lab), 3-1 (Lab)	1
Paper clip, pkg/100	1-2 (Lab), 2-3 (DIS)	1	Toothpick, pkg/250	2-2 (DIS), 2-2 (Lab)	1
*Paper towel, roll	2-1 (Lab), 3-4 (DIS)	1	Tube, cardboard, 1" × 4"	3-1 (Lab)	5
*Paper, graph, sheet	2-2 (Lab)	5	Vinegar, 300 mL	2-1 (Lab)	3
*Paper, tracing, sheet	1-2 (Lab)	5	Wire, copper, 20 gauge, 4 oz.	3-2 (Lab)	1
*Paper, white, ream	1-1 (DIS), 1-4 (Lab), 3-1 (Lab), 4-4 (DIS), 4-5 (DIS), 4-6 (Lab)	6	*Worksheet with 2,000 asterisks	4-6 (Lab)	5

KEY: CP: Chapter Project; **DIS:** Discover; **SA:** Skills Activity; **TT:** Try This; **Lab:** Skills, Consumer, Design Your Own, & Technology and Design
* items are school supplied.

Quantities based on five groups of six students per class.

Master Materials List

Nonconsumable Materials

Description	Textbook Section(s)	Quantity per class	Description	Textbook Section(s)	Quantity per class
*Balance	2-1 (Lab)	5	Hand lens	2-2 (DIS), 3-2 (TT), 3-5 (DIS), 4-1 (DIS)	5
Beaker, plastic, 250 mL	2-1 (DIS), 3-3 (DIS)	10	Magnet, small	4-5 (DIS)	5
Board, wood, 1" × 4" × 8"	3-1 (DIS)	5	*Map, United States	1-2 (Lab)	5
*Bottle, plastic, with screw cap, 2L	2-3 (DIS), 3-3 (DIS)	5	Marble, 5/8"	3-1 (DIS)	5
Bottle, spray, with trigger, 16 oz.	3-2 (Lab)	5	Meter stick	3-2 (TT)	5
Bowl, plastic, 20 oz.	4-1 (TT)	5	*Pan, deep-sided	1-4 (Lab)	5
Block, wooden, 1" × 1" × 1"	3-1 (DIS), 3-2 (TT)	15	*Rock sample	4-1 (DIS)	5
Block, wooden, about 2.5 cm thick	3-2 (Lab)	10	Rod, stirring	2-1 (DIS)	5
*Bucket, 3 L	3-2 (Lab)	1	Ruler, 15 cm	1-4 (Lab), 3-1 (Lab), 4-4 (DIS)	5
*Calculator	3-5 (SA)	5	*Scissors	1-4 (DIS), 3-2 (Lab)	5
Compass, magnetic	1-1 (CP), 1-1 (DIS)	5	*Spoon, metal	3-2 (Lab)	5
Container, plastic, with screw-on lid, 500 mL	2-1 (Lab)	20	*Stereomicroscope	2-2 (Lab)	5
Container, plastic	2-1 (TT), 3-4 (DIS)	5	*Stopwatch	2-1 (DIS), 3-2 (Lab)	5
*Globe	2-2 (TT)	5	*Tray, plastic	3-1 (Lab)	5
Graduated cylinder, polypropylene, 250 mL	2-1 (Lab)	5	*Tub, plastic (27 × 40 × 10 cm)	3-2 (Lab)	1

KEY: CP: Chapter Project; **DIS:** Discover; **SA:** Skills Activity; **TT:** Try This; **Lab:** Skills, Consumer, Design Your Own, & Technology and Design
* items are school supplied.

Quantities based on five groups of six students per class.

Earth's Changing Surface

Book-Specific Resources

Student Edition
StudentExpress™ with Interactive Textbook
Teacher's Edition
All-in-One Teaching Resources
Color Transparencies
Guided Reading and Study Workbook
Student Edition on Audio CD
Discovery Channel School® Video
Lab Activity Video
Consumable and Nonconsumable Materials Kits

Program Print Resources

Integrated Science Laboratory Manual
Computer Microscope Lab Manual
Inquiry Skills Activity Books
Progress Monitoring Assessments
Test Preparation Workbook
Test-Taking Tips With Transparencies
Teacher's ELL Handbook
Reading Strategies for Science Content

Differentiated Instruction Resources

Adapted Reading and Study Workbook
Adapted Tests
Differentiated Instruction Guide for Labs and Activities

Program Technology Resources

Teacher Express™ CD-ROM
Interactive Textbooks Online
PresentationExpress™ CD-ROM
ExamView®, Computer Test Bank CD-ROM
Lab zone™ Easy Planner CD-ROM
Probeware Lab Manual With CD-ROM
Computer Microscope and Lab Manual
Materials Ordering CD-ROM
Discovery Channel School® DVD Library
Lab Activity DVD Library
Web Site at PHSchool.com

Spanish Print Resources

Spanish Student Edition
Spanish Guided Reading and Study Workbook
Spanish Teaching Guide With Tests

Acknowledgments appear on page 198, which constitutes an extension of this copyright page.

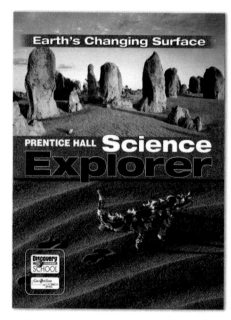

Cover
Sunrise illuminates the Pinnacles in Nambung National Park, Western Australia (top). A thorny devil leaves footprints in the sand (bottom).

PEARSON
Prentice Hall

ISBN 0-13-201150-6
1 2 3 4 5 6 7 8 9 10   10 09 08 07 06

Program Authors

Michael J. Padilla, Ph.D.
Professor of Science Education
University of Georgia
Athens, Georgia

Michael Padilla is a leader in middle school science education. He has served as an author and elected officer for the National Science Teachers Association and as a writer of the National Science Education Standards. As lead author of Science Explorer, Mike has inspired the team in developing a program that meets the needs of middle grades students, promotes science inquiry, and is aligned with the National Science Education Standards.

Ioannis Miaoulis, Ph.D.
President
Museum of Science
Boston, Massachusetts

Originally trained as a mechanical engineer, Ioannis Miaoulis is in the forefront of the national movement to increase technological literacy. As dean of the Tufts University School of Engineering, Dr. Miaoulis spearheaded the introduction of engineering into the Massachusetts curriculum. Currently he is working with school systems across the country to engage students in engineering activities and to foster discussions on the impact of science and technology on society.

Martha Cyr, Ph.D.
Director of K–12 Outreach
Worcester Polytechnic Institute
Worcester, Massachusetts

Martha Cyr is a noted expert in engineering outreach. She has over nine years of experience with programs and activities that emphasize the use of engineering principles, through hands-on projects, to excite and motivate students and teachers of mathematics and science in grades K–12. Her goal is to stimulate a continued interest in science and mathematics through engineering.

Book Author

Michael Wysession, Ph.D.
Associate Professor of Earth and
    Planetary Sciences
Washington University
St. Louis, Missouri

Contributing Writers

Rose-Marie Botting
Science Teacher
Broward County
    School District
Fort Lauderdale,
    Florida

Colleen Campos
Science Teacher
Laredo Middle School
Aurora, Colorado

Holly Estes
Science Teacher
Hale Middle School
Stow, Massachusetts

Edward Evans
Former Science
    Teacher
Hilton Central School
Hilton, New York

Sharon Stroud
Science Teacher
Widefield High School
Colorado Springs,
    Colorado

Consultants

Reading Consultant

Nancy Romance, Ph.D.
Professor of Science
    Education
Florida Atlantic University
Fort Lauderdale, Florida

Mathematics Consultant

William Tate, Ph.D.
Professor of Education and
    Applied Statistics and
    Computation
Washington University
St. Louis, Missouri

Reviewers

Tufts University Content Reviewers

Faculty from Tufts University in Medford, Massachusetts, developed *Science Explorer* chapter projects and reviewed the student books.

Astier M. Almedom, Ph.D.
Department of Biology

Wayne Chudyk, Ph.D.
Department of Civil and Environmental
Engineering

John L. Durant, Ph.D.
Department of Civil and Environmental
Engineering

George S. Ellmore, Ph.D.
Department of Biology

David Kaplan, Ph.D.
Department of Biomedical Engineering

Samuel Kounaves, Ph.D.
Department of Chemistry

David H. Lee, Ph.D.
Department of Chemistry

Douglas Matson, Ph.D.
Department of Mechanical Engineering

Karen Panetta, Ph.D.
Department of Electrical Engineering and
Computer Science

Jan A. Pechenik, Ph.D.
Department of Biology

John C. Ridge, Ph.D.
Department of Geology

William Waller, Ph.D.
Department of Astronomy

Content Reviewers

Paul Beale, Ph.D.
Department of Physics
University of Colorado
Boulder, Colorado

Jeff Bodart, Ph.D.
Chipola Junior College
Marianna, Florida

Michael Castellani, Ph.D.
Department of Chemistry
Marshall University
Huntington, West Virginia

Eugene Chiang, Ph.D.
Department of Astronomy
University of California – Berkeley
Berkeley, California

Charles C. Curtis, Ph.D.
Department of Physics
University of Arizona
Tucson, Arizona

Daniel Kirk-Davidoff, Ph.D.
Department of Meteorology
University of Maryland
College Park, Maryland

Diane T. Doser, Ph.D.
Department of Geological Sciences
University of Texas at El Paso
El Paso, Texas

R. E. Duhrkopf, Ph.D.
Department of Biology
Baylor University
Waco, Texas

Michael Hacker
Co-director, Center for
Technological Literacy
Hofstra University
Hempstead, New York

Michael W. Hamburger, Ph.D.
Department of Geological Sciences
Indiana University
Bloomington, Indiana

Alice K. Hankla, Ph.D.
The Galloway School
Atlanta, Georgia

Donald C. Jackson, Ph.D.
Department of Molecular Pharmacology,
Physiology, & Biotechnology
Brown University
Providence, Rhode Island

Jeremiah N. Jarrett, Ph.D.
Department of Biological Sciences
Central Connecticut State University
New Britain, Connecticut

David Lederman, Ph.D.
Department of Physics
West Virginia University
Morgantown, West Virginia

Becky Mansfield, Ph.D.
Department of Geography
Ohio State University
Columbus, Ohio

Elizabeth M. Martin, M.S.
Department of Chemistry and Biochemistry
College of Charleston
Charleston, South Carolina

Joe McCullough, Ph.D.
Department of Natural and
Applied Sciences
Cabrillo College
Aptos, California

Robert J. Mellors, Ph.D.
Department of Geological Sciences
San Diego State University
San Diego, California

Joseph M. Moran, Ph.D.
American Meteorological Society
Washington, D.C.

David J. Morrissey, Ph.D.
Department of Chemistry
Michigan State University
East Lansing, Michigan

Philip A. Reed, Ph.D.
Department of Occupational & Technical
Studies
Old Dominion University
Norfolk, Virginia

Scott M. Rochette, Ph.D.
Department of the Earth Sciences
State University of New York, College at
Brockport
Brockport, New York

Laurence D. Rosenhein, Ph.D.
Department of Chemistry
Indiana State University
Terre Haute, Indiana

Ronald Sass, Ph.D.
Department of Biology and Chemistry
Rice University
Houston, Texas

George Schatz, Ph.D.
Department of Chemistry
Northwestern University
Evanston, Illinois

Sara Seager, Ph.D.
Carnegie Institution of Washington
Washington, D.C.

Robert M. Thornton, Ph.D.
Section of Plant Biology
University of California
Davis, California

John R. Villarreal, Ph.D.
College of Science and Engineering
The University of Texas – Pan American
Edinburg, Texas

Kenneth Welty, Ph.D.
School of Education
University of Wisconsin–Stout
Menomonie, Wisconsin

Edward J. Zalisko, Ph.D.
Department of Biology
Blackburn College
Carlinville, Illinois

Teacher Reviewers

David R. Blakely
Arlington High School
Arlington, Massachusetts

Jane E. Callery
Two Rivers Magnet Middle
    School
East Hartford, Connecticut

Melissa Lynn Cook
Oakland Mills High School
Columbia, Maryland

James Fattic
Southside Middle School
Anderson, Indiana

Dan Gabel
Hoover Middle School
Rockville, Maryland

Wayne Goates
Eisenhower Middle School
Goddard, Kansas

Katherine Bobay Graser
Mint Hill Middle School
Charlotte, North Carolina

Darcy Hampton
Deal Junior High School
Washington, D.C.

Karen Kelly
Pierce Middle School
Waterford, Michigan

David Kelso
Manchester High School Central
Manchester, New Hampshire

Benigno Lopez, Jr.
Sleepy Hill Middle School
Lakeland, Florida

Angie L. Matamoros, Ph.D.
ALM Consulting, Inc.
Weston, Florida

Tim McCollum
Charleston Middle School
Charleston, Illinois

Bruce A. Mellin
Brooks School
North Andover, Massachusetts

Ella Jay Parfitt
Southeast Middle School
Baltimore, Maryland

Evelyn A. Pizzarello
Louis M. Klein Middle School
Harrison, New York

Kathleen M. Poe
Fletcher Middle School
Jacksonville, Florida

Shirley Rose
Lewis and Clark Middle School
Tulsa, Oklahoma

Linda Sandersen
Greenfield Middle School
Greenfield, Wisconsin

Mary E. Solan
Southwest Middle School
Charlotte, North Carolina

Mary Stewart
University of Tulsa
Tulsa, Oklahoma

Paul Swenson
Billings West High School
Billings, Montana

Thomas Vaughn
Arlington High School
Arlington, Massachusetts

Susan C. Zibell
Central Elementary
Simsbury, Connecticut

Safety Reviewers

W. H. Breazeale, Ph.D.
Department of Chemistry
College of Charleston
Charleston, South Carolina

Ruth Hathaway, Ph.D.
Hathaway Consulting
Cape Girardeau, Missouri

Douglas Mandt, M.S.
Science Education Consultant
Edgewood, Washington

Activity Field Testers

Nicki Bibbo
Witchcraft Heights School
Salem, Massachusetts

Rose-Marie Botting
Broward County Schools
Fort Lauderdale, Florida

Colleen Campos
Laredo Middle School
Aurora, Colorado

Elizabeth Chait
W. L. Chenery Middle School
Belmont, Massachusetts

Holly Estes
Hale Middle School
Stow, Massachusetts

Laura Hapgood
Plymouth Community
    Intermediate School
Plymouth, Massachusetts

Mary F. Lavin
Plymouth Community
    Intermediate School
Plymouth, Massachusetts

James MacNeil, Ph.D.
Cambridge, Massachusetts

Lauren Magruder
St. Michael's Country
    Day School
Newport, Rhode Island

Jeanne Maurand
Austin Preparatory School
Reading, Massachusetts

Joanne Jackson-Pelletier
Winman Junior High School
Warwick, Rhode Island

Warren Phillips
Plymouth Public Schools
Plymouth, Massachusetts

Carol Pirtle
Hale Middle School
Stow, Massachusetts

Kathleen M. Poe
Fletcher Middle School
Jacksonville, Florida

Cynthia B. Pope
Norfolk Public Schools
Norfolk, Virginia

Anne Scammell
Geneva Middle School
Geneva, New York

Karen Riley Sievers
Callanan Middle School
Des Moines, Iowa

David M. Smith
Eyer Middle School
Allentown, Pennsylvania

Gene Vitale
Parkland School
McHenry, Illinois

Contents

Earth's Changing Surface

Reference Section

VIDEO

Enhance understanding through dynamic video.

Preview Get motivated with this introduction to the chapter content.

Field Trip Explore a real-world story related to the chapter content.

Assessment Review content and take an assessment.

Web Links

Get connected to exciting Web resources in every lesson.

SC*LINKS*™ NSTA Find Web links on topics relating to every section.

Active Art Interact with selected visuals from every chapter online.

Planet Diary® Explore news and natural phenomena through weekly reports.

Science News® Keep up to date with the latest science discoveries.

Experience the complete textbook online and on CD-ROM.

Activities Practice skills and learn content.

Videos Explore content and learn important lab skills.

Audio Support Hear key terms spoken and defined.

Self-Assessment Use instant feedback to help you track your progress.

Activities

Fossils Reveal Dinosaur Diet

Inquiry and Paleontology

Paleontologist Karen Chin studies coprolites, or fossilized droppings, to learn what ancient animals ate and what Earth was like in the past. This article explores how Dr. Chin uses inquiry skills, such as observing, measuring, and forming and testing hypotheses, to learn about dinosaurs and the environments in which the animals lived. Fossils are explained in this book, but students can read and understand this article before learning about fossils.

Build Background Knowledge

Ask students to describe fossils that they have seen. Most of these fossils probably will be body fossils. Tell students that some fossils are not parts of an ancient animal's body and that they will be learning about one example of this type of fossil.

Introduce the Career

Before students read the feature, let them read the title, examine the pictures, and read the captions on their own. Then ask: **What questions came into your mind as you looked at these pictures?** *(Students might suggest questions such as the following: Why are thin sections cut from fossils? What is a coprolite? Why does Dr. Chin need a microscope?)* Point out to students that just as they had questions about what they are seeing, scientists, too, have questions about what they observe.

Careers in Science

Fossils Reveal Dinosaur Diet

◀ *Tyrannosaurus rex*

Have you ever wondered what a *Tyrannosaurus rex* might have eaten for lunch? Paleontologist Karen Chin is looking for the answers to this question. She explores the world of ancient animals, including dinosaurs. But she doesn't do her research by digging up fossil bones. Instead, she relies on another kind of clue left behind by these fascinating animals.

Karen is a world-famous expert on coprolites— fossilized animal droppings. Because coprolites contain the undigested remains of food that has passed through an animal's digestive tract, they may provide clues about an animal's diet.

Studying coprolites may sound odd. But research can reveal important information about an animal and its environment. In fact, Karen has made some exciting discoveries about dinosaurs as a result of her research. And she's earned a nickname—The Queen of Coprolites.

Using a slicing machine, Karen cuts thin sections of fossils to examine.

x ◆ G

Career Path

Dr. Karen Chin has a master's degree in biology from Montana State University. She earned a Ph.D. in geology from the University of California at Santa Barbara. Currently, Karen is an Assistant Professor of Geology at the University of Colorado at Boulder. She is also a curator of paleontology at the University of Colorado Museum of Natural History, where she helps oversee the museum's fossil collection.

Background

Facts and Figures Coprolites are a type of trace fossil. Trace fossils are fossils that provide evidence of ancient life but are not body parts. Other examples of trace fossils include burrows and footprints. Another trace fossil that often is attributed to dinosaurs is the gastrolith, which is a smooth, polished stone. Rocks were swallowed by some plant-eating dinosaurs to help them digest their food. Because of the grinding action and acidic environment, the stones were rounded and made smooth.

Talking With
Dr. Karen Chin

? How did you become interested in fossils?

As a child, I was interested in animals and plants. But I wasn't interested in studying extinct animals, so I never thought about becoming a paleontologist. As a young adult, I worked for many summers as a National Park naturalist. I enjoyed talking with the public about nature and science.

When I entered graduate school at Montana State University, I wanted to learn about museums, so I took a part-time job at the Museum of the Rockies. I did all sorts of things there, including helping to glue together fossil dinosaur bones and writing text for fossil exhibits. I became fascinated by the mystery of how we can learn about the prehistoric world by using clues from fossils. It was during this time that I got interested in coprolites.

? How do you identify coprolites?

When a team of paleontologists finds the fossilized bones of dinosaurs or other animals, they sometimes come across coprolites in the same area. Not all coprolites look alike. But they do have some characteristics in common. Coprolites from smaller animals often have a shape that reminds you of dog droppings. But the shapes of coprolites from giant animals like *Tyrannosaurus rex* are not always easy to recognize. In some cases, the coprolites contain clues in the form of chopped-up remains of things an animal ate. I often have to do a lot of investigating to figure out whether a fossil is a coprolite or not.

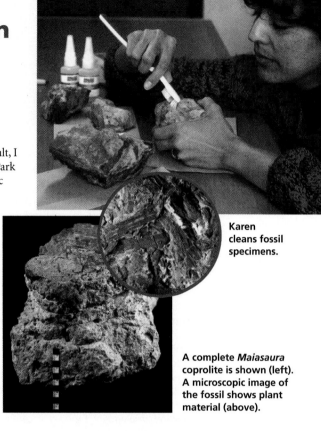

Karen cleans fossil specimens.

A complete *Maiasaura* coprolite is shown (left). A microscopic image of the fossil shows plant material (above).

? What do these fossils tell you?

They can give us a good idea of a dinosaur's diet and digestion. I've seen many different types of food remains, including fish scales, broken bits of dinosaur bone, shells, and fragments of wood and other plant material. Those food remains also tell us what kinds of organisms lived together in the same environment in the ancient past. The coprolites found in Montana are an example of what specimens can reveal.

G ◆ 1

Use Maps Use a map of the United States to show students the location of the Two Medicine Formation in northwestern Montana. Ask: **Why would this area be a good place to find dinosaur fossils?** (*Some students will mention the exposed rock, which makes searching much easier.*) Point out to students that dinosaur fossils can be found only in rock that formed during the time dinosaurs lived and in an environment in which dinosaurs lived. This condition is met by much of the Two Medicine Formation.

Use Visuals Tell students that duck-billed dinosaurs like the ones shown in the artwork were abundant in prehistoric Montana. Ask: **Do you think these dinosaurs ate plants or other animals? Explain.** (*These dinosaurs ate plants. They did not have the jaw structure or teeth that carnivores such as* T. rex *had.*)

Use Math Skills Tell students that dinosaurs existed for about 165 million years before the group became extinct about 65 million years ago. Have students calculate how long ago dinosaurs first appeared. (*65,000,000 + 165,000,000 = 230,000,000 years ago.*)

Two Medicine Formation (above), located in northwestern Montana, is an important dinosaur site. The artwork (left) shows duck-billed dinosaurs in prehistoric Montana.

? What did you find in the fossils?

Many dinosaur fossils have been found at the Two Medicine Formation site in Montana. Dr. Jack Horner, one of the paleontologists who discovered these fossils, also found some specimens he thought might be coprolites. I decided to take a closer look at them.

The specimens looked like nothing more than broken, jagged black rocks. But when I looked closely, I could see they contained plant material. I prepared a very thin section, thin enough for light to shine through, so I could examine it under the microscope. It showed that the rock was filled with chopped-up wood. That material was wood from coniferous trees.

These coprolites were probably produced by duck-billed dinosaurs that lived about 75 million years ago. This particular dinosaur, called *Maiasaura*, was very large, about 7 meters long and about one or two metric tons.

? What else did you learn?

I also noticed burrows in these coprolites. The burrows reminded me of dung beetles. Dung beetles are insects that feed on droppings. Some species of dung beetles create distinctive burrows as they feed. I asked a beetle expert to take a look. He confirmed that the burrows were the type made by dung beetles.

Now we had some new pieces of information. First of all, the presence of the dung beetles confirmed that these fossils were coprolites. Also, the coprolites showed that dung beetles and dinosaurs lived together in prehistoric Montana—something we didn't know before. Other coprolites at the site indicate the presence of snails. So we can infer that duck-billed dinosaurs, coniferous trees, dung beetles, and snails lived in close association.

This large coprolite is thought to be from *Tyrannosaurus rex.* It is being weighed.

Background

Facts and Figures The Two Medicine Formation in Montana consists of a thick stack of sedimentary rocks that include mostly mudstones with some sandstones. The rock layers were deposited during the latter part of the Cretaceous Period of geologic time and represent mostly low-lying river plain environments. In addition to yielding coprolites, the formation has provided a wealth of dinosaur fossils, including fossil eggs and nests.

What fossils did you examine in Canada?

Another paleontologist sent me a possible coprolite collected near where a *T. rex* skeleton was dug up in Saskatchewan, Canada. These giant dinosaur species lived about 65 million years ago. They grew to 14 meters long and weighed as much as 5 metric tons.

I did some chemical tests on the specimen. My results showed that it was a coprolite and that it was produced by a meat-eating animal. The specimen contained many bone fragments. By looking at the cell structure of the bone fragments, I was able to tell that they probably belonged to a young plant-eating dinosaur.

This coprolite specimen was found in the same rock layers as several species of meat-eating dinosaurs. All the dinosaurs were fairly small. The only large one was *T. rex.* Because of the large size of the Saskatchewan coprolite, we inferred that it was probably produced by *T. rex.*

What did you conclude?

This coprolite showed us that it is possible to find coprolites from large meat-eating dinosaurs. It gives us an idea of what to look for when we are searching for fossils. This coprolite provides physical evidence that *T. rex* ate other dinosaurs.

What is your most surprising finding?

I identified a very large tyrannosaur coprolite, though not from *T. rex.* It contains not only bone fragments, but also impressions of muscle tissue. It was surprising to find the fossilized remains of undigested meat in a coprolite. This discovery shows that it is possible for droppings to become fossilized much more quickly than we thought.

Why are these findings important?

It's exciting to use a different kind of fossil evidence to find out how these ancient animals lived and what their environments were like.

Karen looks at a very thin slice of coprolite under her microscope.

Writing in Science

Career Link Karen Chin uses the clues she finds in coprolites to figure out what ancient animals ate and what their environment was like. Make a list of what you'd like to know about animals and plants that lived in prehistoric times. In a paragraph describe ways that studying fossils could help you learn the answers to your questions.

Go Online
PHSchool.com
For: More on this career
Visit: PHSchool.com
Web Code: cfb-2000

G ◆ 3

Research Encourage students to research the *T. rex* coprolite studied by Dr. Chin. The discovery was widely reported in the media, and numerous grade-appropriate articles are available. After students conclude their research, have them prepare a news report about the discovery and present it to the class.

Build Inquiry Skills Tell students that a large object that might be a coprolite has just been found. Ask them to develop a series of tests to help determine whether the object is a coprolite. *(Students might suggest microscopic examination, chemical evidence, shape and size evidence, and proximity evidence, among other possibilities.)*

Discuss Ask: **Why is it important to use a variety of fossil evidence to learn about dinosaurs?** *(Different fossil types provide different information. Dr. Chin's study of coprolites complements other types of evidence.)*

Writing in Science

Writing Mode Description

Scoring Rubric

4 Exceeds criteria, includes a list of at least three things that the student would like to know about prehistoric animals and plants, and includes an organized paragraph that logically describes how studying fossils could answer these questions

3 Meets criteria and includes a list with two entries and a paragraph describing how these questions could be answered

2 Includes one question and a paragraph describing how the question could be answered

1 Includes a list of one or more entries but does not explain how answers could be discovered

---

Go Online
PHSchool.com
For: More on this career
Visit: PHSchool.com
Web Code: cfb-2000

Students can do further research on this career and others that are related to the study of earth science.

Chapter at a Glance

Chapter at a Glance

PRENTICE HALL
TeacherEXPRESS™
Plan · Teach · Assess

 **Chapter Project** *Getting on the Map*

| **Technology** | **Local Standards** |

Teaching Resources
- Chapter Project Teacher Notes, pp. 40–41
- Chapter Project Student Overview, pp. 42–43
- Chapter Project Student Worksheets, pp. 44–45
- Chapter Project Scoring Rubric, p. 46

 DISCOVERY SCHOOL
Video Preview

 Exploring Earth's Surface
G.1.1.1 Explain what the topography of an area includes.
G.1.1.2 Identify the main types of landforms.
1–2 periods
1/2–1 block

 Go Online SCLINKS NSTA

 Models of Earth
G.1.2.1 Explain how maps and globes represent Earth's surface.
2–3 periods
1–1 1/2 blocks **G.1.2.2** Identify latitude and longitude as reference lines that help locate points on Earth.
G.1.2.3 Identify three common map projections.

 Go Online SCLINKS NSTA

 Maps and Computers
G.1.3.1 Explain how computer mapping differs from earlier methods of making maps.
1–2 periods
1/2–1 block **G.1.3.2** Describe the types of data that are used for making computer maps.

 Go Online PHSchool.com
DISCOVERY SCHOOL
Video Field Trip

 Topographic Maps
G.1.4.1 Explain how elevation, relief, and slope are shown on topographic maps.
1–2 periods
1/2–1 block **G.1.4.2** Explain how a topographic map is read.
G.1.4.3 Describe some uses of topographic maps.

 Go Online active art

Review and Assessment

| | **Test Preparation** |

Teaching Resources
- Key Terms Review, p. 81
- Transparency G10
- Performance Assessment Teacher Notes, p. 88
- Performance Assessment Scoring Rubric, p. 89
- Performance Assessment Student Worksheet, p. 90
- Chapter Test, pp. 91–94

 Go Online PHSchool.com
 DISCOVERY SCHOOL
Video Assessment

Test Preparation Blackline Masters

Chapter Activities Planner

For more activities

LAB ZONE Easy Planner CD-ROM

Student Edition	Inquiry	Time	Materials	Skills	Resources
Chapter Project, p. 5	Open-Ended	Ongoing (2 weeks)	**All in One** Teaching Resources See p. 40	Observing, measuring, calculating, making models, communicating	**Lab zone Easy Planner** **All in One** Teaching Resources Support pp. 40–46
Section 1					
Discover Activity, p. 6	Guided	10 minutes	Piece of plain paper, pencil, magnetic compass	Forming operational definitions	**Lab zone Easy Planner**
Skills Activity, p. 9	Guided	10 minutes	Figure 3, pencil, postcard	Classifying	**Lab zone Easy Planner**
Section 2					
Discover Activity, p. 11	Guided	15 minutes	Felt-tip pen, globe, orange or grapefruit, plastic knife	Observing	**Lab zone Easy Planner**
Try This Activity, p. 16	Directed	10 minutes	Globe	Observing	**Lab zone Easy Planner**
Skills Lab, p. 20	Directed	30 minutes	United States map with latitude, longitude, and state borders; tracing paper, paper clips, colored pencils	Classifying, observing, inferring	**Lab zone Easy Planner** **Lab Activity Video** **All in One** Teaching Resources Skills Lab: *A Borderline Case*, p. 63
Section 3					
Discover Activity, p. 21	Guided	15 minutes	Metric ruler, unlined paper, colored pencils	Predicting	**Lab zone Easy Planner**
Section 4					
Discover Activity, p. 26	Guided	20 minutes	8 pieces of cardboard of decreasing size, scissors, unlined paper, pencil, metric ruler	Making models	**Lab zone Easy Planner**
Skills Activity, p. 29	Directed	5 minutes	Figure 14	Interpreting data	**Lab zone Easy Planner**
Skills Lab, p. 31	Guided	40 minutes	deep-sided pan; water; marking pencil; modeling clay; clear, hard sheet of plastic; metric ruler; sheet of unlined white paper; food coloring	Making models, interpreting maps	**Lab zone Easy Planner** **Lab Activity Video** **All in One** Teaching Resources Skills Lab: *A Map in a Pan*, p. 78

Section Lesson Plans

Section 1 Exploring Earth's Surface

1–2 periods, 1 1/2–1 block

Objectives

G.1.1.1 Explain what the topography of an area includes.
G.1.1.2 Identify the main types of landforms.

Key Terms

• topography • elevation • relief • landform • plain • mountain
• mountain range • plateau • landform region

Local Standards

 **Preteach**

Build Background Knowledge

Apply knowledge about maps to understand Earth features.

Lab zone Discover Activity *What Is the Land Like Around Your School?* **L2**

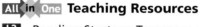 **Targeted Print and Technology Resources**

All in One Teaching Resources

L2 Reading Strategy Transparency
G1: *Comparing and Contrasting*

o **PresentationExpress™ CD-ROM**

Instruct

Topography Compare and contrast topographic features on a map.

Types of Landforms Identify landform types on a map, and connect the types to familiar regions.

 **Targeted Print and Technology Resources**

All in One Teaching Resources

L2 Guided Reading, pp. 49–52
L2 Transparencies G2, G3

www.SciLinks.org Web Code: scn-0711

o **Student Edition on Audio CD**

Assess

Section Assessment Questions

Have students use their graphic organizers comparing and contrasting the characteristics of landforms to answer the questions.

Reteach

Identify and describe landforms from photographs.

Targeted Print and Technology Resources

All in One Teaching Resources

• Section Summary, p. 48
L1 Review and Reinforce, p. 53
L3 Enrich, p. 54

Section 2 Models of Earth

 2–3 periods, 1–1 1/2 blocks

Objectives

G.1.2.1 Explain how maps and globes represent Earth's surface.

G.1.2.2 Identify latitude and longitude as reference lines that help locate points on Earth.

G.1.2.3 Identify three common map projections.

Key Terms

• map • globe • scale • symbol • key • degree • equator • hemisphere • prime meridian • latitude • longitude • map projection

Local Standards

Preteach

Build Background Knowledge

Use a road map to introduce the concept of map scale.

 **Discover Activity** *How Can You Flatten the Curved Earth?* **L1**

Targeted Print and Technology Resources

 **Teaching Resources**

L2 Reading Strategy Transparency G4: *Asking Questions*

PresentationExpress™ CD-ROM

Instruct

Maps and Globes Compare and contrast two models of Earth: maps and globes.

An Earth Reference System Locate the equator and prime meridian on a map, and discern their purposes.

Locating Points on Earth's Surface Use a world map for locating points from lines of latitude and lines of longitude.

Map Projections Consider advantages and disadvantages of different map projections.

 Skills Lab *A Borderline Case* **L2**

Targeted Print and Technology Resources

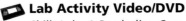 **Teaching Resources**

L2 Guided Reading, pp. 57–60
L2 Transparency G5
L2 Skills Lab: *A Borderline Case*, pp. 63–65

Lab Activity Video/DVD
Skills Lab: *A Borderline Case*

www.SciLinks.org Web Code: scn-0712

Student Edition on Audio CD

Assess

Section Assessment Questions

 Have students use their question-and-answer graphic organizers to help them answer the questions.

Reteach

Students write the latitude and longitude of their town.

Targeted Print and Technology Resources

Teaching Resources

• Section Summary, p. 56
L1 Review and Reinforce, p. 61
L3 Enrich, p. 62

Section 3 Maps and Computers

 *1–2 periods, 1/2–1 block*

ABILITY LEVELS
L1 Basic to Average
L2 For All Students
L3 Average to Advanced

Objectives

G.1.3.1 Explain how computer mapping differs from earlier methods of making maps.

G.1.3.2 Describe the types of data that are used for making computer maps.

Local Standards

Key Terms

• surveying • digitizing • satellite image • pixel • Global Positioning System

---

Preteach

Build Background Knowledge

Elicit knowledge about satellites and their functions.

 **Discover Activity** *Can You Make a Pixel Picture?* L1

Targeted Print and Technology Resources

All in One Teaching Resources

L2 Reading Strategy Transparency G6: *Identifying Main Ideas*

PresentationExpress™ CD-ROM

Instruct

Computer Mapping Consider the advantages of mapping with computers.

Sources of Map Data Consider the advantages of gathering map data with satellites.

Targeted Print and Technology Resources

All in One Teaching Resources

L2 Guided Reading, p. 68

Student Edition on Audio CD

DISCOVERY CHANNEL SCHOOL
Video Field Trip

PHSchool.com Web Code: cfd-2013

Assess

Section Assessment Questions

Have students use their main ideas graphic organizers to answer the questions.

Reteach

Students compare maps made by using different technologies.

Targeted Print and Technology Resources

All in One Teaching Resources

• Section Summary, p. 67

L1 Review and Reinforce, p. 69

L3 Enrich, p. 70

Section 4 Topographic Maps

1–2 periods, 1/2–1 block

Objectives

G.1.4.1 Explain how elevation, relief, and slope are shown on topographic maps.

G.1.4.2 Explain how a topographic map is read.

G.1.4.3 Describe some uses of topographic maps.

Local Standards

Key Terms

• topographic map • contour line • contour interval • index contour

---

Preteach

Build Background Knowledge

Discuss experiences using topographic maps.

 Discover Activity *Can a Map Show Relief?* L1

Targeted Print and Technology Resources

 Teaching Resources

L2 Reading Strategy Transparency G7: *Using Prior Knowledge*

○ **PresentationExpress™ CD-ROM**

Instruct

Mapping Earth's Topography Introduce contour lines and index contours.

Reading a Topographic Map Students contrast road maps and topographic maps and consider the advantages of the latter.

Uses of Topographic Maps Consider how topographic maps are useful to people.

 **Skills Lab** *A Map in a Pan* L2

Targeted Print and Technology Resources

Teaching Resources

L2 Guided Reading, pp. 73–75
L2 Transparencies G8, G9
L2 Skills Lab: *A Map in a Pan,* pp. 78–80

🎞 **Lab Activity Video/DVD**
Skills Lab: *A Map in a Pan*

PHSchool.com Web Code: cfp-2014

○ **Student Edition on Audio CD**

Assess

Section Assessment Questions

⊙ Have students use their prior knowledge graphic organizers to answer the questions.

Reteach

Students describe the symbols, scale, and contour interval of a topographic map.

Targeted Print and Technology Resources

Teaching Resources

• Section Summary, p. 72
L1 Review and Reinforce, p. 76
L3 Enrich, p. 77

Go Online

NSTA-PD*LINKS*

For: Professional Development Support
Visit: www.SciLinks.org/PDLinks
Web Code: scf-0710

Professional Development

Professional Development

Section 1 **Exploring Earth's Surface**

Landforms and Landform Regions Geomorphology is the branch of geology that is concerned with landforms and the processes that create them. Landforms can be thought of as falling into two main groups. The first group includes landforms that are the result of the constructive forces that build up Earth's land surface, such as mountain building and volcanic activity. The second group includes landforms shaped by the destructive forces of weathering and erosion. Those forces slowly wear away the landforms in the first group and create new landforms composed of sediment.

Geomorphologists distinguish many other types of landforms in addition to mountains, plains, and plateaus. Some of these landforms are familiar to people living in the regions where they occur: in the Southwest, canyons and mesas formed by erosion; in the Northeast and Midwest, glacial landforms such as drumlins and eskers formed by deposition; in the Southeast, sinkholes formed by erosion; and in the Rocky Mountain and Pacific coast regions, landforms resulting from the constructive forces of volcanic activity and fault movement.

A landform region can be made up of more than one type of topography. For example, the Great Basin in the western United States is also known as the Basin and Range region because it is characterized by mountain ranges separated by valleys, or basins. Similarly, the Colorado Plateau includes canyons, mesas, and plains.

Section 2 **Models of Earth**

Determining Longitude at Sea For seventeenth-century sailors to determine longitude at sea, they needed to know the local time and the time at the prime meridian, which served as a reference meridian. Local time could be determined by observing the sun, but knowing Greenwich time required having a clock that could keep accurate time at sea. Developing such a clock was a difficult task because of the motion of the ships and the constantly changing

Address Misconceptions

Many people assume that one degree of longitude is always the same distance. However, the distance between meridians of longitude decreases from the equator to the poles. For a strategy for overcoming this misconception, see **Address Misconceptions** in the section *Models of Earth.*

weather conditions. In 1714, the English government offered a reward to whomever could develop a clock that could be used to determine longitude to within one half-degree. The solution would have to be proven on a ship sailing from Great Britain to a port in the West Indies. The problem was finally solved by a working-class carpenter, a self-taught watchmaker with little formal education. John Harrison worked with his brother James to make clocks from various and often odd materials. They made clocks completely from wood, clocks that did not need lubrication, and clocks that had pendulum rods made of alternating wires of brass and steel. Eventually Harrison created two watches, one a pocket watch and the other a larger version of a pocket watch. His son William took the larger watch on a voyage to the West Indies in 1761. Upon arrival in Jamaica in 1762, the watch was found to be only 5.1 seconds slow. A second trial with the same watch showed it to be accurate to within 39.2 seconds on a voyage of 47 days, three times better than needed to win the longitude prize. The Board of Longitude, however, wanted Harrison to show that this feat could be duplicated, so the board commissioned watchmaker Larcum Kendall to make a watch to Harrison's specifications. Captain Cook used Kendall's watch to determine longitude on his second voyage of discovery in 1772.

John Harrison's Marine Chronometer

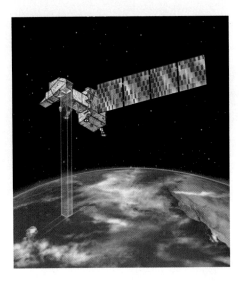

1:24,000-scale topographic maps includes both standard updates, which include revisions of all categories of information and field checks, and limited updates, which do not include revision of contour lines or field checks. The introduction of digital mapping techniques increases production efficiency and allows the production of both computer and paper maps from the same information.

Section 3 **Maps and Computers**

The Landsat Program The Landsat program is a joint project of the USGS and NASA intended to gather data about Earth's resources through the use of satellites. NASA is responsible for developing and launching these satellites. The USGS is responsible for flight operations, maintenance, management of all ground data reception, archiving, and image generation and distribution. Landsat satellites make repeated observations of Earth's land, coastlines, and coral reefs to monitor changes in Earth's surface and environments. The Landsat program began in the early 1970s, and two satellites are still operating today—Landsat 5 and Landsat 7. Landsat 7 was launched on April 15, 1999. It is about 14 feet (4.3 m) long and 9 feet (2.8 m) in diameter. This satellite orbits Earth at an altitude of approximately 438 miles (705 km). The area covered by Landsat images is 115 miles (183 km) wide and 106 miles (170 km) long.

Section 4 **Topographic Maps**

The USGS The primary publisher of topographic maps in the United States is the United States Geological Survey (USGS). During the past several years, the USGS has made changes to many of its 1:24,000-scale topographic maps. Some of these changes were made because of requests from map users who required updated maps.

Maps are created by the USGS as part of the National Mapping Program. This program includes state and federal partners to provide mapping information for the country as a whole. The purpose of the National Mapping Program is to provide information that is useful for managing the nation's natural resources, mitigating natural disasters, understanding the land and the processes that affect it, and many other uses. The public benefits by having access to inexpensive, government-produced maps. Among the materials published by the National Mapping Program are topographic maps and a variety of digital maps and images. The revision of the

Help Students Read

Monitor Your Understanding
Finding Similarities

Strategy Help students read and understand the relationships among grid systems used to locate particular points on Earth's surface. Ask students to look at a globe and a flat map of Earth and locate the equator, the prime meridian, lines of longitude, and lines of latitude. Point out that both longitude and latitude lines are the same distance apart near the equator. Students may note that lines of latitude remain parallel to one another, whereas lines of longitude converge at the poles. Observing the grid system used to locate points on Earth's surface will allow students to see the similarities and differences among the types of lines used for mapmaking. Before students begin, have them read the passage in this chapter that discusses latitude and longitude.

Example

1. Remind students that there are similarities and differences between lines of latitude and lines of longitude. Ask them to identify the similarities between lines of latitude and longitude. *(Similarities are that these lines are shown at 15-degree intervals on both a globe and a flat map and that they divide Earth's surface into segments.)* Ask students to identify differences between lines of latitude and longitude. *(Lines of longitude converge at the poles; lines of latitude are parallel and do not converge.)*

2. Have students identify the similarities and differences between longitude and latitude lines as shown on the globe and on a flat map. Remind them that flat maps always include distortions because they are two-dimensional objects attempting to portray a three-dimensional object, Earth. Ask students to identify the type of map that more closely models the actual size and shape of landmasses on Earth. *(The globe)* Ask students why people use flat maps if they include distortions. *(Students may state that a flat map is easier to carry, open, and consult than a globe.)*

3. Explain to students that they may construct a table to list ways in which latitude and longitude are similar and different. Their tables may include words such as *distance in degrees, east or west, north or south, from the equator,* and *from the prime meridian.*

Interactive Textbook
- Complete student edition
- Video and audio
- Simulations and activities
- Section and chapter activities

Chapter 1

Mapping Earth's Surface

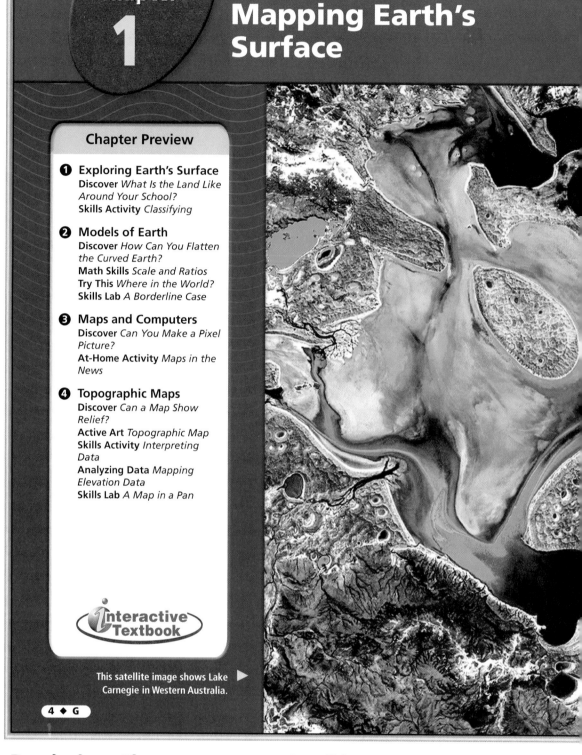

Interactive Textbook

This satellite image shows Lake Carnegie in Western Australia. ▶

Lab zone Chapter Project L3

Objectives
This chapter project will increase students' knowledge of maps and the symbols used in map keys. After this Chapter Project, students will be able to
- Observe and record the natural and human-made features of a neighborhood site
- Measure the boundaries and other relationships at the site
- Calculate scale relationships
- Make a model of the site in the form of a map
- Communicate the features of their map to the class

Skills Focus
Observing, measuring, calculating, making models, communicating

Project Time Line 2 weeks

All in One Teaching Resources
- Chapter Project Teacher Notes
- Chapter Project Overview
- Chapter Project Worksheet 1
- Chapter Project Worksheet 2
- Chapter Project Scoring Rubric

Developing a Plan
A day or two is required for each of the following phases: 1) Select a square or rectangular site in the neighborhood to map; 2) Measure the boundaries of the site and distances between important features; 3) Make a rough sketch of the site, including as many details as possible; 4) Devise a scale to use on the map and brainstorm a list of symbols to represent map features; 5) Create a map of the site with a map scale, a key, features, and contour lines; 6) Present the map to the class.

Possible Materials
- Provide materials for mapmaking, such as a tape measure, rope or string, a ruler or meter stick, a compass, a level, paper, and colored pencils.
- Provide several maps so that students can examine the scale, the contour lines, and the symbols used to identify the features of an area.

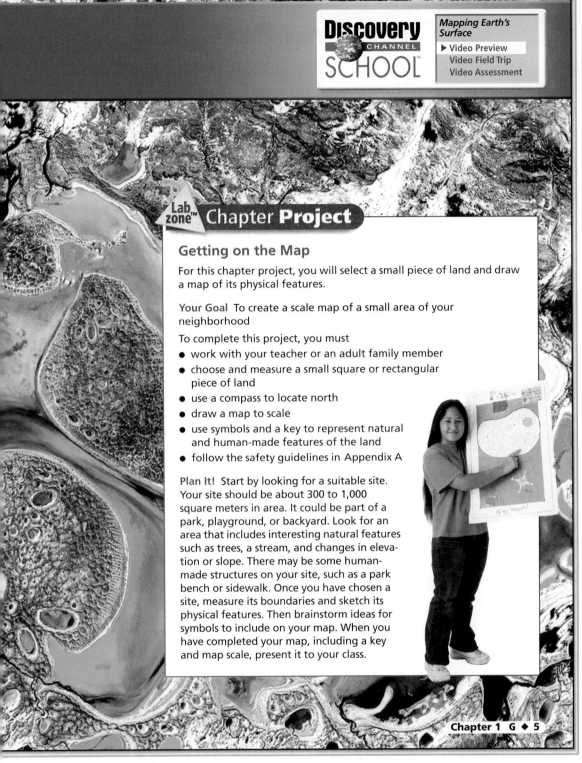

Lab zone™ Chapter **Project**

Getting on the Map

For this chapter project, you will select a small piece of land and draw a map of its physical features.

Your Goal To create a scale map of a small area of your neighborhood

To complete this project, you must
● work with your teacher or an adult family member
● choose and measure a small square or rectangular piece of land
● use a compass to locate north
● draw a map to scale
● use symbols and a key to represent natural and human-made features of the land
● follow the safety guidelines in Appendix A

Plan It! Start by looking for a suitable site. Your site should be about 300 to 1,000 square meters in area. It could be part of a park, playground, or backyard. Look for an area that includes interesting natural features such as trees, a stream, and changes in elevation or slope. There may be some human-made structures on your site, such as a park bench or sidewalk. Once you have chosen a site, measure its boundaries and sketch its physical features. Then brainstorm ideas for symbols to include on your map. When you have completed your map, including a key and map scale, present it to your class.

Chapter 1 G ◆ 5

Discovery CHANNEL SCHOOL™ Video Preview

Mapping Earth's Surface

Show the Video Preview to introduce the Chapter Project and present an overview of the chapter content. Discussion question: **How is GPS technology being used in Kenya to develop maps to help farmers?** (*GPS technology is being used to make maps that show the routes traveled by elephants. This information can be used to designate corridors for farmers to avoid.*)

Possible Shortcuts

You can organize the class in pairs or small groups, or you can designate small areas of the school's grounds for students to map.

Launching the Project

Have students brainstorm areas for the mapping project. Students may suggest a local park or other familiar area. Ask: **How would you begin?** (*Accept all responses at this time, and encourage creative thinking.*) Advise students that the map they will make must be an accurate representation of the area.

Performance Assessment

The Chapter Project Scoring Rubric will help you evaluate how well students complete the Chapter Project. You may want to share the rubric with your students so that they are clear about what is expected of them. Students will be assessed on
● how accurately they measure the mapped site and make their maps to scale
● how many natural and human-made features they map and how effectively they use symbols
● how accurately they show the shape of the land at the mapped site
● how effectively they present their maps to the class **Portfolio**

Objectives
After this lesson, students will be able to
G.1.1.1 Explain what the topography of an area includes.
G.1.1.2 Identify the main types of landform.

Target Reading Skill
Comparing and Contrasting Explain that comparing and contrasting information shows how ideas, facts, and events are similar and different. The results of the comparison can have importance.

Answers
a. Low **b.** High **c.** High **d.** Plateau **e.** Low

All in One Teaching Resources
• Transparency G1

Preteach

Build Background Knowledge   L2

Experience with Reading Maps
Encourage any students who have a background using and reading maps to describe what types of maps they have used and how they identify features on these maps. Students who have gone camping may have used compasses and topographic maps during outings. Ask these students to explain what a map key is and how it can be used to identify features on maps.

Reading Preview

Key Concepts
• What does the topography of an area include?
• What are the main types of landforms?

Key Terms
• topography • elevation
• relief • landform • plain
• mountain • mountain range
• plateau • landform region

Target Reading Skill
Comparing and Contrasting
As you read, compare and contrast the characteristics of landforms by completing a table like the one below.

Characteristics of Landforms

Landform	Elevation	Relief
Plain	a. ___?___	Low
Mountain	b. ___?___	c. ___?___
d. ___?___	High	e. ___?___

Lab zone — Discover Activity

What Is the Land Like Around Your School?
1. On a piece of paper, draw a small square to represent your school.
2. Choose a word that describes the type of land near your school, such as flat, hilly, or rolling. Write the word next to the square.
3. Use a magnetic compass to determine the direction of north. Assume that north is at the top of your piece of paper.
4. If you travel due north 1 kilometer from your school, what type of land do you find? Choose a word to describe the land in this area. Write that word to the north of the square.
5. Repeat Step 4 for areas located 1 kilometer east, south, and west of your school.

Think It Over
Forming Operational Definitions What phrase could you use to describe the land in your area?

In 1804, an expedition set out from St. Louis to explore the land between the Mississippi River and the Pacific Ocean. The United States had just purchased a part of this vast territory, called Louisiana, from France. Before the Louisiana Purchase, the United States stretched from the Atlantic coast westward to the Mississippi River. Few United States citizens had traveled west of the Mississippi. None had ever traveled over land all the way to the Pacific.

Led by Meriwether Lewis and William Clark, the expedition first traveled up the Missouri River. Then the group crossed the Rocky Mountains and followed the Columbia River to the Pacific Ocean. They returned by a similar route. The purpose of the expedition was to map America's interior.

On the journey to the Pacific, the Lewis and Clark expedition traveled more than 5,000 kilometers. As they traveled, Lewis and Clark observed many changes in topography. **Topography** (tuh PAWG ruh fee) is the shape of the land. An area's topography may be flat, sloping, hilly, or mountainous.

◀ The compass used by Meriwether Lewis

6 ◆ G

Lab zone — Discover Activity

Skills Focus Forming operational definitions   L2

Materials piece of plain paper, pencil, magnetic compass

Time 10 minutes

Tips If a compass is unavailable, point out north to students. Give students an idea of how far away a kilometer is by referring to a local landmark.

Expected Outcome By choosing words to describe local areas, students will construct a simple map of the area's topography.

Think It Over Students will develop some generalization about the area's topography according to the landforms, slopes, and other features they observe.

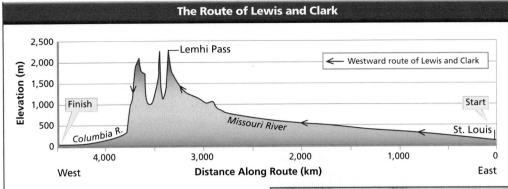

The Route of Lewis and Clark

Elevation (m): 2,500 / 2,000 / 1,500 / 1,000 / 500 / 0

Lemhi Pass

← Westward route of Lewis and Clark

Finish

Start

Columbia R.

Missouri River

St. Louis

Distance Along Route (km): 4,000 / 3,000 / 2,000 / 1,000 / 0

West — East

Topography

The topography of an area includes the area's elevation, relief, and landforms. The desktop where you do homework probably has piles of books, papers, and other objects of different sizes and shapes. Your desktop has both elevation and relief!

Elevation The height above sea level of a point on Earth's surface is its **elevation.** When Lewis and Clark started in St. Louis, they were about 140 meters above sea level. By the time they reached Lemhi Pass in the Rocky Mountains, they were more than 2,200 meters above sea level. Look at Figure 1 to see the changes in elevation along Lewis and Clark's route.

Relief The difference in elevation between the highest and lowest parts of an area is its **relief.** Early in their journey, Lewis and Clark encountered flat or rolling land with low relief, or small differences in elevation. In the Rocky Mountains, they crossed huge mountains separated by deep valleys. These areas had high relief, or great differences in elevation.

Landforms If you followed the route of the Lewis and Clark expedition, you would see many different landforms. A **landform** is a feature of topography, such as a hill or valley, formed by the processes that shape Earth's surface. Different landforms have different combinations of elevation and relief.

 Reading Checkpoint What is the difference between elevation and relief?

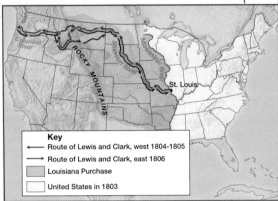

FIGURE 1
The route of the Lewis and Clark expedition crossed regions that differed greatly in elevation and relief. **Interpreting Graphs** *How much elevation did Lewis and Clark gain between St. Louis and Lemhi Pass?*

Key
← Route of Lewis and Clark, west 1804-1805
→ Route of Lewis and Clark, east 1806
Louisiana Purchase
United States in 1803

Chapter 1 G ◆ 7

Address Misconceptions L2

Height and Elevation

Focus Many students think that height and elevation are the same.

Teach Explain that height is the distance of something from the base to the top. Elevation is the distance above sea level. The height of a cliff might be 15 m, whereas its elevation might be 1,500 m. Ask: **What is your standing height above ground?** *(Responses will vary with height and floor number.)* **What is your elevation?** *(The same as that of the landform making up the local area)*

Apply Explain that it is possible for the elevation of an object to be less than its height. Tell students that Mauna Loa, a volcano making up part of the Hawaiian Islands, extends from the ocean floor 5,000 m below sea level to an elevation of about 4,170 m. Ask: **What is the volcano's elevation?** *(4,170 m)* **Height?** *(9,170 m)* You might want to sketch this on the chalkboard. **learning modality: logical/mathematical**

Types of Landforms

Teach Key Concepts L2

Plains, Mountains, and Plateaus

Focus Ask students to recall and describe the land at various places where they have vacationed or visited.

Teach Using a map of the United States that shows topographical features, identify for students regions where each landform type occurs. Ask students to compare and contrast the landform types and identify places they have visited. *(Coastal plains—low relief, low elevation; interior plains—low relief, variable elevation; mountains—high relief, high elevation; plateaus—high elevation, low relief)*

Apply Ask: **Which landform region would have long ocean beaches?** *(Coastal plains)* **In which landform region could you visit many ski resorts ?** *(Mountains)* **learning modality: visual**

FIGURE 2
Landforms
Plains, mountains, and plateaus are just a few of the many landforms that make up the topography of Earth's surface.
Forming Operational Definitions *Based on this illustration, how would you define "mountains"?*

Plains
Plains may occur along a continent's edges or in the interior.

Types of Landforms

Landforms vary greatly in size and shape—from level plains extending as far as the eye can see, to low, rounded hills that you could climb on foot, to jagged mountains that would take you many days to walk around. **There are three main types of landforms: plains, mountains, and plateaus.**

Plains A **plain** is a landform made up of nearly flat or gently rolling land with low relief. A plain that lies along a seacoast is called a coastal plain. In North America, a coastal plain extends around the continent's eastern and southeastern shores. Coastal plains have both low elevation and low relief.

A plain that lies away from the coast is called an interior plain. Although interior plains have low relief, their elevation can vary. The broad interior plains of North America are called the Great Plains.

The Great Plains extend north from Texas into Canada. The Great Plains extend west to the Rocky Mountains from the states of North and South Dakota, Nebraska, Kansas, Oklahoma, and Texas. At the time of the Lewis and Clark expedition, the Great Plains were a vast grassland.

Mountains
A mountain's base usually covers an area of at least several square kilometers, but its peak may rise to a point. Mountains often have steeply sloping sides.

Plateaus
The top of a plateau forms a level surface.

Mountains A **mountain** is a landform with high elevation and high relief. Mountains usually occur as part of a mountain range. A **mountain range** is a group of mountains that are closely related in shape, structure, and age. After crossing the Great Plains, the Lewis and Clark expedition crossed a rugged mountain range in Idaho called the Bitterroot Mountains.

The different mountain ranges in a region make up a mountain system. The Bitterroot Mountains are one mountain range in the mountain system known as the Rocky Mountains.

Mountain ranges and mountain systems in a long, connected chain form a larger unit called a mountain belt. The Rocky Mountains are part of a great mountain belt that stretches down the western sides of North America and South America.

Plateaus A landform that has high elevation and a more or less level surface is called a **plateau.** A plateau is rarely perfectly smooth on top. Streams and rivers may cut into the plateau's surface. The Columbia Plateau in Washington State is an example. The Columbia River, which the Lewis and Clark expedition followed, slices through this plateau. The many layers of rock that make up the Columbia Plateau are stacked about 1,500 meters thick.

Lab zone Skills Activity

Classifying
You take a direct flight across the United States from Walla Walla in Washington State to Washington, D.C. You have a window seat. Write a postcard to friends describing the major landforms that you see on your trip. Use Figure 3 to determine what the land is like along your route.

Modeling Landforms

Materials board or cafeteria tray, three colors of modeling clay

Time 20 minutes

Focus Have students review the first sentence under each subheading about the three major landforms.

Teach Have students draw a quick side view of the three different landforms discussed in this section. Make sure that they include a plain, a plateau, and a mountain in their drawings. Ask student groups to use the modeling clay to model each type of landform. Advise them to use a different color of clay for each type of landform and to connect the landforms to form an unbroken landscape of an area.

Apply Ask each student group to appoint a spokesperson who will describe the characteristics of each landform to the class.
learning modality: kinesthetic

Help Students Read L1

Monitoring Your Understanding
Have students identify similarities and differences among mountains, plains, and plateaus. Students should construct a table to record the similarities and differences. For more information about this strategy, see the Content Refresher.

All in One Teaching Resources
• Transparencies G2, G3

Lab zone Skills Activity

Skills Focus Classifying L2

Materials Figure 3, pencil, postcard

Time 10 minutes

Tips Remind students to write their postcards from the perspective of a person on a plane.

Expected Outcome Students describe these features in order: plateaus leading to mountains (Columbia Plateau and northern Rocky Mountains), interior plains (the Great Plains and Central Lowlands), a plateau and mountainous region (the Appalachian Plateau and Appalachian Mountains), and coastal plains (Atlantic Coastal Plain).

Extend Ask students to describe what they might see if they were to stand on the ground in each landform region. **learning modality: visual**

Monitor Progress L2

Skills Check Have students make a compare/contrast table that includes elevation, relief, and a description for each type of landform. Students can place their tables in their portfolios.

Portfolio

Answer
Figure 2 Sample answer: A mountain is a landform with steep sides and peaks that rises high above the surrounding land.

Answers

Figure 3 Charleston, Coastal Plain; Santa Fe, Mountains; Topeka, Interior Plain (or Great Plains)

✓ **Reading Checkpoint** Landform regions can be described by specific terms, such as the Great Plains and the Rocky Mountains, or by more general terms, such as uplands and lowlands.

Assess

Reviewing Key Concepts

1. a. The height above sea level of a point on Earth's surface **b.** Relief is the difference in elevation between the highest and the lowest parts of an area; elevation refers to distance above sea level, whereas relief refers to the maximum difference in elevation in a region. **c.** 1,000 m (1,200 m − 200 m)
2. a. Plains, plateaus, and mountains **b.** A mountain is a landform with high elevation and high relief. **c.** Mountain, mountain range, mountain system, mountain belt

Reteach   L1
Show students a variety of photographs that depict various landforms. Work together as a class to identify and describe each.

Performance Assessment   L2
Drawing Have student groups work together to draw and illustrate a map of Lewis and Clark's journey. Students should include descriptions and drawings of the landform regions encountered on the journey.

All in One Teaching Resources

- Section Summary: *Exploring Earth's Surface*
- Review and Reinforce: *Exploring Earth's Surface*
- Enrich: *Exploring Earth's Surface*

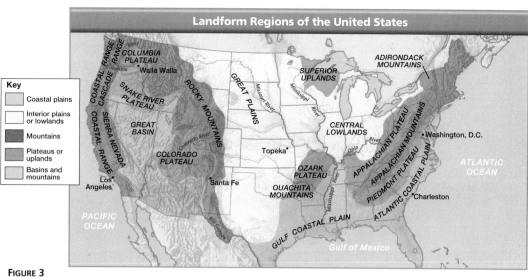

FIGURE 3
The United States has many different landform regions.
Interpreting Maps *In what regions are Charleston, Santa Fe, and Topeka?*

Landform Regions A large area of land where the topography is made up mainly of one type of landform is called a **landform region.** The Great Plains and Rocky Mountains are major landform regions. Other terms can be used to describe landform regions. For example, an upland is a region of hilly topography. A lowland is a region of plains with low elevation. A basin is lower than the mountains around it.

✓ **Reading Checkpoint** What terms can be used to describe landform regions?

Section 1 Assessment

⊙ **Target Reading Skill** Comparing and Contrasting Use the information in your table to help answer Question 2 below.

Reviewing Key Concepts

1. **a. Defining** What is elevation?
   b. Comparing and Contrasting What is relief? How does it differ from elevation?
   c. Calculating What is the relief in an area where the highest point is 1,200 meters above sea level and the lowest point is 200 meters above sea level?
2. **a. Listing** What are the three main types of landforms?
   b. Describing What are the characteristics of a mountain?
   c. Sequencing Place these features in order from smallest to largest: mountain system, mountain range, mountain belt, mountain.

10 ◆ G

Writing in Science

Description Look at Figure 3. Choose one of the landform regions on the map. Research the characteristics of your landform region using an encyclopedia or other reference. Write a description of the region, including characteristics such as elevation, relief, and the types of landforms found there.

Writing in Science

Writing Mode Description
Scoring Rubric
4 Exceeds criteria by including more than three characteristics
3 Meets criteria by including three characteristics
2 Includes only two characteristics
1 Includes inaccurate information

Lab zone Chapter Project

Keep Students on Track Confirm that students have chosen sites and that these are as square or rectangular as possible. Remind students to obtain permission from the property owner to study the site. Students can begin measuring the boundaries, recording the distances, and sketching the topography.

Reading Preview

Key Concepts
- How do maps and globes represent Earth's surface?
- What reference lines are used to locate points on Earth?
- What are three common map projections?

Key Terms
- map • globe • scale
- symbol • key • degree
- equator • hemisphere
- prime meridian • latitude
- longitude • map projection

Target Reading Skill

Asking Questions Before you read, preview the red headings. In a graphic organizer like the one below, ask a question for each heading. As you read, write the answers to your questions.

Models of Earth

Question	Answer
What are maps and globes?	

Lab zone Discover Activity

How Can You Flatten the Curved Earth?

1. Using a felt-tip pen, make a rough sketch of the outlines of the continents on the surface of an orange or grapefruit.
2. Using a plastic knife, carefully peel the orange. If possible, keep the peel in one large piece so that the continents remain intact.
3. Try to lay the pieces of orange peel flat on a table.

Think It Over

Observing What happens to the continents when you try to flatten the pieces? Is there any way to keep the shapes of the continents from being distorted?

Today, people know that Earth is a sphere located in space and moving around the sun. But it took hundreds of years to develop this scientific model of Earth. Around 600 B.C., one early Greek scientist, Thales of Miletus, hypothesized that Earth is a disk floating in a pool of water. Another Greek scientist, Anaximander, suggested that Earth is a cylinder floating in space. (He thought that people lived on the flat top of the cylinder!)

Around 350 B.C., the Greek scientist Aristotle used evidence from everyday observations to support the idea that Earth is a sphere. For example, Aristotle pointed out that a ship sailing away from shore appears to sink beneath the horizon because Earth's surface is curved. If Earth were flat, the ship would simply appear smaller as it moved away.

After Aristotle, other Greek scientists used the knowledge that Earth is a sphere to help them measure the size of Earth. Eratosthenes, a Greek scientist who lived in Egypt more than 2,200 years ago, calculated Earth's size. Using measurements and principles of geometry and astronomy, he arrived at a figure that was accurate to within 14 percent.

Chapter 1 G ◆ 11

Lab zone Discover Activity

Skills Focus Observing   **L1**

Materials felt-tip pen, globe, orange or grapefruit, plastic knife

Time 15 minutes

Tips Have a globe available for reference. Make sure that the felt-tip pens are dark enough to make strong lines on the fruit peel. Point out that the continents need only be roughly sketched.

Expected Outcome Students will find that the peel cannot be placed flat on a table. To do so would require stretching or tearing the peel.

Think It Over The outlines of the continents are distorted or torn. Some students may suggest that the size of the continents would have to be adjusted.

Objectives

After this lesson, students will be able to

G.1.2.1 Explain how maps and globes represent Earth's surface.

G.1.2.2 Identify latitude and longitude as reference lines that help locate points on Earth.

G.1.2.3 Identify three common map projections.

Target Reading Skill

Asking Questions Explain that changing a head into a question helps students anticipate the ideas, facts, and events they are about to read.

Answers

Possible questions and their answers:

Q. What is meant by an Earth reference system?

A. *Just like a checkerboard, a grid system is needed to locate points on Earth.*

Q. How do you locate points on Earth's surface?

A. *Lines of latitude and longitude can be used to locate any place.*

Q. Why are there different types of map projections?

A. *Different types are useful for different purposes.*

All in One Teaching Resources

- Transparency G4

Preteach

Build Background Knowledge   **L2**

Distances on a Map

Display a road map of your state, point out two major cities, and use a ruler to measure the distance between them. Ask: **What is the relationship between distance on the map and real distance?** *(Students may express the concept of proportionality in some way.)* Explain that students will learn how maps are made to a scale that provides a proportional representation.

Instruct

Maps and Globes

Teach Key Concepts ▪L1▪
Representations of Earth's Surface

Focus Ask: **What is a model?** *(Something that represents an object or a system, such as a model car)* **What are some models of Earth?** *(Globes, maps)*

Teach Display a globe and a map. Ask: **What is the difference between a map and a globe?** *(A map is flat and shows all or part of Earth's surface. A globe is a sphere and shows all of Earth's surface.)* **How are they alike?** *(Both are drawn to scale and use symbols to represent features on Earth's surface.)*

Apply Ask: **Why are models of Earth useful?** *(They allow people to visualize an object that is very large.)* **learning modality: visual**

Independent Practice ▪L2▪

All in One Teaching Resources

- Guided Reading and Study Worksheet: *Models of Earth*

⊙ **Student Edition on Audio CD**

Math Skill Scales and Ratios

Focus Ask: **What is the purpose of a scale?** *(It relates distance on a map to real distance.)*

Teach Point out that if the scale of a map is 1:250,000, actual distance is 250,000 times the distance shown on the map. The sample problem shows how to set up the ratio. If the first number in the ratio is always 1, then a quick method to find actual distance is to multiply the denominator by the distance on the map (250,000 × 23.5).

Answer
117,500 cm or 1.175 km; (1 × d = 25,000 × 4.7 cm) or (25,000 × 4.7 cm)

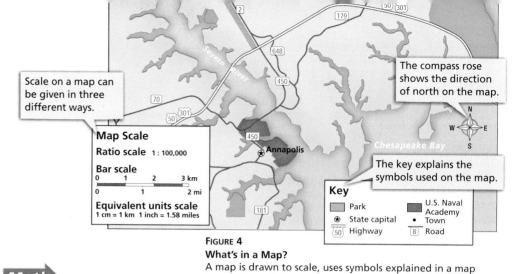

FIGURE 4
What's in a Map?
A map is drawn to scale, uses symbols explained in a map key, and usually has a compass rose to show direction. This map shows the area around Annapolis, Maryland.
Interpreting Maps What is the scale of this map?

Math Skills

Scale and Ratios

A ratio compares two numbers by division. For example, the scale of a map given as a ratio is 1 : 250,000. At this scale, the distance between two points on the map measures 23.5 cm. How would you find the actual distance?

1. Write the scale as a fraction.

$$\frac{1}{250,000}$$

2. Write a proportion. Let *d* represent the distance between the two points.

$$\frac{1}{250,000} = \frac{23.5 \text{ cm}}{d}$$

3. Write the cross products.

$$1 \times d = 250,000 \times 23.5 \text{ cm}$$
$$d = 5,875,000 \text{ cm}$$

(*Hint:* To convert cm to km, divide *d* by 100,000.)

Practice Problem A map's scale is 1 : 25,000. If two points are 4.7 cm apart on the map, how far apart are they on the ground?

Maps and Globes

Maps and globes show the shape, size, and position of Earth's surface features. A **map** is a flat model of all or part of Earth's surface as seen from above. A **globe** is a sphere that represents Earth's entire surface. A globe correctly shows the relative size, shape, and position of landmasses and bodies of water, much as if you were viewing Earth from space.

Maps and globes are drawn to scale and use symbols to represent topography and other features on Earth's surface. A map's **scale** relates distance on a map to a distance on Earth's surface. Scale is often given as a ratio. For example, one unit on a map could equal 25,000 units on the ground. So one centimeter on the map would represent 0.25 kilometer. This scale, "one to twenty-five thousand," would be written "1 : 25,000." Figure 4 shows three ways of giving a map's scale.

Mapmakers use shapes and pictures called **symbols** to stand for features on Earth's surface. A symbol can represent a physical feature, such as a river, lake, mountain, or plain. A symbol also can stand for a human-made feature, such as a highway, city, or airport. A map's **key,** or legend, is a list of all the symbols used on the map with an explanation of their meaning.

Maps also include a compass rose or north arrow. The compass rose helps relate directions on the map to directions on Earth's surface. North usually is located at the top of the map.

✓ **Reading Checkpoint** Where can you find the meaning of the symbols on a map?

FIGURE 5
A Grid System
The checkerboard pattern made by this farmland is based on the grid lines used on maps and globes.

An Earth Reference System

When you play checkers, the grid of squares helps you to keep track of where each piece should be. To find a point on Earth's surface, you need a reference system like the grid of squares on a checkerboard. Of course, Earth itself does not have grid lines, but most maps and globes show a grid. Because Earth is a sphere, the grid curves to cover the entire planet. **Two of the lines that make up the grid, the equator and prime meridian, are the baselines for measuring distances on Earth's surface.**

Measuring in Degrees To locate positions on Earth's surface, scientists use units called degrees. You probably know that degrees are used to measure the distance around a circle. As you can see in Figure 6, a **degree** (°) is $\frac{1}{360}$ of the distance around a circle. Degrees can also be used to measure distances on the surface of a sphere. On Earth's surface, each degree is a measure of an angle formed by lines drawn from the center of Earth to points on the surface. To help locate points precisely, degrees are further divided into smaller units called minutes and seconds.

FIGURE 6
Degrees Around
Distances around a circle are measured in degrees.
Interpreting Diagrams *How many degrees are there in one quarter of the distance around the circle?*

An Earth Reference System

An Earth Reference System

Teach Key Concepts 〔L2〕
Locating Points on Earth

Focus Ask students to look at a globe or a wall map of Earth and locate the equator and the prime meridian.

Teach Ask: **Why are these two lines placed on globes and maps?** *(They are the baselines for a grid used to locate positions on Earth's surface.)* Explain to students that the equator, prime meridian, and lines of latitude and longitude drawn on maps and globes do not really exist on Earth's surface. These lines allow people to locate points on Earth's surface and measure distances between points.

Apply Ask: **Why was it necessary to establish a prime meridian?** *(There needed to be a starting point for measuring longitude.)* **If you started at the prime meridian and traveled east, how many degrees would you have to travel to return to it?** *(360°)* **learning modality: visual**

Measuring in Degrees

Materials round protractor, paper, pencil
Time 25 minutes

Focus Refer students to Figure 6. Beginning with a full circle, review the number of degrees in a full, half, and quarter circle. *(360, 180, 90)*

Teach Challenge students to use a protractor to draw angles measuring 135°, 90°, 75°, 60°, 45°, and 30°. Each angle should be labeled with the appropriate value.

Apply Ask: **Which of the angles is more than a quarter circle?** *(135°)*, **Which is less than one-eighth of a circle?** *(30°)* **learning modality: logical/mathematical**

Monitor Progress _____ 〔L2〕

Writing Have students explain in their own words what it means to draw a map "to scale."

Answers
Figure 4 1:100,000 or 1 cm = 1 km
Figure 6 90 degrees

 Reading Checkpoint   In the map's key

Use Visuals: Figure 7

L2

Equator and Prime Meridian

Focus Direct students' attention to the illustration of Earth showing the equator and the prime meridian.

Teach Ask: **How is the equator like the prime meridian, and how are they different?** *(Both are imaginary lines that provide a basis for an imaginary grid on Earth's surface. The equator is a line that circles Earth in an east-west direction, whereas the prime meridian makes a half circle in a north-south direction.)*

Apply The equator divides Earth into Northern and Southern Hemispheres. Ask: **What is a hemisphere?** *(A hemisphere is one half of the sphere that makes up Earth.)* **learning modality: visual**

Lab zone Teacher **Demo**

Modeling Hemispheres **L1**

Materials one orange, one grapefruit, one cantaloupe, a sharp knife, a permanent marker, paper towels for cleanup

Time 10 minutes

Focus Tell students that each piece of fruit represents Earth.

Teach Model Earth by using the marking pen to draw the equator and the prime meridian on all three fruits. Using a sharp knife, cut the orange in half along the equator line. Then cut the grapefruit in half along the prime meridian.

Apply Hold up the cantaloupe, and point out the equator and the prime meridian. Then hold the two halves of the orange so that the North Pole area is pointing up. Ask: **What do the two halves of the orange represent?** *(They represent the Northern and Southern Hemispheres of Earth).* Hold the two halves of the grapefruit so that the North Pole area is pointing up. Ask: **What do the two halves of the grapefruit represent?** *(They represent the Eastern and Western Hemispheres of Earth.)* **learning modality: visual**

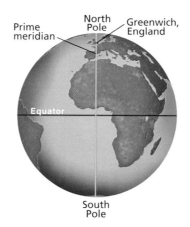

FIGURE 7
Equator and Prime Meridian
The equator and prime meridian divide Earth's surface into hemispheres.

The Equator Halfway between the North and South poles, the **equator** forms an imaginary line that circles Earth. The equator divides Earth into the Northern and Southern hemispheres. A **hemisphere** (HEM ih sfeer) is one half of the sphere that makes up Earth's surface. If you started at the equator and traveled to one of the poles, you would travel 90 degrees—one quarter of the distance in a full circle.

Science and History

Maps and Technology
Centuries ago, people invented instruments for determining compass direction, latitude, and longitude. Mapmakers developed techniques to show Earth's surface accurately.

1154
Scientific Mapmaking
The Arab mapmaker Al-Idrisi made several world maps for King Roger of Sicily. Idrisi's maps marked a great advance over other maps of that time. They showed the Arabs' grasp of scientific mapmaking and geography. But unlike modern maps, these maps placed south at the top!

Around 1100
Magnetic Compass
Because the needle of a magnetic compass points north, ships at sea could tell direction even when the sun and stars were not visible. Arabs and Europeans adopted this Chinese invention by the 1200s.

Around 1300
Charts for Navigation
Lines representing wind directions criss-crossed a type of map called a portolan chart. These charts also showed coastlines and harbors. A sea captain would use a portolan chart and a compass when sailing from one harbor to another.

| 1100 | 1200 | 1300 | 1400 |

14 ◆ G

Background

History of Science The oldest map discovered so far is a clay tablet from about 2300 B.C. The map shows a settlement in a river valley in ancient Babylonia (in present-day Iraq). Ancient Egyptians and ancient Greeks used maps extensively. Ptolemy, a Greek geographer, was the most famous mapmaker of ancient times. Ptolemy's mapmaking ideas had great influence for more than a thousand years.

European voyages of discovery in the 1500s required maps that could show a spherical world on a flat surface. Mercator's solution was to imagine a hollow cylinder around Earth, touching it at the equator. A light at the center of Earth would then "project" the lines of latitude and longitude onto the cylinder. If the cylinder were then unwrapped and laid flat, the result would be the Mercator projection.

The Prime Meridian Another imaginary line, called the **prime meridian**, makes a half circle from the North Pole to the South Pole. The prime meridian passes through Greenwich, England. Places east of the prime meridian are in the Eastern Hemisphere. Places west of the prime meridian are in the Western Hemisphere.

If you started at the prime meridian and traveled west along the equator, you would travel through 360 degrees before returning to your starting point. At 180 degrees east or west of the prime meridian is another half circle that lies directly opposite the prime meridian.

 Reading Checkpoint What two hemispheres are separated by the equator?

Writing in Science

Writing in Science Choose one period on the timeline to learn more about. Use the library to find information about maps in that time. Who used maps? Why were they important? Share what you learn in the form of a letter written by a traveler or explorer who is using a map of that period.

1569
Map Projections
Flemish mapmaker Gerardus Mercator invented the first modern map projection, which bears his name. Mercator and his son, Rumold, also made an atlas and maps of the world such as the one shown above.

1595
Determining Latitude
To find latitude, sailors used a variety of instruments, including the backstaff. The navigator sighted along the backstaff's straight edge to measure the angle of the sun or North Star above the horizon. Later improvements led to modern instruments for navigation.

1763
Determining Longitude
John Harrison, a carpenter and mechanic, won a prize from the British navy for building a highly accurate clock called a chronometer. Harrison's invention made finding longitudes quicker and easier. With exact longitudes, mapmakers could greatly improve the accuracy of their maps.

1500	1600	1700	1800

Chapter 1   G ◆ 15

Address Misconceptions L2

Distance Between Lines of Longitude

Focus Many people assume that lines of longitude are always the same distance apart.

Teach Ask: **How does the distance between lines of longitude change from the equator toward the poles?** *(It decreases.)* **Is the distance represented by one degree of longitude always the same?** *(No. The distance is greatest at the equator and least at the poles.)*

Apply Tell students that one common size of map shows areas that are one degree of latitude high and one degree of longitude wide. Ask: **How would the land area shown by these maps change from the equator to the poles?** *(The land area shown would decrease toward the poles.)*

Science and History

Focus Ask: **Why was it so important for people to develop better maps and technology during this time period?** *(People were beginning to travel long distances, especially by sea.)*

Teach Ask students to speculate about how each advance in the timeline made navigation easier.

Writing in Science

Writing Mode Research

Scoring Rubric

4 Exceeds criteria by thoroughly researching a time period from the timeline and writing a letter from the perspective of a traveler that includes many details

3 Meets criteria by writing a letter about a selected time period that includes the requested information

2 Includes only some of the requested information

1 Includes inaccurate and incomplete information

Differentiated Instruction

Gifted and Talented L3
Finding North Challenge small groups of students to write a procedure by which a mapmaker at a certain location could find true north without the use of a compass. Give students the following information: At this location and day, the sun is directly south at noon. *(Possible procedure: Place a stick in the ground so that it stands upright. At noon, mark the stick's shadow with a pebble. Draw a line along this length of shadow. This line now points to true north.)*

Monitor Progress L2

Drawing Have each student make a simple sketch of a globe that shows the different hemispheres.

Answer

Reading Checkpoint The Northern and Southern Hemispheres

Locating Points on Earth's Surface

Teach Key Concepts L2
Latitude and Longitude

Focus Tell students that lines of latitude and lines of longitude are somewhat similar to city streets. Lines of latitude are similar to east-west streets, and lines of longitude are similar to north-south streets. The intersection of two streets defines a location.

Teach Ask: **Is 30° N a latitude or a longitude?** *(It is a latitude because latitude lines are identified as being north or south of the equator. A latitude of 30° N indicates a circle 30° north of the equator.)* **Is 30° E a latitude or a longitude?** *(It is a longitude because longitude lines are east or west of the prime meridian. A longitude of 30° E indicates a half-circle that is 30° east of the prime meridian.)*

Apply Ask: **Why do you need both latitude and longitude to locate a place on Earth's surface?** *(The intersection of lines of latitude and lines of longitude are specific points.)* **learning modality: logical/ mathematical**

All in One Teaching Resources

• Transparency G5

Integrating Life Science

Ask: **What is the vegetation like near the equator?** *(Tropical plants that include trees and vines and some grasses)* **What is vegetation like at high latitudes?** *(Hearty plants such as mosses and sedges and some low shrubs)* **Are animals also different at different latitudes?** *(Yes. Monkeys might live near the equator, and polar bears might live in Arctic regions.)* **How does latitude affect the distribution of life?** *(Because climate changes with latitude, plant and animal communities also change with latitude.)* **learning modality: verbal**

Help Students Read

Making Inferences Students' understanding often depends on how they apply prior knowledge toward making inferences about new situations. Have students examine Figure 9. Then, ask them to make the inference: **How could you use the grid lines to find a location?** *(Find the line with degrees east or west at the bottom and the line with degrees north or south on the side, then locate the point where the two lines intersect.)*

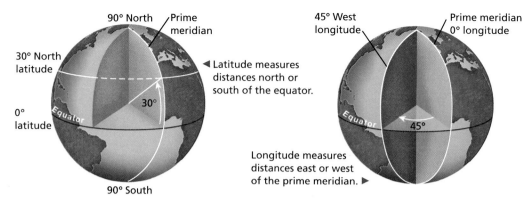

FIGURE 8
Latitude and Longitude
Points on Earth's surface can be located using the grid of latitude and longitude lines.

Lab zone Try This Activity

Where in the World?
Using a globe, determine what city is found at each of the following points:

2° S 79° W

38° N 9° W

34° N 135° E

34° S 58° W

55° N 3° W

1° N 103° E

What word is spelled by the first letters of these cities?

Locating Points on Earth's Surface

Using the equator and prime meridian, mapmakers have constructed a grid made up of lines of latitude and longitude. **The lines of latitude and longitude form a grid that can be used to find locations anywhere on Earth.**

Latitude The equator is the starting line for measuring **latitude,** or distance in degrees north or south of the equator. The latitude of the equator is 0°. Between the equator and each pole are 90 evenly spaced, parallel lines called lines of latitude. Each degree of latitude is equal to about 111 kilometers.

A line of latitude is defined by the angle it makes with the equator and the center of Earth. Figure 8 shows how lines drawn from the center of Earth to the equator and from the center of Earth to 30° North form an angle of 30 degrees.

Longitude The distance in degrees east or west of the prime meridian is called **longitude.** There are 360 lines of longitude that run from north to south, meeting at the poles. Each line represents one degree of longitude. A degree of longitude equals about 111 kilometers at the equator. But at the poles, where the lines of longitude come together, the distance decreases to zero.

The prime meridian, which is the starting line for measuring longitude, is at 0°. The longitude lines in each hemisphere are numbered up to 180 degrees. Half of the lines of longitude are in the Eastern Hemisphere, and half are in the Western Hemisphere.

Each line of longitude is defined by the angle it makes with the prime meridian and the center of Earth. As you can see in Figure 8, a line drawn from the center of Earth to the prime meridian and a line drawn from the center of Earth to 45° West form an angle of 45 degrees at the equator.

Lab zone Try This Activity

Skills Focus Observing

Materials globe

Time 10 minutes

Tips Tell students to identify the major city closest to the coordinates given.

Expected Outcome In order, the cities are Guayaquil, Ecuador; Lisbon, Portugal; Osaka, Japan; Buenos Aires, Argentina;

L2 Edinburgh, Great Britain; and Singapore, Singapore. The word spelled by the first letter of these cities is *GLOBES*.

Extend Have students research the five largest cities in the world and determine the latitude and longitude for each. **learning modality: visual**

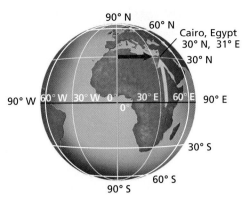

90° N
60° N
Cairo, Egypt
30° N, 31° E
30° N
90° W 60° W 30° W 0° 30° E 60° E 90° E
0°
30° S
60° S
90° S

◀ Cairo, Egypt, is located where the latitude line 30° N crosses the longitude line 31° E.

Go Online
SCI LINKS NSTA

For: Links on latitude and longitude
Visit: www.SciLinks.org
Web Code: scn-0712

Using Latitude and Longitude The location of any point on Earth's surface can be expressed in terms of the latitude and longitude lines that cross at that point. For example, you can see on the map in Figure 9 that New Orleans is located where the line for 30° North latitude crosses the line for 90° West longitude. Notice that each longitude line crosses the latitude lines, including the equator, at a right angle.

 Reading Checkpoint How are longitude lines numbered?

FIGURE 9
Every point on Earth's surface has a particular latitude and longitude.
Interpreting Maps *What are the latitude and longitude of Mexico City? Of Sydney?*

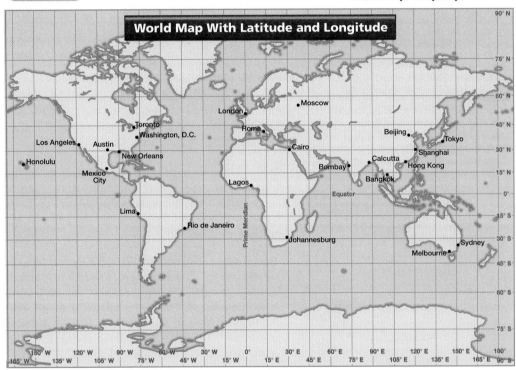

World Map With Latitude and Longitude

London
Moscow
Toronto
Rome
Washington, D.C.
Beijing
Tokyo
Los Angeles
Austin
Cairo
Shanghai
Honolulu
New Orleans
Calcutta
Hong Kong
Mexico City
Bombay
Bangkok
Lagos
Equator
Lima
Rio de Janeiro
Johannesburg
Sydney
Melbourne

Chapter 1 G ◆ 17

Go Online
SCI LINKS NSTA

For: Links on latitude and longitude
Visit: www.SciLinks.org
Web Code: scn-0712

Download a worksheet that will guide students' review of Internet resources on latitude and longitude.

Lab zone Teacher **Demo**

Walking Around Earth L1

Materials globe
Time 5 minutes

Focus Holding up the globe, challenge students to answer this question: **Is it possible to walk around the world, crossing all 360° of longitude, in less than a minute?** *(Accept all responses at this time.)*

Teach Allow students a few minutes to discuss the question. Then repeat the question: **Is it possible? If so, where?** *(It is possible to walk around 360° of longitude at the poles. If a pole were planted at the South Pole, one could simply walk a small circle around the pole.)* Ask: **Is it possible to walk across all lines of latitude?** *(No. One would have to walk from the North Pole to the South Pole or vice versa)* Use the globe to show students how lines of longitude converge at the poles and how lines of latitude are parallel.

Apply Tell students that one plane is flying around the world at 30° N latitude, and another plane is flying around the world at 40° N latitude. Ask: **Which plane must travel farther?** *(The plane at 30° N latitude)* **learning modality: visual**

Monitor Progress L2

Skills Check Have students compare and contrast longitude and latitude lines and explain why both types of lines are needed to locate a point on Earth's surface.

Answers
Figure 9 The latitude and longitude of Mexico City are approximately 19° N 99° W. The latitude and longitude of Sydney are approximately 34° S 151° E.

Reading Checkpoint Longitude lines are numbered up to 180 degrees east and west of the prime meridian.

Differentiated Instruction

English Learners/Beginning L1
Comprehension: Link to Visual Use Figure 9 to help students understand latitude and longitude. Ask students to use their fingers to trace the 30° N line of latitude. Ask them to trace the 90° W line of longitude. Students should identify New Orleans at the intersection. **learning modality: visual**

English Learners/Intermediate L2
Comprehension: Link to Visual Have students use Figure 9 to identify the hemispheres in which the following cities lie: Johannesburg, South Africa; Lima, Peru; Toronto, Canada; and Bangkok, Thailand. *(Johannesburg and Lima, Southern; Toronto and Bangkok, Northern; Lima and Toronto, Western; Bangkok and Johannesburg, Eastern)* **learning modality: visual**

Map Projections

Teach Key Concepts L2

Uses of Maps

Focus Ask: **What advantages do flat maps have over globes?** *(A flat map can be rolled up and carried easily.)* **Why do you think different types of flat maps are made?** *(Different types of maps are useful for different purposes.)*

Teach Ask: **Which map would be most useful for comparing the sizes of continents?** *(Equal-area projection)* **Which map is useful for showing relatively small areas, such as the United States?** *(Conic projection)* **Which map best shows the shapes of continents away from the poles?** *(Mercator projection)*

Apply Ask: **Why are map distortions less of a problem on maps that show a smaller region?** *(These maps represent a smaller section of Earth's surface that is nearly flat.)* **learning modality: logical/ mathematical**

 **Build Inquiry** L2

Sequencing the Sizes of Landmasses

Materials Mercator projection, paper, pencil
Time 15 minutes

Focus Show students a Mercator projection of Earth, or refer them to Figure 10. Remind students that Mercator projections are made by projecting points from a sphere onto a cylinder.

Teach Ask students to look at the map and order the landmasses from largest to smallest: Antarctica, Asia and Europe, North America, Greenland, Africa, South America, Australia. Now ask students to compare this sequence with the actual sequence: Asia and Europe, Africa, North America, South America, Antarctica, Australia, Greenland.

Apply Ask: **Which continents appeared larger than they actually are?** *(Those near the poles—Antarctica and Greenland)* **Why?** *(Mercator projections produce distortions of areas near the poles.)* **learning modality: visual**

FIGURE 10
A Mercator projection is based on a cylinder with grid lines that has been flattened. On a Mercator projection, lines of longitude are parallel, so shapes near the poles are distorted.

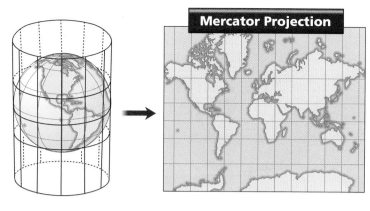

Map Projections

To show Earth's curved surface on a flat map, mapmakers use map projections. A **map projection** is a framework of lines that helps in transferring points on Earth's three-dimensional surface onto a flat map. Features such as continents, oceans, islands, rivers, and lakes might appear to have somewhat different sizes and shapes on different map projections. All projections distort the shapes of these features to some extent. **Three common map projections are the Mercator projection, the equal-area projection, and the conic projection.** Each map projection has advantages and disadvantages.

Mercator Projection On a Mercator projection, all the lines of latitude and longitude appear as straight, parallel lines that form a rectangle. On a Mercator projection, the size and shape of landmasses near the equator are distorted only a little. But as you can see in Figure 10, size and shape become more and more distorted as you go toward the poles. The reason for this distortion is that the lines of longitude on the map do not come together at the poles as they do on a globe. In fact, the North and South poles cannot be shown using a Mercator projection.

Equal-Area Projection To solve the problem of distortion on Mercator projections, mapmakers developed equal-area projections. An equal-area projection correctly shows the relative sizes of Earth's landmasses. But an equal-area projection also has distortion. The shapes of landmasses near the edges of the map appear stretched and curved.

FIGURE 11
An equal-area projection shows areas correctly, but distorts some shapes around its edges.
Comparing and Contrasting *Why does Greenland appear larger on the Mercator projection than on the equal-area projection?*

18 ◆ G

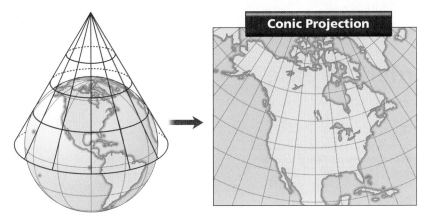

Conic Projection

Conic Projection Suppose you placed a clear plastic cone over a globe, as shown in Figure 12. Then you could trace the lines of latitude and longitude onto the cone, unwrap the cone, and place it flat. The result would be a conic projection. In a conic projection, lines of longitude appear as straight lines while lines of latitude are curved. There is little distortion on maps that use this projection to show limited parts of Earth's surface. A conic projection is frequently used for maps of the continental United States.

FIGURE 12
A conic projection is based on a cone that covers part of Earth and is then rolled out flat. A conic projection's grid is formed from straight lines of longitude and curved lines of latitude.

 Reading Checkpoint Why is a conic projection best suited to showing only part of Earth's surface?

Section 2 Assessment

🎯 **Target Reading Skill** Asking Questions
Work with a partner to check the answers in your graphic organizer.

Reviewing Key Concepts

1. a. **Defining** What is a map?
   b. **Explaining** What information does a globe present?
   c. **Comparing and Contrasting** How are maps and globes similar? How are they different?
2. a. **Identifying** What two lines are baselines for measurements on Earth's surface?
   b. **Explaining** How are these baselines used to locate points on Earth's surface?
   c. **Interpreting Maps** Look at the map in Figure 9. If you fly due north from Lima, through how many degrees of latitude must you travel to reach Washington, D.C.?

3. a. **Listing** What are three common map projections?
   b. **Comparing and Contrasting** What are the advantages and disadvantages of each of the three projections?

Math ▶ **Practice**

4. **Scales and Ratios** A globe has a scale of 1 : 40,000,000. Using a piece of string, you determine that the shortest distance between two cities on the globe is 7 cm. What is the actual distance between the two cities?

Chapter 1 G ◆ 19

Lab zone **Chapter Project**

Keep Students on Track Encourage volunteers to describe any difficulties they had with choosing an area to map. Have students review the sites they chose, explain how they measured the area, describe how they located north on their maps, and discuss the features they are placing on their maps. Emphasize the need to identify features with symbols and a key.

Monitor Progress _____ L2

Answers
Figure 11 Mercator projections exaggerate the sizes of landmasses near the poles. This is because the lines of longitude are parallel, instead of curving in and meeting at the North and South poles, as they do on the equal-area projection.

✓ **Reading Checkpoint** Little distortion occurs when conic projection maps are used to show limited parts of Earth's surface.

Assess

Reviewing Key Concepts

1. a. A map is a flat model of all or part of Earth's surface as seen from above. **b.** A globe shows the relative size, shape, and position of landmasses and bodies of water on Earth's surface. **c.** Both maps and globes are drawn to scale and use symbols to represent features on Earth's surface. Maps often distort the sizes or shapes of landmasses, but globes do not.
2. a. The equator for latitude and the prime meridian for longitude **b.** They form the basis for a grid of latitude and longitude lines that cover Earth's surface and can be used to locate any point on the surface. **c.** Approximately 51° of latitude
3. a. Mercator, equal-area, conic **b.** Mercator projections show the correct shape of landmasses near the equator but distort areas near the poles. Equal-area projections correctly show the relative sizes of Earth's landmasses but distort the shapes of these landmasses near the edges of the maps. Conic projections have little distortion but can be used to show only limited parts of Earth's surface.

4. **Math** ▶ **Practice** 2,800 km

Reteach L1

Ask students to use the appropriate map in this section to locate their town. Ask them to write down the approximate latitude and longitude for their town.

All in One Teaching Resources
• Section Summary: *Models of Earth*
• Review and Reinforce: *Models of Earth*
• Enrich: *Models of Earth*

G ● 19

A Borderline Case ☐2

Prepare for Inquiry

Skills Objectives
Students will be able to
- Observe features that are used to define state borders
- Infer which state borders were drawn along latitude and longitude lines
- Classify state borders according to type

Prep Time 5 minutes
Class Time 30 minutes

All in One Teaching Resources
- Lab Worksheet: *A Borderline Case*

Guide Inquiry

Invitation
Tell students to look at the map of the United States. Ask: **What feature of the borders of a state tells you that the border was drawn along lines of latitude or longitude?** *(Students may respond that some states have borders that are straight lines running either east and west or north and south.)*

Introduce the Procedure
Before students begin, remind them that other surface features may form boundaries between states. Ask: **What other surface features could form natural boundaries between states?** *(Lakes, rivers, and mountain ranges.)*

Troubleshooting the Experiment
Caution students that some state borders may be straight but not parallel to lines of latitude or longitude.

Expected Outcome
Students should be able to infer the basis for determining most state boundaries, whether lines of latitude and longitude or physical features.

Analyze and Conclude
1. Three states are completely defined by lines of latitude and longitude: Wyoming, Colorado, and Utah. Thirty-nine states are partially defined by lines of latitude and longitude. Eight states do not have borders defined by latitude or longitude. These states are Hawaii, Delaware, New Jersey, and five of the New England states (with the exception of Maine).

A Borderline Case

Problem
Which was more important in locating state borders: lines of latitude and longitude or physical features?

Skills Focus
classifying, observing, inferring

Materials
- United States map with latitude, longitude, and state borders
- tracing paper
- paper clips
- colored pencils
- physical map of the U.S.

Procedure
1. Lay a sheet of tracing paper on top of a map of the United States.
2. Trace over the Pacific and Atlantic coasts of the United States with a blue pencil.
3. Using the blue pencil, trace all Great Lakes shorelines that reach nearby states.
4. Trace all state borders that go exactly north-south with a red pencil. (*Hint:* Some straight-line borders that appear to run north-south, such as the western border of Maine, do not follow lines of longitude.)
5. Use a green pencil to trace all state borders or sections of state borders that go exactly east-west. (*Hint:* Straight-line borders that are slanted, such as the southern border of Nevada, do not follow lines of latitude.)
6. Now use a blue pencil to trace the borders that follow rivers.
7. Use a brown pencil to trace any borders that are not straight lines or rivers.

Analyze and Conclude
1. **Classifying** How many state boundaries are completely defined by longitude and latitude? How many are partially defined by longitude and latitude? How many states do not use either one to define their borders?
2. **Observing** What feature is most often used to define a state border when longitude and latitude are not used? Give specific examples.
3. **Observing** Study the physical map of the United States. What other physical features are used to define borders? Which state borders are defined by these features?
4. **Inferring** In which region of the country were lines of latitude and longitude most important in determining state borders? What do you think is the reason for this?
5. **Communicating** Pick any state and describe its borders as accurately as you can in terms of latitude, longitude, and physical features.

More to Explore
Research the history of your state to find out when and how its borders were established. Are your state's borders based on longitude and latitude, landforms and topography, or both?

Review a map of your county or state. Are any features other than borders related to longitude and latitude? Which features seem to follow landforms and topography?

---

2. Rivers, as in the border between Ohio and Kentucky

3. A lake is used between New York and Vermont. Mountain ranges are used between Virginia and West Virginia.

4. The states west of the Mississippi River; this is because the borders were established by land surveys; but some students will notice the lack of significant physical features.

5. Students may choose any state that has easily defined borders.

Extend Inquiry

More to Explore Have students study a state map and make predictions about how the borders were drawn. They can then use encyclopedias and history books to check their predictions.

Maps and Computers

Reading Preview

Key Concepts
- How does computer mapping differ from earlier ways of making maps?
- What sources of data are used in making computer maps?

Key Terms
- surveying • digitizing
- satellite image • pixel
- Global Positioning System

Target Reading Skill
Identifying Main Ideas As you read the Maps and Computers section, write the main idea in a graphic organizer like the one below. Then write three supporting details that further explain the main idea.

Main Idea

Computers use digitized data to make maps.

Detail	Detail	Detail

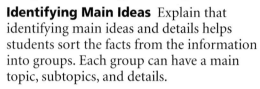

Lab zone Discover **Activity**

Can You Make a Pixel Picture?
1. With a pencil, draw a square grid of lines spaced 1 centimeter apart. The grid should have 6 squares on each side.
2. On the grid, draw the outline of a simple object, such as an apple.
3. Using a different color pencil, fill in all squares that are completely inside the object. If a square is mostly inside the object, fill it in completely. If it is mostly outside, leave it blank.
4. Each square on your grid represents one pixel, or bit of information, about your picture. Looking at your pixel picture, can you recognize the shape you started with?

Think It Over
Predicting How would the pixel picture change if you drew the object smaller? How would the pixel picture look if you used graph paper with squares that are smaller than your grid?

For centuries, mapmakers drew maps by hand. Explorers made maps by sketching coastlines as seen from their ships. More accurate maps were made by locating points on Earth's surface in a process called surveying. In **surveying,** mapmakers determine distances and elevations using instruments and the principles of geometry. In the twentieth century, people learned to make maps using photographs taken from airplanes.

Computer Mapping

Since the 1970s, computers have revolutionized mapmaking. **With computers, mapmakers can store, process, and display map data electronically.**

All of the data used in computer mapping must be written in numbers. The process by which mapmakers convert the location of map points to numbers is called **digitizing.** These numbers are stored on a computer as a series of 0's and 1's. The digitized data can easily be displayed on a computer screen, modified, and printed in map form.

▲ A computer produced this digital model of part of Earth's surface.

Chapter 1 G ◆ 21

Objectives
After this lesson, students will be able to
G.1.3.1 Explain how computer mapping differs from earlier methods of making maps.
G.1.3.2 Describe the types of data that are used for making computer maps.

Target Reading Skill

Identifying Main Ideas Explain that identifying main ideas and details helps students sort the facts from the information into groups. Each group can have a main topic, subtopics, and details.

Answers
One way students might organize the information is to write these three details: Digitizing is converting the location of map points to numbers, much of the data is gathered by satellites, and the Global Positioning System (GPS) is used to find latitude, longitude, and elevation.

All in One Teaching Resources
- Transparency G6

Preteach

Build Background Knowledge [L2]
Using Satellites to Map Earth
Remind students that satellites are launched into Earth's orbit for various purposes. Ask: **What functions do satellites perform?** *(Students may mention a variety of functions, such as military spying and collection of weather data.)* Explain that some satellites gather data about Earth's surface and that these data are used to make maps.

Lab zone Discover **Activity**

Skills Focus Predicting [L1]

Materials metric ruler, unlined paper, colored pencils

Time 15 minutes

Tips Advise students to begin by drawing a horizontal line six centimeters long and marking each centimeter length along that line. Next, have them draw a perpendicular line up from the left edge of the first line and mark each centimeter length along that line. Then, they should complete the square and draw lines from each centimeter mark to the mark on the opposite line. They will make a grid of 36 squares. You might want to provide graph paper so that students can test their predictions.

Expected Outcome Students will observe that the pixel picture and the original outline have a similar though not identical shape.

Think It Over If the squares remain the same size, the smaller object will look less like the original. Conversely, using graph paper with smaller squares will make the pixel picture look more like the original.

Computer Mapping

Teach Key Concepts L2

Mapping Using Computers

Focus Review with students some of the traditional ways of mapmaking, such as exploring coastlines from ships and surveying overland.

Teach Ask: **What is the advantage of using computers for mapmaking?** *(Computers can store, process, and display map data electronically. This allows data to be displayed rapidly and in different ways, depending on the need.)*

Apply Ask: **How has the advance of computerized mapmaking made maps more readily available to the people who need them?** *(Because the data are digitized, the maps can be made available via the Internet.)* **learning modality: logical/mathematical**

Independent Practice L2

All in One Teaching Resources

• Guided Reading and Study Worksheet: *Maps and Computers*

○ **Student Edition on Audio CD**

Sources of Map Data

Teach Key Concepts L2

Data for Mapping

Focus Remind students that satellites are devices that orbit Earth.

Teach Ask: **What can satellites do that mapmakers on the ground cannot?** *(Satellites acquire data from large regions of Earth in a short amount of time.)* **What do satellites detect to get the data?** *(Often some type of electromagnetic radiation, which could include visible light and infrared light, is detected.)*

Apply Ask: **How might people use the maps created from satellite data?** *(The maps could be used to identify vegetation patterns, study the growth of cities, and describe how ocean currents change, among many other uses.)*

Go Online
PHSchool.com

For: More on satellite mapping
Visit: PHSchool.com
Web Code: cfd-2013

Sources of Map Data

Computer mapmakers use these up-to-the-minute data to produce maps quickly and easily. Computers can automatically make maps that might take a person hundreds of hours to draw by hand. **Computers produce maps using data from many sources, including satellites and the Global Positioning System.**

Data From Satellites Much of the data used in computer mapping is gathered by satellites in space. Mapping satellites use electronic devices to collect computer data about the land surface. Pictures of the surface based on these data are called **satellite images.**

A satellite image is made up of thousands of tiny dots called **pixels.** A painting made of pixels would have many separate dots of color. Each pixel in a satellite image contains information on the color and brightness of a small part of Earth's surface. For example, the pixels that represent a forest differ in color and brightness from the pixels that represent farmland. The data in each pixel are stored on a computer. When the satellite image is printed, the computer translates these digitized data into colors.

FIGURE 13
Views of Yellowstone

These views of Yellowstone National Park show how computers have changed the technology of mapmaking. Yellowstone Lake is near the center of both images.

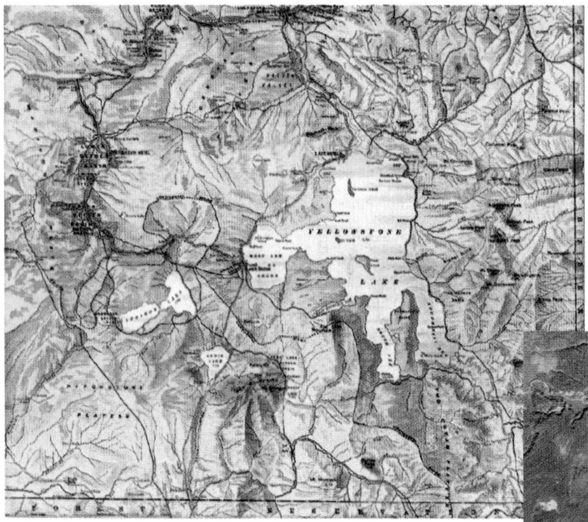

◄ This early map of the Yellowstone region was produced through surveys on the ground.

This satellite image made by the Landsat Thematic Mapper enables scientists to compare areas affected by forest fires (orange) with unburnt forest (green). ►

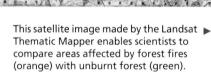

Differentiated Instruction

Special Needs L1
Analyzing Visuals Provide several Landsat images to student pairs. Remind students that in Landsat images, areas covered by grass or trees often show up as red, water often shows up as black or blue, and cities often are bluish gray. Give student pairs clear sheets of acetate and colored markers. Ask students to place the acetate over one Landsat image, and have

them use the markers to color in grass and trees in green, water in blue, and cities in gray. Have students compare their completed drawings with the Landsat images on which they are based. Ask: **Which image is more like an aerial photograph?** *(Students may respond that the colored image on acetate is more like an actual photograph because the image has true colors.)* **learning modality: visual**

Beginning in 1972, the United States launched a series of Landsat satellites designed to observe Earth's surface. Today, Landsat is just one of many different satellites used for this purpose. As a Landsat satellite orbits Earth, it collects and stores data about a strip of the surface that is 185 kilometers wide. The satellite relays the data back to a station on Earth, where computers use the data to create images. Landsat images show what covers the land surface—plants, soil, sand, rock, water, or snow and ice. Large, human-made features such as cities are also visible.

Scientists learn to identify specific features by the "signature," or combination of colors and shapes, that the feature makes on a satellite image. In a satellite image, areas covered by grass, trees, or crops are often shown as red, water as black or blue, and cities as bluish gray. Landsat images may show features such as grasslands, forests, and agricultural crops, as well as deserts, mountains, or cities.

Data From the Global Positioning System Today mapmakers can collect data for maps using the Global Positioning System, or GPS. The **Global Positioning System** is a method of finding latitude, longitude, and elevation of points on Earth's surface using a network of satellites. To learn more about GPS, look at the Technology and Society feature on the next pages.

Reading Checkpoint What is a satellite image?

Mapping Earth's Surface

Video Preview
► Video Field Trip
Video Assessment

Section 3 Assessment

🎯 **Target Reading Skill** Identifying Main Ideas Use your graphic organizer to help you answer Question 1 below.

Reviewing Key Concepts

1. a. **Explaining** In what form is the information for a map stored on a computer?
   b. **Defining** What is digitizing?
   c. **Applying Concepts** What are the advantages of computer mapping?
2. a. **Reviewing** How do satellites gather data for a satellite image?
   b. **Explaining** In what form are data for a satellite image stored?
   c. **Summarizing** Summarize the process by which Landsat produces a satellite image of part of Earth's surface.

Lab zone At-Home Activity

Maps in the News Most of the maps that you see today in newspapers and magazines are made using computers. With family members, look through newspapers and news magazines. How many different types of maps can you find? Explain to your family the map's scale, symbols, and key. After you have studied the map, try to state the main point of the information shown on the map.

Chapter 1 G ◆ 23

Lab zone At-Home Activity

Maps in the News [L2] Students will find a variety of maps, including weather maps, political maps of areas of world interest, and any number of specialized maps, such as those showing population or distribution of natural resources. Review some of these types of maps in class, and then encourage students to convey their knowledge to family members at home.

Technology and Society

Global Positioning System (GPS)

Key Concept

The global positioning system allows users to locate their position on or above Earth.

Build Background Knowledge L2

Recalling Science Concepts

Many students have seen television commercials about smart cars that provide a driver with his or her precise location. Ask: **How can equipment in these cars determine the car's location?** *(Many students will suggest that satellites are used.)* Tell students that GPS satellites have a great variety of uses, including navigation and mapping.

Introduce the Debate

To establish context for a debate about the GPS, ask: **Do you think that the benefits of GPS justify the costs of placing satellites in orbit?** *(Accept all answers as a prelude to debate.)*

Facilitate the Debate

- Before students debate, have them brainstorm lists of both costs and benefits of GPS technology.
- Have students read the feature as a homework assignment. The next day, organize the class in small groups for debate. Have some groups argue for expanded use of GPS technology. Have other groups argue that the costs associated with such expansion are too high.

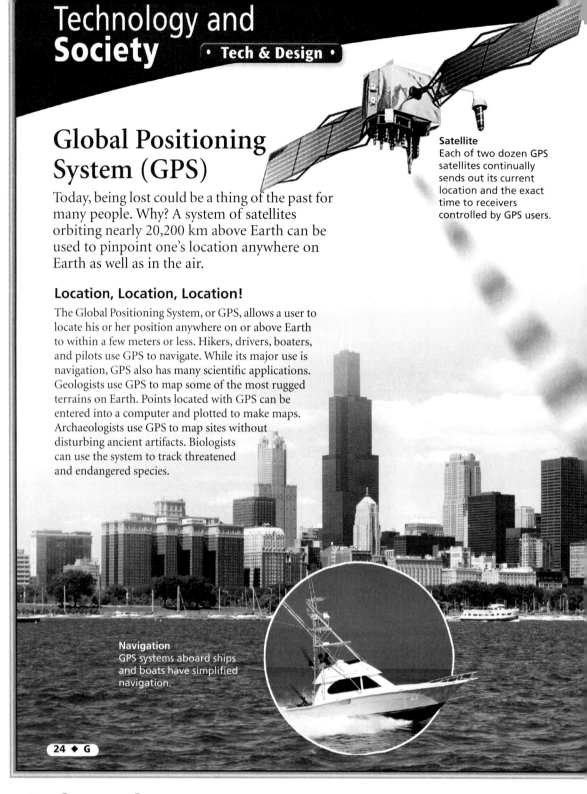

Global Positioning System (GPS)

Today, being lost could be a thing of the past for many people. Why? A system of satellites orbiting nearly 20,200 km above Earth can be used to pinpoint one's location anywhere on Earth as well as in the air.

Satellite
Each of two dozen GPS satellites continually sends out its current location and the exact time to receivers controlled by GPS users.

Location, Location, Location!

The Global Positioning System, or GPS, allows a user to locate his or her position anywhere on or above Earth to within a few meters or less. Hikers, drivers, boaters, and pilots use GPS to navigate. While its major use is navigation, GPS also has many scientific applications. Geologists use GPS to map some of the most rugged terrains on Earth. Points located with GPS can be entered into a computer and plotted to make maps. Archaeologists use GPS to map sites without disturbing ancient artifacts. Biologists can use the system to track threatened and endangered species.

Navigation
GPS systems aboard ships and boats have simplified navigation.

Background

Facts and Figures Global positioning system technology was originally developed for military use. The system still is managed by the Department of Defense. However, during the past decade, civilian use of the system has increased rapidly. Today, with the purchase of appropriate equipment, anyone can make use of the highly accurate GPS system. Costs of using the system continue to decrease, but significant costs are associated with maintaining the system.

Keeping GPS on Track

GPS has become indispensable to surveyors and mappers, many types of scientists and engineers, and many ordinary people who need to know where they are. But like all technologies, GPS has limitations. To receive signals from GPS satellites, receivers need an unobstructed view of the sky. Dense forests and tall buildings can prevent the receivers from picking up signals.

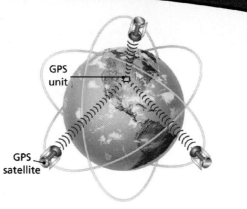

System of Satellites
At least three satellites must be above the horizon to pinpoint a location.

Receiver
GPS receivers are the size of a typical cellular phone. These devices receive and process satellite signals to determine the receiver's precise location.

Weigh the Impact

1. Identify the Need
Think about activities in which knowing one's precise location is important. Make a list of at least five activities.

2. Research
Research the activities you listed in Question 1 to find out if GPS has been applied to them.

3. Write
Choose one application of GPS mentioned in this feature. Or, propose an application of this guidance system that you think might be useful. Write one or two paragraphs to explain the application or how you think GPS might be applied to an activity.

For: More on GPS
Visit: PHSchool.com
Web Code: cfh-2010

Weigh the Impact

1. Students' lists might include the following activities: boating, flying a plane, hiking, tracking wildlife, driving a car, mapmaking, and surveying.

2. GPS has been applied to all activities listed above.

3. Students should explain how GPS makes the activity easier or more accurate.

For: More on GPS
Visit: PHSchool.com
Web Code: cfh-2010

Students can research this issue online.

Extend

Remind students that GPS provides information about location. Provide groups of students with latitude and longitude information for two points: a current location and a destination. Ask them to explain how to reach the destination.

Objectives

After this lesson, students will be able to

G.1.4.1 Explain how elevation, relief, and slope are shown on topographic maps.

G.1.4.2 Explain how a topographic map is read.

G.1.4.3 Describe some uses of topographic maps.

Target Reading Skill

Using Prior Knowledge Explain that using prior knowledge helps students connect what they already know to what they are about to read.

Answers

One possible way to complete the graphic organizer:

What You Know

1. Some maps show where mountains and plains are. 2. Many people use maps to plan a trip or hike in unfamiliar areas.

What You Learned

1. Mapmakers use contour lines to represent elevation, relief, and slope on topographic maps. 2. A map's scale and symbols will help interpret the map's contour lines.

3. Topographic maps have many uses in science and engineering, business, government, and everyday life.

All in One Teaching Resources

• Transparency G7

Preteach

Build Background Knowledge ■L2

Reading Topographic Maps

Provide a topographic map, and ask students to identify familiar features. Ask students to point out contour lines and explain how these lines show changes in elevation. Then draw a series of three concentric circles on the chalkboard. Write the number 10 on the largest circle, 20 on the middle circle, and 30 on the innermost circle. Ask: **What do these numbers suggest about the shape of this feature?** (*Many students will infer that the numbered circles represent a hill as seen from above.*)

Topographic Maps

Reading Preview

Key Concepts

• How do mapmakers represent elevation, relief, and slope?

• How do you read a topographic map?

• What are some uses of topographic maps?

Key Terms

• topographic map
• contour line
• contour interval
• index contour

Target Reading Skill

Using Prior Knowledge Before you read, write what you know about topographic maps in a graphic organizer like the one below. As you read, write what you learn.

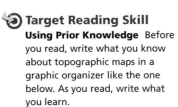

What You Know

1. Some maps show where mountains and plains are.
2.

What You Learned

1.
2.

Lab zone Discover Activity

Can a Map Show Relief?

1. Carefully cut the corners off 8 pieces of cardboard so that they look rounded. Each piece should be at least 1 centimeter smaller than the one before.

2. Trim the long sides of the two largest pieces so that the long sides appear wavy. Don't cut more than 0.5 centimeter into the cardboard.

3. Trace the largest cardboard piece on a sheet of paper.

4. Trace the next largest piece inside the tracing of the first. Don't let any lines cross.

5. Trace the other cardboard pieces, from largest to smallest, one inside the other, on the same paper.

6. Stack the cardboard pieces beside the paper in the same order they were traced. Compare the stack of cardboard pieces with your drawing. How are they alike? How are they different?

Think It Over

Making Models If the cardboard pieces are a model of a landform, what do the lines on the paper represent?

An orienteering meet is not an ordinary race. Participants compete to see how quickly they can find a series of locations called control points. The control points are scattered over a large park or state forest. Orienteers choose a set number of control points, and then visit the points in any order. In this sport, your ability to read a map and use a compass is often more important than how fast you can run. In a major meet, there may be several hundred orienteers on dozens of teams.

At the start of an orienteering meet, you would need to consult your map. But the maps used in orienteering are different from road maps or maps in an atlas—they're topographic maps.

FIGURE 14
Orienteering
Orienteering helps people develop the skill of using a map and compass.

Lab zone Discover Activity

Skills Focus Making models

Materials 8 pieces of cardboard of decreasing size, scissors, unlined paper, pencil, metric ruler

Time 20 minutes

Tips Cut the cardboard pieces in advance. Suggested sizes of cardboard pieces, in centimeters, are 4×4, 6×8, 8×10, 10×12, 12×14, 16×18, 18×22, and ■L1 20×26. Thicker cardboard works best for this activity.

Expected Outcome Students will trace a series of contour lines indicating the "topography" of the stacked pieces of cardboard.

Think It Over The lines on the paper represent contour lines, which are lines that represent various heights.

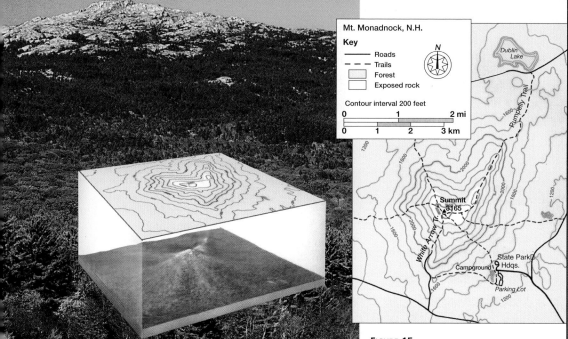

Mt. Monadnock, N.H.

Key

— Roads
- - - Trails
Forest
Exposed rock

Contour interval 200 feet

0   1   2 mi
0   1   2   3 km

Summit 3165
Campground
State Park Hdqs.
Parking Lot

FIGURE 15
Contour Lines
The contour lines on a topographic map represent elevation and relief. **Comparing and Contrasting** *What information does the topographic map provide that the photograph does not?*

For: Topographic Map activity
Visit: PHSchool.com
Web Code: cfp-2014

Mapping Earth's Topography

A **topographic map** (tahp uh GRAF ik) is a map showing the surface features of an area. Topographic maps use symbols to portray the land as if you were looking down on it from above. Topographic maps provide highly accurate information on the elevation, relief, and slope of the ground surface.

Mapmakers use contour lines to represent elevation, relief, and slope on topographic maps. On a topographic map, a **contour line** connects points of equal elevation. In the United States, most topographic maps give contour intervals in feet rather than in meters.

The change in elevation from contour line to contour line is called the **contour interval.** The contour interval for a given map is always the same. For example, the map in Figure 15 has a contour interval of 200 feet. If you start at one contour line and count up 10 contour lines, you have reached an elevation 2,000 feet above where you started. Usually, every fifth contour line, known as an index contour, is darker and heavier than the others. **Index contours** are labeled with the elevation in round units, such as 1,600 or 2,000 feet above sea level.

Reading Checkpoint   What do all the points connected by a contour line have in common?

Reading a Topographic Map

Teach Key Concepts

L2

Topographic Maps

Focus Remind students about the road maps that they have seen. Tell them that topographic maps include all of this information and much more.

Teach Ask: **What features on a road map are also on a topographic map?** (*Scale and some symbols, such as roads and rivers*) **What features are on topographic maps but not on road maps?** (*Additional symbols for marshes, gravel pits, glaciers, and so on; more important, topographic maps also show elevation, relief, and slope with contour lines.*)

Apply Ask: **If you were hiking a mountain trail, what information would you want to know?** (*Possible responses include how long the hike might be, how high the top of the trail is, how steep the trail is, the direction of the climb, and whether any natural features such as glaciers or rock slides exist.*) Tell students that a topographic map of the region would provide all of this information. **learning modality: logical/mathematical**

Observing a Map Compass

L3

Materials topographic map with compass

Time 10 minutes

Focus Explain to students that Earth has a true geographic north pole, which is its north rotational pole, and a magnetic North Pole, which is the north pole of Earth's magnetic field.

Teach Show students a topographic map. Point out that the map has a north arrow and a magnetic north arrow. Ask: **Toward which direction will a compass needle point?** (*Magnetic north*) Show students the angular measure between the two arrows. This angle (declination) is different from place to place and through time.

Apply Ask: **Why are some hand compasses made so that they can be adjusted to point toward true north?** (*When using a compass, it often is more important to know the direction of true north.*) **learning modality: visual**

Figure 16
Topographic Map
The different types of symbols on topographic maps provide data on elevation, relief, slopes, and human-made features. This United States Geological Survey map shows part of Tennessee.

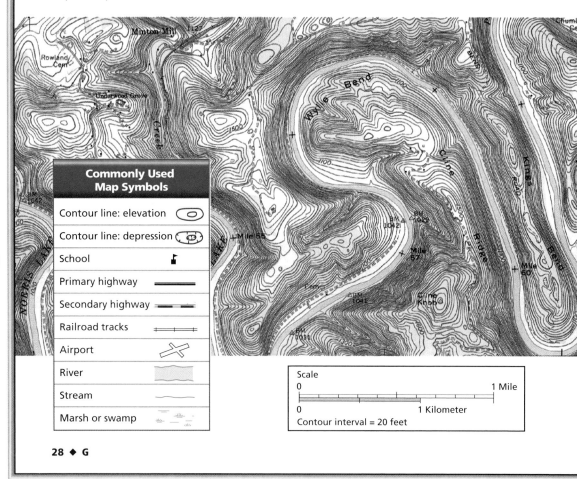

Reading a Topographic Map

Looking at a topographic map with many squiggly contour lines, you may feel as if you are gazing into a bowl of spaghetti. But with practice, you can learn to read a topographic map like the one in Figure 16. **To read a topographic map, you must familiarize yourself with the map's scale and symbols and interpret the map's contour lines.**

Scale Topographic maps are usually large-scale maps. Large-scale maps show a close-up view of part of Earth's surface. In the United States, many topographic maps are at a scale of 1 : 24,000, or 1 centimeter equals 0.24 kilometers. At this scale, a map can show the details of elevation and features such as rivers and coastlines. Large buildings, airports, and major highways appear as outlines at the correct scale. Symbols are used to show houses and other small features.

Mapping Elevation Data

The map shows the elevation data points on which the contour lines are based. Study the map and the map key, then answer the questions.

1. **Reading Maps** What is the contour interval on this map?

2. **Reading Maps** What color are the lowest points on the map? What range of elevations do these points represent?

3. **Reading Maps** What color are the highest points on the map?

4. **Applying Concepts** What is the elevation of the contour line labeled A?

5. **Inferring** Is the area between B and C a ridge or a valley? How can you tell?

6. **Interpreting Data** Describe how elevation changes along the trail from point D to point C.

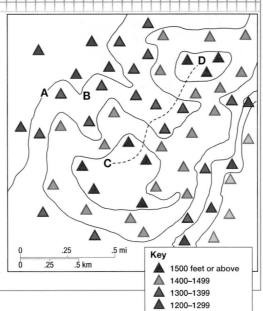

Key

▲	1500 feet or above
▲	1400–1499
▲	1300–1399
▲	1200–1299
△	Below 1200 feet
—	Contour line
--	Trail

Contour interval = 100 feet

Symbols Mapmakers use a great variety of symbols on topographic maps. If you were drawing a map, what symbols would you use to represent a forest, a campground, an orchard, a swamp, or a school? Look at Figure 16 to see the symbols that are often used for these and other features.

Interpreting Contour Lines To find the elevation of a feature, begin at the labeled index contour, which is a heavier line than regular contour lines. Then, count the number of contour lines up or down to the feature.

Reading contour lines is the first step toward "seeing" an area's topography. Look at the topographic map in Figure 16. The closely spaced contour lines indicate steep slopes. The widely spaced contour lines indicate gentle slopes or relatively flat areas. A contour line that forms a closed loop with no other contour lines inside it indicates a hilltop. A closed loop with dashes inside indicates a depression, or hollow in the ground.

The shape of contour lines also help to show ridges and valleys. V-shaped contour lines pointing downhill indicate a ridge line. V-shaped contour lines pointing uphill indicate a valley. A stream in the valley flows toward the open end of the V.

 Reading Checkpoint How are hilltops and depressions represented using contour lines?

Lab zone Skills Activity

Interpreting Data

Study the topographic map in Figure 16. Where are the steepest slopes on the map found? How can you tell? What is the difference in elevation between the river and the top of Cline Knob?

Lab zone Skills Activity

Skills Focus Interpreting data **L2**

Materials Figure 16

Time 5 minutes

Tips Encourage students to go online for the active art before completing this activity.

Expected Outcome Students will identify the steepest slopes along the sides

of the major river, where contour lines are close together. The difference in elevation between the river and the top of Cline Knob is approximately 800 feet.

Extend Have students draw a contour diagram of a hill that has one steep side and one gentle side. **learning modality: visual**

Math Skill Interpreting Maps

Focus Remind students that contour lines connect points of equal elevation.

Teach Ask: **What symbol represents the elevation data points?** (*Triangles*) **What are the wiggly lines on the map?** (*Contour lines*)

Answers

1. 100 feet

2. Yellow, points below 1,200 feet

3. Red, 1,500 feet or above

4. 1,300 feet

5. A valley, contour lines curve uphill

6. At point D, elevation is above 1,500 feet. It then decreases to about midway along the trail where elevation is less than 1,400 feet. Elevation then increases again to point C, which is above 1,500 feet.

Help Students Read **L2**

Relating Text and Visuals Instruct students to refer to Figure 16 after reading *Reading a Topographic Map*. Have them find and explain the scale, locate several objects using the map symbols, and identify hilltops and depressions. Then provide another topographic map and ask questions about its scale, symbols, and contour lines. Encourage students to refer to the text as needed to answer the questions.

Monitor Progress _____ **L2**

Drawing Have each student draw a hill that begins at an elevation of 1,000 feet and has a height of 2,080 feet. Make sure that students draw contour lines, including index contour lines, and that they indicate the contour interval of their lines. Students can place their drawings in their portfolios.

Portfolio

Answer

Reading Checkpoint Hilltops are indicated by a closed loop with no other contour lines inside it. Depressions are indicated by a closed loop with dashes inside it.

Answer

 Businesses use topographic maps to help decide where to locate new stores, housing, or factories.

Uses of Topographic Maps

Teach Key Concepts [L2]

Using Topographic Maps

Focus Remind students that topographic maps show elevation, relief, and slope.

Teach Ask: **Who would need to know the elevation, relief, or slope of a portion of Earth's surface?** (*Students may infer that anyone planning to build something on Earth's surface will need to know about the elevation, relief, or slope of the building site.*)

Apply Ask: **In which type of area would you build a ski resort?** (*A hilly or mountainous area*) **Where would you build a shopping mall?** (*On a flat area with highway access*) **learning modality: logical/mathematical**

Assess

Reviewing Key Concepts

1. a. A map that shows the surface features of an area including elevation and relief **b.** Elevation and relief are represented by contour lines. **c.** 50 m/interval × 12 intervals = 600 m
2. a. The scale, the meaning of the map symbols, and the contour interval **b.** Steep slopes are represented by contour lines that are close together; gentle slopes have contour lines that are farther apart. **c.** A valley
3. a. Science and engineering, business, government, and everyday life **b.** You would look for areas that have few contour lines, or contour lines that are very far apart.

Reteach [L1]

Give student groups a topographic map. Ask students to list the symbols, identify the scale, and describe the contour interval of the map.

All in One Teaching Resources

• Section Summary: *Topographic Maps*
• Review and Reinforce: *Topographic Maps*
• Enrich: *Topographic Maps*

FIGURE 17
Using Topographic Maps
Topographic maps provide the data necessary for the planning of highways, bridges, and other large construction projects.

Uses of Topographic Maps

Topographic maps have many uses in science and engineering, business, government, and everyday life. Suppose that you are an engineer planning a route for a highway over a mountain pass. Your design for the highway needs to solve several problems. To design a safe highway, you need a route that avoids the steepest slopes. To protect the area's water supply, the highway must stay a certain distance from rivers and lakes. You also want to find a route that avoids houses and other buildings. How would you solve these problems and find the best route for the highway? You would probably begin by studying topographic maps.

Businesses use topographic maps to help decide where to build new stores, housing, or factories. Local governments use them to decide where to build new schools and other public buildings. Topographic maps have recreational uses, too. If you were planning a bicycle trip, you could use a topographic map to see where your trip would be flat or hilly.

✓ **Reading Checkpoint** How do businesses use topographic maps?

Section 4 Assessment

🎯 **Target Reading Skill** Using Prior Knowledge Review your graphic organizer and revise it based on what you just learned in the section.

Reviewing Key Concepts

1. **a. Defining** What is a topographic map?
   b. Explaining How do topographic maps represent elevation and relief?
   c. Calculating If the contour interval on a topographic map is 50 meters, how much difference in elevation do 12 contour lines represent?
2. **a. Reviewing** What do you need to know about a topographic map in order to read it?
   b. Comparing and Contrasting Compare the way steep slopes are represented on a topographic map with the way gentle slopes are represented.
   c. Inferring Reading a map, you see V-shaped contour lines that point uphill. What land feature would you find in this area?

3. **a. Listing** What are four main uses of topographic maps?
   b. Problem Solving Suppose that your community needs a large, flat site for a new athletic field. How could you use a topographic map of your area to identify possible sites?

Writing in Science

Giving Directions Write a descriptive paragraph of a simple route from one point on the map in Figure 16 to another point. Your paragraph should provide the starting point, but not the end point. Include details such as distance, compass direction, and topography along the route. Share your paragraph with classmates to see if they can follow your directions.

Writing in Science

Writing Mode Description
Scoring Rubric
4 Exceeds criteria by including more types of details than required
3 Meets criteria by including all required details
2 Includes one or two types of details
1 Includes incomplete or inaccurate description

Lab zone Chapter Project

Keep Students on Track Review all students' work to this point. Make sure that students have made a scale and an initial sketch, brainstormed a list of symbols to use, and begun thinking about making the final map. Talk with students about how to show topography on the map. Encourage students to revise the map if it does not turn out as they envisioned it.

A Map in a Pan

Problem
How can you make a topographic map?

Skills Focus
making models, interpreting maps

Materials
- deep-sided pan
- water
- marking pencil
- modeling clay
- clear, hard sheet of plastic
- metric ruler
- sheet of unlined white paper
- food coloring

Procedure
1. Place a lump of clay on the bottom of a pan. Shape the clay into a model of a hill.
2. Pour colored water into the pan to a depth of 1 centimeter to represent sea level.
3. Place a sheet of hard, clear plastic over the container.
4. Trace the outline of the pan on the plastic sheet with a marking pencil. Then, looking straight down into the pan, trace the outline the water makes around the edges of the clay model. Remove the plastic sheet from the pan.
5. Add another centimeter of water to the pan, bringing the depth of the water to 2 centimeters. Replace the plastic sheet exactly as before, then trace the water level again.
6. Repeat Step 5 several times. Stop when the next addition of water would completely cover your model.
7. Remove the plastic sheet. Trace the outlines that you drew on the plastic sheet onto a sheet of paper.

Analyze and Conclude
1. **Interpreting Maps** Looking at your topographic map, how can you tell which parts of your model hill have a steep slope? A gentle slope?
2. **Interpreting Maps** How can you tell from the map which point on the hill is the highest?
3. **Interpreting Maps** Are there any ridges or valleys on your map?
4. **Applying Concepts** Is there any depression on your map where water would collect after it rained? What symbol should you use to identify this depression?
5. **Making Models** Compare your map with the clay landform. How are they alike? How are they different? How could you improve your map as a model of the landform?

More to Explore
Obtain a topographic map that includes an interesting landform such as a mountain, canyon, river valley, or coastline. After studying the contour lines on the map, make a sketch of what you think the landform looks like. Then build a scale model of the landform using clay or layers of cardboard or foamboard. How does your model landform compare with your sketch?

Prepare for Inquiry

Skills Objectives
After this lab, students will be able to
- Make a topographic map of a model landform
- Interpret a topographic map

Prep Time 1 hour
Class Time 40 minutes

Advance Planning
An aluminum baking pan is a good choice for the deep-sided pan; gather enough pans for each student or group. Cut a rectangular piece of clear plastic for each student or group. This plastic is available at building or hardware stores; it could be cut to order or cut from large sheets with a utility knife. Prepare water colored with food coloring ahead of time.

Alternative Materials
If clear, hard plastic is unavailable, students can use clear plastic wrap, although they will have to be very precise in its placement each time.

All in One Teaching Resources
- Lab Worksheet: *A Map in a Pan*

Guide Inquiry

Invitation
Ask: **What is the orientation of the surface of a body of water?** (*Horizontal*) **What forms when a horizontal surface intersects an object?** (*A line*)

Introduce the Procedure
Give students time to read the whole procedure. Then ask: **What will the outline that you trace onto the plastic become on the sheet of paper?** (*Contour line*) **How will adding 1 cm of water each time be reflected on the map you make?** (*The addition of 1 cm will become the contour interval between contour lines on the map.*)

Expected Outcome
Each student will produce a contour map of the model landform.

Analyze and Conclude
1. Closely-spaced contour lines represent steep slopes. Widely-spaced contour lines represent gentle slopes.

2. The highest point is indicated by a closed loop with no other contour lines inside it.

3. Where V-shaped contour lines point uphill

4. If a depression exists, it should be shown as a closed loop with dashes inside.

5. Both model a natural landform. The clay model has three dimensions, whereas the map has only two dimensions. One possible way to improve the map is to reduce the contour interval.

Extend Inquiry

More to Explore State and national parks make topographic maps available; public libraries often have these maps. Maps also can be obtained from the U.S. Geological Survey or from state surveys.

Study Guide

- Complete student edition
- Section and chapter self-assessments
- Assessment reports for teachers

Help Students Read

Building Vocabulary

Paraphrasing Help students define the key terms in their own words. By paraphrasing, students can use words that are already familiar to them to define new terms. Have students write down the key terms *degree, latitude, longitude, equator, prime meridian,* and *hemisphere.* Then, have them read the text associated with these terms. Finally, have them use the definitions they find to help them write another definition in their own words.

Word Origins Have students write the key terms from the chapter that they have not heard before. These terms may include *digitizing, pixel, plateau, contour line,* and *topography.* Ask students to look up these words in a dictionary and find the origins of the words. For example, the word *topography* is made up from two Greek words—*topos,* meaning "place," and *graphein,* meaning "to write." Therefore, topography is the art or practice of mapmaking, that is, writing down information about the natural and human-made features of a place or region. Have students explore the origins of any word with which they are unfamiliar.

Connecting Concepts

Concept Maps Help students develop one way to show how the information in this chapter is related. The topography of an area includes the area's elevation, relief, and landforms. Types of landforms can be identified on a map through the use of symbols and contour lines. Have students brainstorm to identify the key concepts, key terms, details, and examples, and then write each one on a sticky note and attach it at random on chart paper or on the board.

Tell students that this concept map will be organized in hierarchical order and to

① Exploring Earth's Surface

Key Concepts

- The topography of an area includes the area's elevation, relief, and landforms.
- There are three main types of landforms: plains, mountains, and plateaus.

Key Terms

topography
elevation
relief
landform
plain
mountain
mountain range
plateau
landform region

② Models of Earth

Key Concepts

- Maps and globes are drawn to scale and use symbols to represent topography and other features on Earth's surface.
- Two of the lines that make up the grid, the equator and prime meridian, are the baselines for measuring distances on Earth's surface.
- The lines of latitude and longitude form a grid that can be used to find locations anywhere on Earth.
- Three common map projections are the Mercator projection, the equal-area projection, and the conic projection.

Key Terms

map
globe
scale
symbol
key
degree
equator
hemisphere
prime meridian
latitude
longitude
map projection

③ Maps and Computers

Key Concepts

- With computers, mapmakers can store, process, and display map data electronically.
- Computers produce maps using data from many sources, including satellites and the Global Positioning System.

Key Terms

surveying
digitizing
satellite image
pixel
Global Positioning System

④ Topographic Maps

Key Concepts

- Mapmakers use contour lines to represent elevation, relief, and slope on topographic maps.
- To read a topographic map, you must familiarize yourself with the map's scale and symbols and interpret the map's contour lines.
- Topographic maps have many uses in science and engineering, business, government, and everyday life.

Key Terms

topographic map
contour line
contour interval
index contour

begin at the top with the key concepts. Ask students these questions to guide them to categorize the information on the sticky notes: **How many different types of landforms are there? What lines make up the grid that can be used to locate points on Earth?**

Prompt students by using connecting words or phrases, such as "include" and "used for," to indicate the basis for the organization of the map. The phrases should form a sentence between or among a set of concepts.

Answer

Accept logical presentations by students.

All in One Teaching Resources

- Key Terms Review: *Mapping Earth's Surface*
- Connecting Concepts: *Mapping Earth's Surface*

Review and Assessment

Organizing Information

Concept Mapping Copy the concept map. Then complete the map to show the characteristics of the different types of landforms. (For more about Concept Mapping, see the Skills Handbook.)

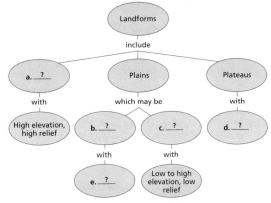

Reviewing Key Terms

Choose the letter of the best answer.

1. A landform that has high elevation but a mostly flat surface is a
   a. plain.
   b. mountain.
   c. mountain range.
   d. plateau.

2. The equator divides Earth into two equal halves called
   a. globes.
   b. hemispheres.
   c. degrees.
   d. pixels.

3. Latitude is a measurement of distance north or south of the
   a. hemisphere.
   b. equator.
   c. index contour.
   d. prime meridian.

4. To show Earth's curved surface on a flat map, mapmakers choose different
   a. map projections.
   b. globes.
   c. scales.
   d. landform regions.

5. The digitized data on a computer map is made up of
   a. index contours.
   b. pixels.
   c. contour intervals.
   d. symbols.

6. On a topographic map, relief is shown using
   a. lines of latitude.
   b. lines of longitude.
   c. map projections.
   d. contour lines.

If the statement is true, write *true*. If it is false, change the underlined word or words to make the statement true.

7. <u>Relief</u> is a landform's height above sea level.

8. The <u>equator</u> is a half circle that extends from the North Pole to the South Pole.

9. If an airplane flew around Earth in a straight line from east to west, the airplane would cross lines of <u>longitude.</u>

10. An <u>index contour</u> is labeled to indicate the elevation along a contour line.

Writing in Science

Advertisement Suppose that you are a manufacturer of GPS tracking and mapping devices. Write an advertisement that describes as many uses for your device as you can think of.

Discovery
CHANNEL
SCHOOL

Mapping Earth's Surface
Video Preview
Video Field Trip
▶ Video Assessment

Chapter 1 G ◆ 33

Review and Assessment

Organizing Information

a. Mountains
b. Coastal
c. Interior
d. High elevation, low relief
e. Low elevation, low relief

Reviewing Key Terms

1. d **2.** b **3.** b **4.** a **5.** b **6.** d
7. false; Elevation
8. false; prime meridian
9. true
10. true

Writing in Science

Writing Mode Persuasion
Scoring Rubric
4 Exceeds criteria by writing an advertisement that includes at least four uses for the device
3 Meets criteria by writing an advertisement that includes three uses for the device
2 Includes two uses for the device
1 Includes one use for the device

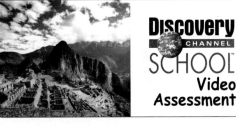

Discovery
CHANNEL
SCHOOL™
Video
Assessment

Mapping Earth's Surface

Show the Video Assessment to review chapter content and as a prompt for the writing assignment. Discussion questions: **List three ways which GPS technology is making it easier for us to know where we are.** (*It is used to locate emergency vehicles, ships at sea, and to display on a map a lost motorists position.*)

Go Online
PHSchool.com
For: Self-Assessment
Visit: PHSchool.com
Web Code: cfa-2010

Students can take an online practice test that is automatically scored.

All in One Teaching Resources
• Transparency G10: Concept Mapping
• Chapter Test
• Performance Assessment Teacher Notes
• Performance Assessment Student Worksheet
• Performance Assessment Scoring Rubric

ExamView® **Computer Test Bank CD-ROM**

Checking Concepts

11. A coastal plain has low elevation, but an interior plain can have low or high elevation.

12. A mountain range is a series of mountains that have the same general shape and structure.

13. A large area of land where the topography is similar is called a landform region.

14. It is in the Eastern Hemisphere because it lies 170 degrees east of the prime meridian.

15. On a Mercator projection, the size and shape of landmasses near the equator are distorted only a little; but as you move towards the poles, size and shape become more distorted.

16. A map's contour interval states the amount by which elevation changes between each contour line.

17. Contour lines that are far apart indicate flat or gently sloping land. Contour lines that are close together indicate steeply sloping land.

Math Practice

18. 1:26,000,000; 26,000,000 cm or 260 km

Thinking Critically

19. A 1.5-meter-deep depression would not show on a map with a 5-meter contour interval because that interval shows only changes in elevation greater than 5 meters. The depression would show on a map with a 1-meter contour interval because the depression is greater than 1 meter.

20. Approximately 8° N latitude and 24° E longitude, (accept reasonable answers); Point A is located in the Northern and Eastern Hemispheres.

21. The colors in the photograph and the satellite image would be different. For example, in a satellite image, vegetation often appears red, water appears black, and cities appear grayish blue.

22. Answers will vary. Students may state that a topographic map could be used to help them plan a bicycle ride or other recreational activity.

Review and Assessment

Checking Concepts

11. Compare the elevation of a coastal plain to that of an interior plain.

12. What is a mountain range?

13. What do geologists call an area where there is mostly one kind of topography?

14. The South Island of New Zealand lies at about 170° E. What hemisphere is it in?

15. What is one advantage of a Mercator projection? What is one disadvantage?

16. What information does a map's contour interval provide?

17. How do the contour lines on a topographic map indicate the slope of the land?

Math Practice

18. Scale and Ratios Earth's diameter is about 13,000 kilometers. If a globe has a diameter of 0.5 meter, write the globe's scale as a ratio. What distance on Earth would 1 centimeter on the globe represent?

Thinking Critically

19. Applying Concepts Which would be more likely to show a shallow, 1.5-meter-deep depression in the ground: a 1-meter contour interval or a 5-meter contour interval?

20. Interpreting Maps Use the map below to answer the question. What is the latitude and longitude of Point A? In which two hemispheres is Point A located?

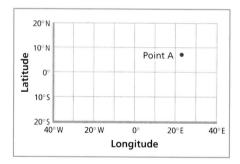

21. Comparing and Contrasting How would the colors in a satellite image of an area compare with a color photograph of the same area?

22. Problem Solving Describe one way in which you could use a topographic map of your community.

Applying Skills

Use the map below to answer Questions 23–25.

This map shows part of Acadia National Park in Maine. The contour interval is 20 feet.

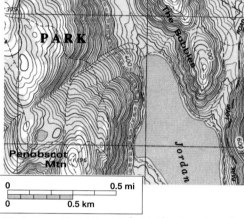

23. Interpreting Maps What is the elevation of the large lake? Which of the two Bubbles is higher?

24. Calculating Use the map scale to calculate the distance from the top of Penobscot Mountain to the large lake.

25. Inferring How can you tell whether the streams flow into or out of the large lake?

Lab zone Chapter Project

Performance Assessment Present your map to the class. What symbols did you use to represent the natural and physical features of your site? How did you measure and locate them on your map? How accurate is your map? Does your map give others a clear idea of what the land looks like?

Lab zone Chapter Project

Project Wrap Up **L3** Help students think about what is important to present and the order in which to present it. Ask other students to come to the front of the class, and have the presenter give directions to these students to determine whether the map can be used easily by others. Encourage constructive suggestions for improvements in each map.

Reflect and Record Advise students to assess the quality of their maps by comparing them with the maps of other students. Suggest that they write in their journals which features they would change if they made another map.

Standardized Test Prep

Choose the letter of the best answer.

1. On a map, what is the height above sea level of a point on Earth's surface?
   A topography   B relief
   C elevation   D latitude

2. You are an engineer preparing to build a new highway exit. You will need to look at details of the area where the new exit will be located. Which map scale would it be best to use, in order to see the needed topographic details?
   F 1 centimeter = 0.25 kilometers
   G 1 centimeter = 10.0 kilometers
   H 1 centimeter = 5.0 kilometers
   J 1 centimeter = 2.5 kilometers

Use the map below and your knowledge of science to answer Questions 3–4.

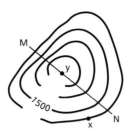

Contour interval = 15 meters

3. A topographic profile shows the shape or relief of the land along a given line. Along line M-N on the map, which of the following would the profile most closely resemble?

A   B

C   D

4. What is the elevation of the point marked *x* on the map?
   F 1400 meters   G 1500 meters
   H 1485 meters   J 1515 meters

5. How is longitude measured?
   A in degrees east or west of the prime meridian
   B in degrees east or west of the equator
   C in degrees north or south of the prime meridian
   D in kilometers east or west of the prime meridian

Constructed Response

6. Write a paragraph comparing a topographic map of an area with a satellite image of the same area. Assume that both are at the same scale. In your answer, explain how the topographic map and the satellite image are similar and how they are different.

Applying Skills

23. **a.** between 260 and 280 feet; **b.** The north Bubble has an elevation of more than 860 feet, which is higher than the south Bubble, at just more than 760 feet.

24. The distance is 0.5 km.

25. The streams flow into the large lake because V-shaped contours point upstream.

Standardized Test Prep

1. C **2.** F **3.** A **4.** H **5.** A
6. Both maps represent the same area at the same scale. The topographic map displays the topography of the land. The satellite image might show land features, such as vegetation.

Chapter at a Glance

PRENTICE HALL

Plan • Teach • Assess

 Chapter **Project** *Soils for Seeds*

Technology

Local Standards

All in One Teaching Resources

- Chapter Project Teacher Notes, pp. 102–103
- Chapter Project Student Overview, pp. 104–105
- Chapter Project Student Worksheets, pp. 106–107
- Chapter Project Scoring Rubric, p. 108

Video Preview

Rocks and Weathering

G.2.1.1 Explain how weathering and erosion affect Earth's surface.

G.2.1.2 Identify what causes mechanical weathering and chemical weathering.

G.2.1.3 Describe the factors that determine how fast weathering occurs.

2–3 periods
1–1 1/2 blocks

PHSchool.com

How Soil Forms

G.2.2.1 Describe the composition of soil, and explain how it forms.

G.2.2.2 Explain how scientists classify soils.

G.2.2.3 Identify the roles of plants and animals in soil formation.

2–3 periods
1–1 1/2 blocks

active art

Soil Conservation

G.2.3.1 Explain why soil is a valuable resource.

G.2.3.2 List ways that soil can lose its value.

G.2.3.3 Identify ways that soil can be conserved.

1 period
1/2 block

Video Field Trip

Review and Assessment

Test Preparation

All in One Teaching Resources

- Key Terms Review, p. 137
- Transparency G18
- Performance Assessment Teacher Notes, p. 144
- Performance Assessment Scoring Rubric, p. 145
- Performance Assessment Student Worksheet, p. 146
- Chapter Test, pp. 147–150

PHSchool.com

Video Assessment

Test Preparation Blackline Masters

Lab zone Chapter Activities Planner

For more activities

LAB ZONE
Easy Planner
CD-ROM

Student Edition	Inquiry	Time	Materials	Skills	Resources
Chapter Project, p. 37	Open-Ended	Ongoing (2–3 weeks)	**All in One** Teaching Resources See p. 102	Observing, comparing and contrasting	**Lab zone Easy Planner** **All in One** Teaching Resources Support, pp. 102–103
Section 1					
Discover Activity, p. 38	Guided	10 minutes	2 fizzing antacid tablets, 2 beakers, warm water, plastic stirring rod, plastic bowl, stopwatch	Drawing conclusions	**Lab zone Easy Planner**
Try This Activity, p. 43	Directed	5 minutes on the first day, 5 minutes three days later	2 pads of steel wool, water, jar with lid	Predicting	**Lab zone Easy Planner**
Skills Lab, pp. 46–47	Guided	Prep 30 minutes; Class 30 minutes on two consecutive days	300 mL of water; balance; paper towels; masking tape; 2 pieces of thin cloth; marking pen or pencil; 300 mL of vinegar; plastic graduated cylinder, 250 mL; 80 small pieces of water-soaked limestone; 4 watertight plastic containers with screw-on caps, 500 mL	Interpreting data, calculating, drawing conclusions	**Lab zone Easy Planner** **Lab Activity Video** **All in One** Teaching Resources Skills Lab: *Rock Shake*, pp. 117–119
Section 2					
Discover Activity, p. 48	Guided	15 minutes	Soil sample, paper plate, paper towel, toothpick, hand lens	Forming operational definitions	**Lab zone Easy Planner**
Try This Activity, p. 51	Directed	30 minutes	Metric ruler, string, stakes, trowel, white poster board, hand lens	Drawing conclusions	**Lab zone Easy Planner**
Consumer Lab, p. 55	Guided	Prep 30 minutes; Class 40 minutes	20–30 grams of local soil, 20–30 grams of bagged topsoil, plastic spoon, plastic dropper, toothpick, water, stereomicroscope, plastic petri dish or jar lid, graph paper ruled with 1- or 2-mm spacing	Observing, inferring, developing hypotheses	**Lab zone Easy Planner** **Lab Activity Video** **All in One** Teaching Resources Consumer Lab: *Comparing Soils*, pp. 128–129
Section 3					
Discover Activity, p. 56	Open-Ended	15 minutes	Soil, pie plate, water, container, craft sticks, paper clips, pebbles, modeling clay, paper	Observing	**Lab zone Easy Planner**

Section 1 **Rocks and Weathering**

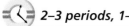 *2–3 periods, 1–1 1/2 blocks*

Objectives

G.2.1.1 Explain how weathering and erosion affect Earth's surface.

G.2.1.2 Identify what causes mechanical weathering and chemical weathering.

G.2.1.3 Describe the factors that determine how fast weathering occurs.

Key Terms

• weathering • erosion • uniformitarianism • mechanical weathering
• abrasion • ice wedging • chemical weathering • oxidation • permeable

Local Standards

Preteach

Build Background Knowledge

Speculate about how headstones change through the years.

Discover Activity *How Fast Can It Fizz?* L1

Targeted Print and Technology Resources

All in One Teaching Resources

L2 Reading Strategy Transparency G11: *Relating Cause and Effect*

PresentationExpress™ CD-ROM

Instruct

Weathering and Erosion Compare the Appalachian and Sierra Nevada Mountains, and consider natural examples of weathering and erosion.

Mechanical Weathering Describe different types of mechanical weathering, and identify examples of each type.

Chemical Weathering Differentiate chemical weathering from mechanical weathering.

Rate of Weathering Identify factors that affect the rate at which weathering occurs.

Skills Lab Rock Shake L2

Targeted Print and Technology Resources

All in One Teaching Resources

L2 Guided Reading, pp. 111–114
L2 Transparencies G12, G13
L2 Skills Lab: *Rock Shake,* pp. 117–119

Lab Activity Video/DVD
Skills Lab: *Rock Shake*

PHSchool.com Web Code: cfd-2021

Student Edition on Audio CD

Assess

Section Assessment Questions

Have students use their completed relating cause and effect graphic organizers to answer the questions.

Reteach

Review the five types of mechanical weathering.

Targeted Print and Technology Resources

All in One Teaching Resources

• Section Summary, p. 110
L1 Review and Reinforce, p. 115
L3 Enrich, p. 116

Section 2 How Soil Forms

 2–3 periods, 1–1 1/2 blocks

Objectives

G.2.2.1 Describe the composition of soil and explain how it forms.
G.2.2.2 Explain how scientists classify soils.
G.2.2.3 Identify the roles of plants and animals in soil formation.

Local Standards

Key Terms

• soil • bedrock • humus • fertility • loam • soil horizon • topsoil • subsoil
• litter • decomposer

Preteach

Build Background Knowledge

Describe local soil, and compare it with commercial potting soil.

 **Discover Activity** *What Is Soil?* **L2**

Targeted Print and Technology Resources

All in One Teaching Resources

L2 Reading Strategy:
Building Vocabulary

⊙ **PresentationExpress™ CD-ROM**

Instruct

What Is Soil? Explain the composition and importance of soil.

The Process of Soil Formation Describe soil horizons and how they form.

Soil Types Describe factors that affect soil type.

Living Organisms in Soil Explain how organic matter becomes humus.

 **Consumer Lab** *Comparing Soils* **L2**

Targeted Print and Technology Resources

All in One Teaching Resources

L2 Guided Reading, pp. 122–125
L2 Transparencies G14, G15, G16
L2 Consumer Lab: *Comparing Soils,* pp. 128–129

📼 **Lab Activity Video/DVD**
Consumer Lab: *Comparing Soils*

PHSchool.com Web Code: cfp-2022

⊙ **Student Edition on Audio CD**

Assess

Section Assessment Questions

Have students use their definitions of key terms to help them answer the questions.

Reteach

Summarize soil formation, classification, and organisms, using a concept map.

Targeted Print and Technology Resources

All in One Teaching Resources

• Section Summary, p. 121
L1 Review and Reinforce, p. 126
L3 Enrich, p. 127

Section 3 **Soil Conservation**

 1 period, 1/2 block

Objectives

G.2.3.1 Explain why soil is a valuable resource.

G.2.3.2 List ways that soil can lose its value.

G.2.3.3 Identify ways that soil can be conserved.

Key Terms

• sod • natural resource • Dust Bowl • soil conservation
• contour plowing • conservation plowing • crop rotation

Local Standards

Preteach

Build Background Knowledge

Describe how wind can pick up and move exposed soil.

 **Discover Activity** *How Can You Keep Soil From Washing Away?* **L1**

Targeted Print and Technology Resources

All in One Teaching Resources

L2 Reading Strategy Transparency
G17: *Previewing Visuals*

⊙ **PresentationExpress™ CD-ROM**

Instruct

The Value of Soil Consider the finite amount of soil on Earth and the consequences of losing it.

Soil Damage and Loss Describe exhausted soil, and explain how the nutrients can be replaced.

Soil Conservation Describe methods to conserve soil, and explain their importance.

Targeted Print and Technology Resources

All in One Teaching Resources

L2 Guided Reading, pp. 132–134

DISCOVERY CHANNEL
SCHOOL
Video Field Trip

www.SciLinks.com Web Code: scn-0723

⊙ **Student Edition on Audio CD**

Assess

Section Assessment Questions

Have students use their graphic organizers to help them answer the questions.

Reteach

Students make a cause-and-effect chart about why people left the Great Plains during the Dust Bowl.

Targeted Print and Technology Resources

All in One Teaching Resources

• Section Summary, p. 131
L1 Review and Reinforce, p. 135
L3 Enrich, p. 136

Chapter 2 Content Refresher

Go Online

NSTA-PDLINKS

For: Professional development support
Visit: www.SciLinks.org/PDLinks
Web Code: scf-0720

Professional Development

Section 1 Rocks and Weathering

Mechanical and Chemical Weathering Mechanical weathering includes a variety of surface processes that break apart rock without changing it chemically. The availability of water in an area and the area's mean annual temperature determine the type of weathering that is most important in that area. As shown in the graph below, chemical weathering is the most important form of weathering in regions with high precipitation and high temperatures. One of the most important forms of mechanical weathering is ice wedging, or "frost action." This process also requires water. Ice wedging predominates in regions with frequent freezing and thawing.

> **Address Misconceptions**
>
> *Some students think that weathering, especially chemical weathering, occurs as large and dramatic events.* For a strategy for overcoming this misconception, see **Address Misconceptions** in *Rocks and Weathering*.

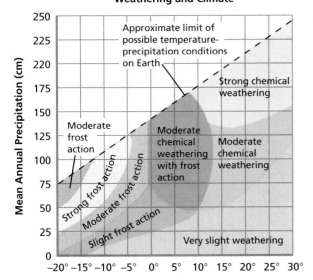

Weathering and Climate

Graph axes: Mean Annual Precipitation (cm) from 0 to 250; Mean Annual Temperature (°C) from −20° to 30°.

Approximate limit of possible temperature-precipitation conditions on Earth

Strong chemical weathering

Moderate frost action

Moderate chemical weathering with frost action

Moderate chemical weathering

Strong frost action

Moderate frost action

Slight frost action

Very slight weathering

Section 2 How Soil Forms

Characteristics of Soils The air and water in soil are important for plants and also for microorganisms and animals in the soil. Without air, plants and other living things would not have the oxygen and carbon dioxide they need to carry out life processes. Too much water in soil can reduce the amount of oxygen available for soil organisms.

The amount of living organic matter in soil varies greatly. In typical topsoil in the eastern United States, living organisms make up about 0.2 percent of the top 15 cm of soil. In one hectare (which is more than twice the size of an acre), there are about 2,000 kg of living roots, about 700 kg of animals (mostly worms), about 500 kg of bacteria, and about 400 kg of fungi.

Section 3 Soil Conservation

Dust Bowl Topsoil is not just dirt. It is a complex mixture of organic and inorganic materials that forms an ideal growing medium for crops. Topsoil doesn't form rapidly enough to be considered a renewable resource—it must be conserved. The topsoil of the prairies in the Midwest formed over several thousand years following the retreat of the glaciers at the end of the last Ice Age. Since the prairies were first plowed for agriculture in the mid-nineteenth century, about half of this topsoil has eroded away. In addition to wind and water erosion, other factors result in loss of topsoil for agricultural purposes. Two such factors are nutrient depletion and the buildup of salts and other minerals in irrigated soils.

Help Students Read

Summarizing

Identifying the Main Ideas

Strategy Use this strategy to help students extract and synthesize the main ideas from a reading passage. Choose several passages from the text, such as explanations about how soil forms, how ice wedging occurs, or methods for conserving soil. After students have read a passage, their summaries can take the form of written summaries, diagrams, or concept maps.

Example

1. Have students read the paragraphs about methods for conserving soil. After students have finished reading, ask each of them to draw a picture illustrating each method. Pictures should be annotated with captions.

2. Have students read the paragraph about ice wedging and examine the accompanying figure. Then ask students to write the main ideas about how ice wedging occurs. After students have written the ideas as a journal entry, the ideas can be assembled into a concept map.

Chapter 2
Weathering and Soil Formation

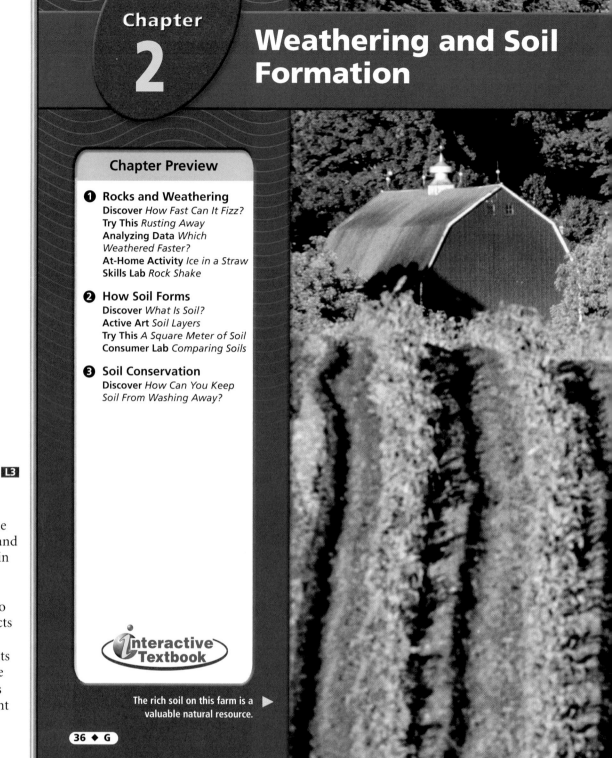

Chapter Preview

interactive Textbook

The rich soil on this farm is a valuable natural resource. ▶

Lab zone Chapter **Project**   L3

Objectives
This project will provide students with the opportunity to examine soils and collect and record data about how bean plants grow in different soils. After this Chapter Project, students will be able to

- design and implement an experiment to investigate different soils and their effects on plant growth
- control variables and take measurements of plant growth during a period of time
- create data tables and draw conclusions about how soil composition affects plant growth
- communicate their conclusions

Skills Focus
Designing experiments, controlling variables, measuring, creating data tables, drawing conclusions, communicating

Project Time Line 2 to 3 weeks

All in One Teaching Resources
- Chapter Project Teacher Notes
- Chapter Project Overview
- Chapter Project Worksheet 1
- Chapter Project Worksheet 2
- Chapter Project Scoring Rubric

Developing a Plan
Observing plant growth requires a minimum of two weeks. Advise students to spend one or two days deciding which soils to use, planting the seeds, and setting up the experiment. After setup, they can create their data tables. Allow class time each day for students to record the growth and health of the plants in their data tables.

Possible Materials
- Sand, gravel, vermiculite, and potting soil can be purchased from a local garden or large home supply store. Students can also collect topsoil from local environments.
- Each group will need 12 to 15 pinto beans and three or four small pots. You may use plastic foam cups with a small hole punched in the bottom as pots.
- Students can use metric rulers to take their measurements.

Lab zone™ Chapter Project

Soils for Seeds

The process of weathering affects all rocks exposed on Earth's surface. Weathering breaks rock into smaller and smaller particles. When the rock particles mix with other ingredients, such as leaves, the mixture is called soil. In this project you will test how soil and other growing materials affect the growth of plants.

Your Goal To determine how soil composition affects the growth of bean seeds

To complete this project, you must

- compare the particle size, shape, and composition of different growing materials
- compare how bean seeds grow in several different growing materials
- determine what type of soil or growing material is best for young bean plants
- follow the safety guidelines in Appendix A

Plan It! In a group, brainstorm what types of soil and other growing materials you will use in your experiment. What are the different variables that affect the growth of plants? How will you measure the growth of your bean plants? Plan your experiment and obtain your teacher's approval. As you carry out your experiment, observe and record the growth of your plants. Then present your results to your class.

Chapter 2 G ◆ 37

Weathering and Soil Formation

Show the Video Preview to introduce the Chapter Project and overview the chapter content. Discussion question: **How are prairie fires vital to the prairie's survival?** *(The fires have prevented trees from becoming plentiful on the prairie and given these grasslands the characteristics they have today.)*

Performance Assessment

The Chapter Project Scoring Rubric will help you evaluate how well students complete the Chapter Project. You may want to share the rubric with your students so that they know what is expected. Students will be assessed on

- how well they set up the experiment and control variables
- how well they measure and record the growth of plants in their data tables
- how effectively they present their results and conclusions to the class
- how much they contribute to their group's effort

Portfolio

Possible Shortcuts

To reduce the time that students spend on the project, you may plant the bean seeds a week in advance. Give each group of students three or four pots to observe. Each pot should contain plants in a different type of soil.

Launching the Project

Display a healthy potted plant, and ask: **How can you meet a plant's requirements?** *(Most students will mention that the right amounts of sunlight and water are necessary. Some might mention good soil.)* Point out that each of the above factors could be investigated; in this project, students will investigate the type of soil. Students will control other factors so that only soil makes a difference in how the plants grow.

Objectives

After this lesson, students will be able to

G.2.1.1 Explain how weathering and erosion affect Earth's surface.

G.2.1.2 Identify what causes mechanical weathering and chemical weathering.

G.2.1.3 Describe the factors that determine how fast weathering occurs.

Target Reading Skill 🔄

Relating Cause and Effect Explain that cause is the reason for what happens. The effect is what happens because of the cause. Relating cause and effect helps students relate the reason for what happens to what happens as a result.

Answer

Possible answers:

oxygen

water

acid rain

All in One Teaching Resources

• Transparency G11

Preteach

Build Background Knowledge　**L2**

Old Headstones

Ask students whether anyone has seen old headstones in a cemetery. Ask: **How would you describe the difference between a new headstone and one that is one hundred years old?** (*A typical answer might describe the old headstone as rounded and crumbling with a faded inscription.*) Invite students to speculate about what processes change a headstone through the years.

Section

1 Rocks and Weathering

Reading Preview

Key Concepts

• How do weathering and erosion affect Earth's surface?

• What are the causes of mechanical weathering and chemical weathering?

• What determines how fast weathering occurs?

Key Terms

• weathering
• erosion
• uniformitarianism
• mechanical weathering
• abrasion
• ice wedging
• chemical weathering
• oxidation
• permeable

🔄 **Target Reading Skill**

Relating Cause and Effect A cause makes something happen. An effect is what happens. As you read, identify the causes of chemical weathering. Write them in a graphic organizer like the one below.

Lab zone　Discover **Activity**

How Fast Can It Fizz?

1. Place a fizzing antacid tablet in a small beaker. Then grind up a second tablet and place it in another beaker. The whole tablet is a model of solid rock. The ground-up tablet is a model of rock fragments.

2. Add 100 mL of warm water to the beaker containing the whole tablet. Then stir with a stirring rod until the tablet dissolves completely. Use a stopwatch to time how long it takes.

3. Add 100 mL of warm water to the beaker containing the ground-up tablet. Then stir until all of the ground-up tablet dissolves. Time how long it takes.

Think It Over

Drawing Conclusions Which dissolved faster, the whole antacid tablet or the ground-up tablet? What variable affected how long it took each of them to dissolve?

Imagine a hike that lasts for months and covers hundreds of kilometers. Each year, many hikers go on such treks. They hike trails that run the length of America's great mountain ranges. For example, the John Muir Trail follows the Sierra Nevada mountains. The Sierras extend about 640 kilometers along the eastern side of California. In the east, the Appalachian Trail follows the Appalachian Mountains. The Appalachians stretch more than 3,000 kilometers from Alabama to Canada.

The two trails cross very different landscapes. The Sierras are rocky and steep, with many peaks rising 3,000 meters above sea level. The Appalachians are more rounded and gently sloping, and are covered with soil and plants. The highest peaks in the Appalachians are less than half the elevation of the highest peaks in the Sierras. Which mountain range do you think is older? The Appalachians formed more than 250 million years ago. The Sierras formed only within the last 10 million years. The forces that wear down rock on Earth's surface have had much longer to grind down the Appalachians.

Lab zone　Discover **Activity**

Skills Focus Drawing conclusions　**L1**

Materials 2 fizzing antacid tablets, 2 beakers, warm water, plastic stirring rod, plastic bowl, stopwatch

Time 10 minutes

Tips Demonstrate how to grind up a tablet by using the stirring rod in a plastic bowl. Have students use warm water from the tap. If stopwatches are unavailable, students can observe a second hand on a watch or wall clock.

Expected Outcome Typical dissolving times are 30 seconds for the whole tablet and 10 seconds for the ground-up tablet.

Think It Over The ground-up tablet dissolved faster than the whole tablet.

Inferences will vary. Some students might correctly suggest that the ground-up tablet had more surface area exposed to water than the whole tablet did and therefore dissolved faster.

Weathering and Erosion

The process of mountain building thrusts rock up to the surface of Earth. There, the rock is exposed to weathering. **Weathering** is the process that breaks down rock and other substances at Earth's surface. Heat, cold, water, and ice all contribute to weathering. So do the oxygen and carbon dioxide in the atmosphere. Repeated freezing and thawing, for example, can crack rock apart into smaller pieces. Rainwater can dissolve minerals that bind rock together. You don't need to go to the mountains to see examples of weathering. The forces that wear down mountains also cause bicycles to rust, paint to peel, sidewalks to crack, and potholes to form.

The forces of weathering break rocks into smaller and smaller pieces. Then the forces of erosion carry the pieces away. **Erosion** (ee ROH zhun) is the removal of rock particles by wind, water, ice, or gravity. **Weathering and erosion work together continuously to wear down and carry away the rocks at Earth's surface.** The weathering and erosion that geologists observe today also shaped Earth's surface millions of years ago. How do geologists know this? Geologists make inferences based on the principle of **uniformitarianism** (yoon uh fawrm uh TAYR ee un iz um). This principle states that the same processes that operate today operated in the past.

There are two kinds of weathering: mechanical weathering and chemical weathering. Both types of weathering act slowly, but over time they break down even the biggest, hardest rocks.

 What is the difference between weathering and erosion?

FIGURE 1
Effects of Weathering
The jagged peaks of the Sierra Nevadas (bottom) formed within the last 10 million years. The more gently sloping Appalachians (top) have been exposed to weathering for 250 million years.
Inferring How can you tell that the Sierra Nevadas formed much more recently than the Appalachians?

G ◆ 39

G ● 39

Mechanical Weathering

Teach Key Concepts L2
Causes of Mechanical Weathering

Focus Point out that all kinds of mechanical weathering have the same effect: breaking apart rock.

Teach Discuss the five types of mechanical weathering shown in Figure 2, and have volunteers describe the pictures and types of weathering in their own words. Ask: **In which of the different types is the composition of rock different after mechanical weathering occurs?** *(None; in each case, the composition of the rock remains the same.)*

Apply Ask: **What are some examples of each type of mechanical weathering that you have seen?** *(Students might have seen very smooth, rounded rocks at a beach, an example of abrasion; they might have seen cracks in sidewalks because of freezing and thawing or plant growth.)* **learning modality: logical/mathematical**

All in One Teaching Resources
• Transparency G12

Mechanical Weathering L1

Materials two pieces of sandstone, newspaper

Time 5 minutes

Focus Tell students that this activity will demonstrate mechanical weathering.

Teach As students watch, have a volunteer rub two pieces of sandstone together over a sheet of newspaper. Students will observe that particles fall on the paper.

Apply Ask: **What kind of mechanical weathering does this model?** *(Abrasion)* **How could such abrasion occur in nature?** *(Water or wind could carry sand particles into rock, grinding part of it away.)* **learning modality: logical/mathematical**

FIGURE 2
Forces of Mechanical Weathering
Mechanical weathering affects all the rock on Earth's surface.
Forming Operational Definitions *Study the examples of mechanical weathering, and then write a definition of each term in your own words.*

Freezing and Thawing
When water freezes in a crack in a rock, it expands and makes the crack bigger. The process of ice wedging also widens cracks in sidewalks and causes potholes in streets.

Release of Pressure
As erosion removes material from the surface of a mass of rock, pressure on the rock is reduced. This release of pressure causes the outside of the rock to crack and flake off like the layers of an onion.

Animal Actions
Animals that burrow in the ground—including moles, gophers, prairie dogs, and some insects—loosen and break apart rocks in the soil.

Mechanical Weathering

If you hit a rock with a hammer, the rock may break into pieces. Like a hammer, some forces of weathering break rock into pieces. The type of weathering in which rock is physically broken into smaller pieces is called **mechanical weathering.** These smaller pieces of rock have the same composition as the rock they came from. If you have seen rocks that are cracked or split in layers, then you have seen rocks that are undergoing mechanical weathering. Mechanical weathering works slowly. But over very long periods of time, it does more than wear down rocks. Mechanical weathering eventually wears away whole mountains.

Abrasion
Sand and other rock particles that are carried by wind, water, or ice can wear away exposed rock surfaces like sandpaper on wood. Wind-driven sand helped shape the rocks shown here.

Plant Growth
Roots of trees and other plants enter cracks in rocks. As roots grow, they force the cracks farther apart. Over time, the roots of even small plants can pry apart cracked rocks.

The causes of mechanical weathering include freezing and thawing, release of pressure, plant growth, actions of animals, and abrasion. The term **abrasion** (uh BRAY zhun) refers to the grinding away of rock by rock particles carried by water, ice, wind, or gravity.

In cool climates, the most important force of mechanical weathering is the freezing and thawing of water. Water seeps into cracks in rocks and then freezes when the temperature drops. Water expands when it freezes. Ice therefore acts like a wedge that forces things apart. Wedges of ice in rocks widen and deepen cracks. This process is called **ice wedging.** When the ice melts, the water seeps deeper into the cracks. With repeated freezing and thawing, the cracks slowly expand until pieces of rock break off.

 Reading Checkpoint How does ice wedging weather rock?

Go Online
PHSchool.com

For: More on weathering
Visit: PHSchool.com
Web Code: cfd-2021

Differentiated Instruction

Gifted and Talented **L3**
Analyzing Visuals Encourage students to look through nature books and magazines to find photographs of the different types of mechanical weathering. Have students classify the type of weathering illustrated and write a sentence explaining why the example demonstrates this type of weathering. Display students' examples on a bulletin board to share with the class.
learning modality: visual

Go Online
PHSchool.com

For: More on weathering
Visit: PHSchool.com
Web Code: cfd-2021

Students can review weathering in an online interactivity.

Help Students Read **L1**
Comparing and Contrasting This technique helps students identify similarities and differences of processes or things. Have students read about mechanical weathering and chemical weathering. After they have read the appropriate passages, have each student draw a Venn diagram that includes ways that the two types of weathering are similar and different.

Monitor Progress _____ **L2**

Drawing Have students draw pictures illustrating the five types of mechanical weathering. Students can place their drawings in their portfolios.

Answers
Figure 2 Release of pressure—the removal of rock layers reduces the pressure on underlying layers, causing cracks. Freezing and thawing—freezing water expands in the cracks in rocks and breaks them apart. Animal action—animals dig holes and burrows, which loosen soil and rock particles. Plant growth—the pressure of growing plant roots breaks apart the cracks in rocks. Abrasion—rock particles carried by wind, water, or ice grind away at rock surfaces.

Reading Checkpoint Wedges of ice in the cracks in rock widen and deepen these cracks. When the ice melts, water seeps deeper into the cracks. With repeated freezing and thawing, the rock eventually breaks apart.

Chemical Weathering

Teach Key Concepts   L2

Mechanical Versus Chemical Weathering

Focus Share with students the meanings of the words *mechanical* and *chemical*. The word *mechanical* implies physical processes. The word *chemical* suggests processes related to chemical reactions.

Teach Help clarify the difference between mechanical and chemical weathering by referring to physical and chemical change. Physical changes include changes in size, shape, state, and so on. These changes do not alter the makeup of a substance. Chemical changes, in contrast, are changes resulting from chemical reactions, in which substances change into other substances.

Apply Have students identify the following as examples of mechanical weathering or chemical weathering: **reddish soil** (*Chemical*), **rock in a desert breaking because of repeated heating and cooling** (*Mechanical*), **ants making large hills** (*Mechanical*). **learning modality: logical/ mathematical**

Use Visuals: Figure 3   L2

Weathering and Surface Area

Focus Remind students that more surface area means more weathering.

Teach Propose that the faces of the unbroken cube in the figure are each 10 m × 10 m and that the rock is on Earth's surface. Ask: **How many square meters of rock are exposed to the forces of chemical weathering?** (*600 m², 6 × 100 m², are exposed to weathering.*)

Apply **If the rock fractures into eight pieces as shown, how much surface area is exposed?** (*Now each face is 5 m × 5 m, or 25 m². Therefore, 1200 m² would be exposed to chemical weathering; 8 pieces × 6 sides each = 48 sides; 48 sides × 25 m²/side = 1200 m².*) **learning modality: logical/mathematical**

All in One Teaching Resources

• Transparency G13

Chemical Weathering

In addition to mechanical weathering, another type of weathering attacks rock. **Chemical weathering** is the process that breaks down rock through chemical changes. **The causes of chemical weathering include the action of water, oxygen, carbon dioxide, living organisms, and acid rain.**

Each rock is made up of one or more minerals. Chemical weathering can produce new minerals as it breaks down rock. For example, granite is made up of several minerals, including feldspar, quartz, and mica. As a result of chemical weathering, granite eventually changes the feldspar minerals to clay minerals.

Chemical weathering creates holes or soft spots in rock, so the rock breaks apart more easily. Chemical and mechanical weathering often work together. As mechanical weathering breaks rock into pieces, more surface area becomes exposed to chemical weathering. The Discover activity at the beginning of this section shows how increasing the surface area increases the rate of a chemical reaction.

FIGURE 3
Weathering and Surface Area
As weathering breaks apart rock, the surface area exposed to weathering increases. The total volume of the rock stays the same even though the rock is broken into smaller and smaller pieces.
Predicting *What will happen to the surface area if each cube is again divided into four cubes?*

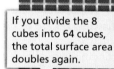
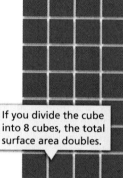

The surface area of a cube is equal to 6 times the area of each side.

If you divide the cube into 8 cubes, the total surface area doubles.

If you divide the 8 cubes into 64 cubes, the total surface area doubles again.

FIGURE 4
Effects of Chemical Weathering
Acid rain chemically weathered these stone gargoyles on the cathedral of Notre Dame in Paris, France.

Water Water is the most important cause of chemical weathering. Water weathers rock by dissolving it. When a rock or other substance dissolves in water, it mixes uniformly throughout the water to make a solution. Over time, many rocks will dissolve in water.

Oxygen The oxygen gas in air is an important cause of chemical weathering. If you have ever left a bicycle or metal tool outside in the rain, then you have seen how oxygen can weather iron. Iron combines with oxygen in the presence of water in a process called **oxidation.** The product of oxidation is rust. Rock that contains iron also oxidizes, or rusts. Rust makes rock soft and crumbly and gives it a red or brown color.

Carbon Dioxide Another gas found in air, carbon dioxide, also causes chemical weathering. Carbon dioxide dissolves in rainwater and in water that sinks through air pockets in the soil. The result is a weak acid called carbonic acid. Carbonic acid easily weathers rocks such as marble and limestone.

Living Organisms Imagine a seed landing on a rock face. As it sprouts, its roots push into cracks in the rock. As the plant's roots grow, they produce weak acids that slowly dissolve rock around the roots. Lichens—plantlike organisms that grow on rocks—also produce weak acids that chemically weather rock.

Acid Rain Over the past 150 years, people have been burning large amounts of coal, oil, and gas for energy. Burning these fuels can pollute the air with sulfur, carbon, and nitrogen compounds. Such compounds react chemically with the water vapor in clouds, forming acids. These acids mix with raindrops and fall as acid rain. Acid rain causes very rapid chemical weathering.

 Reading Checkpoint How can plants cause chemical weathering?

Lab zone **Try This Activity**

Rusting Away
Here's how you can observe weathering.

1. Moisten some steel wool and place it in a closed container so it will not dry out.
2. Observe the steel wool after a few days. What has happened to it?
3. Take a new piece of steel wool and squeeze it between your fingers. Remove the steel wool from the container and squeeze it between your fingers. What happens? Wash your hands when you have finished.

Predicting If you kept the steel wool moist for a longer time, what would eventually happen to it? How is the weathering of steel wool like the weathering of a rock?

Chapter 2 G ◆ 43

Rate of Weathering

Teach Key Concepts   L1

Type of Rock and Climate

Focus Ask students to recall the activity with the fizzing antacid tablets that they did at the beginning of this section. Point out that in addition to surface area, the type of rock and climate also affect the rate of weathering.

Teach Ask: **Do you think chemical weathering occurs faster in hot or cold climates?** (*Most students will choose hot.*) **Why?** (*Higher temperatures speed up chemical reactions.*) **Why might different types of rock weather at different rates?** (*The minerals in some rocks are more easily affected by weathering.*)

Apply Display a map of the world, and locate the United States. Ask: **In which countries would you expect weathering to occur more quickly than it does in the United States?** (*Possible answers include countries that are located in the tropics.*) **learning modality: logical/mathematical**

Math ▶ Analyzing Data

Math Skill Making and interpreting graphs

Focus Review with students what each axis means and how the graph is structured. Point out that line graphs are a good way to show changes over time.

Teach Ask: **What change is being shown over time?** (*The thickness of stone lost to weathering*) **Why would weathering reduce the thickness of the stone?** (*Because the exposed surfaces of stone dissolve during weathering*)

Answers

1. Time in years

2. The thickness of stone lost to weathering

3. Stone A lost about 8.5 millimeters; stone B lost slightly more than 4 millimeters.

4. Stone A weathered at a faster rate.

5. They were exposed to different climate conditions.

Math ▶ Analyzing Data

Which Weathered Faster?
The graph shows the rate of weathering for two identical pieces of limestone that weathered in different locations.

1. Reading Graphs What does the *x*-axis of the graph represent?

2. Reading Graphs What does the *y*-axis of the graph represent?

3. Reading Graphs How much thickness did Stone A lose in 1,000 years? How much thickness did Stone B lose in the same period?

4. Drawing Conclusions Which stone weathered at a faster rate?

5. Inferring Since the two identical pieces of limestone weathered at different rates, what can you infer caused the difference in their rates of weathering?

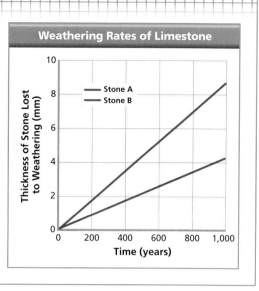

Weathering Rates of Limestone

Rate of Weathering

Visitors to New England's historic cemeteries may notice a surprising fact. Slate tombstones carved in the 1700s are less weathered and easier to read than marble gravestones from the 1800s. Why is this so? Some kinds of rocks weather more rapidly than others. **The most important factors that determine the rate at which weathering occurs are the type of rock and the climate.**

Type of Rock The minerals that make up the rock determine how fast it weathers. Rock made of minerals that do not dissolve easily in water weathers slowly. Rock made of minerals that dissolve easily in water weathers faster.

Some rock weathers more easily because it is permeable. **Permeable** (PUR mee uh bul) means that a material is full of tiny, connected air spaces that allow water to seep through it. Permeable rock weathers chemically at a fast rate. Why? As water seeps through the spaces in the rock, it dissolves and removes material broken down by weathering.

Climate Climate refers to the average weather conditions in an area. Both chemical and mechanical weathering occur faster in wet climates. Rainfall provides the water needed for chemical changes as well as for freezing and thawing.

Differentiated Instruction

English Learners/Beginning   L1
Comprehension: Ask Questions To help students understand factors that affect the rate of weathering, distribute a rewritten, simplified version of the content on this page and the next. Then ask students simple questions that can be answered directly from the rewritten text. **learning modality: logical/ mathematical**

English Learners/Intermediate   L2
Comprehension: Ask Questions Have students read the simplified paragraph that you prepared for *Beginning*. Then challenge students to explain various observations: the inscription on a limestone headstone is less readable than the one on a granite headstone; rock weathers faster in wet climates. **learning modality: logical/ mathematical**

Granite

Marble

Chemical reactions occur faster at higher temperatures. That is why chemical weathering occurs more quickly where the climate is both hot and wet. Granite, for example, is a very hard rock that forms when molten material cools inside Earth. Granite weathers so slowly in cool climates that it is often used as a building stone. But in hot and wet climates, granite weathers more rapidly and eventually crumbles apart.

 Reading Checkpoint How does rainfall affect the rate of weathering?

FIGURE 5
Which Rock Weathers Faster?
These two tombstones are about the same age and are in the same cemetery, yet one has weathered much less than the other.
Inferring Which type of stone weathers faster, granite or marble? Explain.

Section 1 Assessment

Target Reading Skill Relating Cause and Effect Refer to your graphic organizer about the causes of chemical weathering to help you answer Question 2 below.

Reviewing Key Concepts

1. a. **Defining** What is weathering?
   b. **Defining** What is erosion?
   c. **Predicting** Over millions of years, how do weathering and erosion change a mountain made of solid rock?
2. a. **Defining** What is chemical weathering?
   b. **Comparing and Contrasting** Compare and contrast mechanical weathering and chemical weathering.
   c. **Classifying** Classify each as chemical or mechanical weathering: freezing or thawing, oxidation, water dissolving chemicals in rock, abrasion, acid rain.
3. a. **Identifying** What are two factors that affect the rate of weathering?
   b. **Relating Cause and Effect** A granite monument is placed outside for 200 years in a region with a cool, dry climate. What would its rate of weathering be? Explain.

Lab zone **At-Home Activity**

Ice in a Straw Demonstrate one type of weathering for your family. Plug one end of a drinking straw with a small piece of clay. Fill the straw with water. Now plug the top of the straw with clay. Make sure that the clay plugs do not leak. Lay the straw flat in the freezer overnight. Remove the straw the next day. What happened to the clay plugs? What process produced this result? Be sure to dispose of the straw so that no one will use it for drinking.

Chapter 2 G ◆ 45

Rock Shake

Prepare for Inquiry

Key Concept
Mechanical weathering and chemical weathering break down rock into smaller pieces.

Skills Objectives
After this lab, students will be able to
- interpret data about whether acid or water causes more weathering of limestone pieces
- calculate the change in mass of limestone pieces and the percentage change in mass
- draw conclusions about weathering from their data

Prep Time 30 minutes
Class Time 30 minutes on day 1; 30 minutes on day 2

All in One Teaching Resources
- Lab Worksheet: *Rock Shake*

Advance Planning
Collect and prepare the pieces of limestone at least one day in advance. Each student will need 80 pieces. Small limestone gravel is the best material to use. Use a hammer to break up any large pieces. Soak the pieces in water for 24 hours.

The cloth students use should measure about 10 × 10 centimeters; cheesecloth will work best. Prepare in advance a vinegar-water solution that is 75 percent white vinegar and 25 percent distilled water. Use distilled water in containers A and B because tap water is slightly acidic.

Because there are many varieties of limestone, you might want to perform the experiment in advance. Some limestone is very susceptible to change from acid, but other limestone is resistant to such change. Some limestone might break up more easily during shaking. By doing the activity in advance, you can determine likely changes in mass for the pieces in each container.

Safety
Caution students that vinegar can irritate the eyes. Make sure that they wear goggles when pouring the vinegar and shaking the containers. Have students check that the caps are screwed on tightly.

Rock Shake

Problem
How will shaking and acid conditions affect the rate at which limestone weathers?

Skills Focus
interpreting data, calculating, drawing conclusions

Materials
- 300 mL of water
- balance
- paper towels
- masking tape
- 2 pieces of thin cloth
- marking pen or pencil
- 300 mL of vinegar, an acid
- plastic graduated cylinder, 250 mL
- 80 small pieces of water-soaked limestone
- 4 watertight plastic containers with screw-on caps, 500 mL

Procedure

PART 1 Day 1

1. Using masking tape, label the four 500-mL containers A, B, C, and D.
2. Separate the 80 pieces of limestone into four sets of 20.
3. Copy the data table in your notebook. Then place the first 20 pieces of limestone on the balance and record their mass in the data table. Place the rocks in container A.
4. Repeat Step 3 for the other sets of rocks and place them in containers B, C, and D.
5. Pour 150 mL of water into container A and container B. Put caps on both containers.
6. Pour 150 mL of vinegar into container C and container D. Put caps on both containers.
7. Predict the effect of weathering on the mass of the limestone pieces. Which will weather more: the limestone in water or the limestone in vinegar? (*Hint:* Vinegar is an acid.) Also predict the effect of shaking on the limestone in containers B and D. Record your predictions in your notebook.
8. Allow the pieces to soak overnight.

Data Table				
Container	Total Mass at Start	Total Mass Next Day	Change in Mass	Percent Change in Mass
A (water, no shaking)				
B (water, shaking)				
C (vinegar, no shaking)				
D (vinegar, shaking)				

Guide Inquiry

Introduce the Procedure
After students have read the procedure, ask: **What variables are you testing in this experiment?** (*The effects of acid and shaking on limestone*) **What is the purpose of container A?** (*Because container A contains no acid and the pieces are not shaken, it is the control.*)

Troubleshooting the Experiment
- On Day 2, have students look at a clock so that they can time the shaking of containers B and D. If students get tired, they can rest, as long as each container is shaken for the same total amount of time.
- Demonstrate how to pour the water through the cloth. Advise students to pick out the 20 largest pieces, ignoring any sediment.

PART 2 Day 2

9. Screw the caps tightly on containers B and D. Shake both containers for 10 to 15 minutes. Make sure that each container is shaken for exactly the same amount of time and at the same intensity. After shaking, set the containers aside. Do not shake containers A and C.

10. Open the top of container A. Place one piece of thin cloth over the opening of the container. Carefully pour all of the water out through the cloth into a waste container. Be careful not to let any of the pieces flow out with the water. Dry these pieces carefully and record their mass in your data table.

11. Next, determine how much limestone was lost through weathering in container A. (*Hint*: Subtract the mass of the limestone pieces remaining on Day 2 from the mass of the pieces on Day 1.)

12. Repeat Steps 10 and 11 for containers B, C, and D.

Analyze and Conclude

1. **Calculating** Calculate the percent change in mass of the 20 pieces for each container.

$$\% \text{ change} = \frac{\text{Change in mass} \times 100}{\text{Total mass at start}}$$

Record the results in the data table.

2. **Interpreting Data** Do your data show a change in mass of the 20 pieces in each of the four containers?

3. **Interpreting Data** Is there a greater change in total mass for the pieces in one container than for the pieces in another? Explain.

4. **Drawing Conclusions** How correct were your predictions of how shaking and acid would affect the weathering of limestone? Explain.

5. **Developing Hypotheses** If your data showed a greater change in the mass of the pieces in one of the containers, how might this change be explained?

6. **Drawing Conclusions** Based on your data, which variable do you think was more responsible for breaking down the limestone: the vinegar or the shaking? Explain.

7. **Communicating** Write a paragraph that explains why you allowed two of the containers to stand without shaking, and why you were careful to shake the other two containers for the same amount of time.

Design an Experiment

Would your results for this experiment change if you changed the variables? For example, you could soak or shake the pieces for a longer time, or test rocks other than limestone. You could also test whether adding more limestone pieces (30 rather than 20 in each set) would make a difference in the outcome. Design an experiment on the rate of weathering of changing one of these variables. *Have your teacher approve your plan before you begin.*

Extend Inquiry

Design an Experiment Encourage students to continue testing limestone or other types of rock. Granite, for example, is more resistant to both acid and shaking.

Expected Outcome

The pieces in container D will show the greatest change in mass because those pieces were subjected to both chemical and mechanical weathering (acid and shaking). The pieces in container A will show little or no change in mass because they were subjected to neither chemical nor mechanical weathering. The pieces in container C will probably show a greater change in mass than the pieces in container B, depending on the type of limestone.

Analyze and Conclude

1. The percent change in mass of the pieces in each container will vary significantly, depending on the type of limestone used, the original mass of the pieces, the strength of the acid, and the amount of shaking. The exact figures are not important but how the figures compare is important.

2. There should be a change in the mass of the pieces in containers B, C, and D. There should be little or no change in mass of the pieces in container A.

3. The pieces in container D should show the greatest change in total mass because they were subjected to both acid and shaking. The pieces in container A should show the least change because they were not subjected to acid or shaking.

4. Most students will have correctly predicted that the acid and shaking will cause the greatest amount of weathering.

5. The mass of the pieces in container D showed the greatest change because those pieces were soaked in acid overnight and shaken the next day.

6. Most students will suggest that the acid was more responsible for breaking down the limestone because the change in mass of the pieces in container C was greater than the change in mass of the pieces in container B.

7. Two variables were tested in this experiment—the effect of shaking and the effect of acid. The two containers that were not shaken differ only in the absence or presence of acid, so this variable is tested exclusively. Shaking the two containers the same amount of time allowed the acidity variable to be tested with shaking. The shaking variable is tested in water by the "water, no shaking" and "water, shaking" containers. The shaking variable is tested in acid by the "vinegar, no shaking" and "vinegar, shaking" containers.

Objectives

After this lesson, students will be able to

G.2.2.1 Describe the composition of soil and explain how it forms.

G.2.2.2 Explain how scientists classify soils.

G.2.2.3 Identify the roles of plants and animals in soil formation.

Target Reading Skill

Building Vocabulary Explain that knowing the definitions of key-concept words helps students understand what they read.

Answers

As students read each passage that contains a key term, remind them to write a sentence in their own words. Encourage students to write one or two descriptive phrases to help them remember the key term. Call on students to share their definitions.

All in One Teaching Resources

• Guided Reading and Study Worksheet: *How Soil Forms, Use Target Reading Skills*

Preteach

Build Background Knowledge   **L1**

Local Soil

Ask students: **How would you describe the color, feel, and makeup of soil in this area?** (*Answers will vary, depending on local soil type. Students may mention whether the soil is black, brown, or red; sandy or clayey; moist or very dry, and so on.*) Then let students examine and feel a commercial potting soil. Challenge students to explain why that soil is different from the local soil.

Reading Preview

Key Concepts

• What is soil made of and how does it form?

• How do scientists classify soils?

• What is the role of plants and animals in soil formation?

Key Terms

• soil
• bedrock
• humus
• fertility
• loam
• soil horizon
• topsoil
• subsoil
• litter
• decomposer

Target Reading Skill

Building Vocabulary A definition states the meaning of a word or phrase by telling about its most important feature or function. Carefully read the definition of each Key Term and also read the neighboring sentences. Then write a definition of each Key Term in your own words.

Lab zone Discover **Activity**

What Is Soil?

1. Use a toothpick to separate a sample of soil into individual particles. With a hand lens, try to identify the different types of particles in the sample. Wash your hands when you are finished.

2. Write a "recipe" for the sample of soil, naming each of the "ingredients" that you think the soil contains. Include what percentage of each ingredient would be needed to make up the soil.

3. Compare your recipe with those of your classmates.

Think It Over

Forming Operational Definitions Based on your observations, how would you define *soil*?

A bare rock surface does not look like a spot where a plant could grow. But look more closely. In that hard surface is a small crack. Over many years, mechanical and chemical weathering will slowly enlarge the crack. Rain and wind will bring bits of weathered rock, dust, and dry leaves. The wind also may carry tiny seeds. With enough moisture, a seed will sprout and take root. Then, a few months later, the plant blossoms.

What Is Soil?

The crack in the rock seems to have little in common with a flower garden containing thick, rich soil. But soil is what the weathered rock and other materials in the crack have started to become. **Soil** is the loose, weathered material on Earth's surface in which plants can grow.

One of the main ingredients of soil comes from bedrock. **Bedrock** is the solid layer of rock beneath the soil. Once exposed at the surface, bedrock gradually weathers into smaller and smaller particles that are the basic material of soil.

Lab zone Discover **Activity**

Skills Focus Forming operational definitions

Materials soil sample, paper plate, paper towel, toothpick, hand lens

Time 15 minutes

Tips Provide each student with about 50 mL of soil on a paper plate.

L2

Expected Outcome Recipes should reflect a variety of different particles in the soil, including rock fragments and organic matter.

Think It Over Answers will vary. A typical answer might suggest that soil is a mixture of different particles, including sand, clay, rock fragments, and material derived from living things.

Soil Composition Soil is more than just particles of weathered bedrock. **Soil is a mixture of rock particles, minerals, decayed organic material, water, and air.** Together, sand, silt, and clay make up the portion of soil that comes from weathered rock.

The decayed organic material in soil is called humus. **Humus** (HYOO mus) is a dark-colored substance that forms as plant and animal remains decay. Humus helps create spaces in soil for the air and water that plants must have. Humus also contains substances called nutrients, including nitrogen, sulfur, phosphorus, and potassium. Plants need nutrients in order to grow. As plants grow, they absorb nutrients from the soil.

Fertile soil is rich in the nutrients that plants need to grow. The **fertility** of soil is a measure of how well the soil supports plant growth. Soil that is rich in humus has high fertility. Sandy soil containing little humus has low fertility.

Soil Texture Sand feels coarse and grainy, but clay feels smooth and silky. These differences are differences in texture. Soil texture depends on the size of individual soil particles.

The particles of rock in soil are classified by size. As you can see in Figure 7, the largest soil particles are gravel. The smallest soil particles are clay. Clay particles are smaller than the period at the end of this sentence.

Soil texture is important for plant growth. Soil that is mostly clay has a dense, heavy texture. Some clay soils hold a lot of water, so plants grown in them may "drown" for lack of air. In contrast, sandy soil has a coarse texture. Water quickly drains through it, so plants may die for lack of water.

Soil that is made up of about equal parts of clay, sand, and silt is called **loam.** It has a crumbly texture that holds both air and water. Loam is best for growing most types of plants.

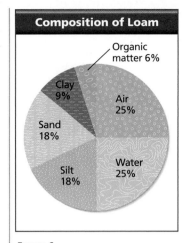

Composition of Loam

Organic matter 6%
Clay 9%
Air 25%
Sand 18%
Water 25%
Silt 18%

Figure 6
Loam, a type of soil, is made up of air, water, and organic matter as well as materials from weathered rock. **Interpreting Graphs** *What two materials make up the major portion of this soil?*

Figure 7
Soil particles range in size from gravel to clay particles too small to be seen by the unaided eye. The sand, silt, and clay shown here have been enlarged.

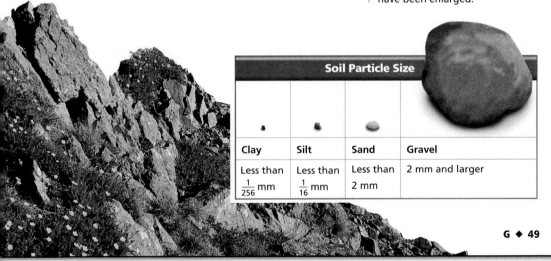

Soil Particle Size

Clay	Silt	Sand	Gravel
Less than $\frac{1}{256}$ mm	Less than $\frac{1}{16}$ mm	Less than 2 mm	2 mm and larger

G ◆ 49

G ● 49

The Process of Soil Formation

Teach Key Concepts [L2]

Soil Horizons and Their Formation

Focus Remind students that a soil horizon is a layer of soil that has unique properties.

Teach Ask: **Which soil horizon is most similar to bedrock?** (*The C horizon; it consists mostly of pieces of bedrock.*) Refer students to Figure 8. Ask: **Which soil horizon forms last?** (*The B horizon forms last as particles wash down from the A horizon.*)

Apply Ask: **Which soil horizon is most important for growing food?** (*The A horizon*) **learning modality: logical/mathematical**

All in One Teaching Resources

• Transparency G14

Examining Soil Horizons [L3]

Materials soil samples from different levels of a roadcut, white paper, toothpick or probe, hand lens

Time 15 minutes

Focus Review with students the characteristics of each soil horizon.

Teach Have students compare and contrast the samples from each horizon and identify them as coming from the A, B, or C horizon.

Apply Ask: **How are the samples different and similar?** (*The A horizon will be darker, the B horizon will be lighter and might be clayey, the C horizon will have larger rock particles.*) **learning modality: kinesthetic**

FIGURE 8
Soil Layers
Soil horizons form in three steps.
Inferring *Which soil horizon is responsible for soil's fertility? Explain.*

The Process of Soil Formation

Soil forms as rock is broken down by weathering and mixes with other materials on the surface. Soil is constantly being formed wherever bedrock is exposed. Soil formation continues over a long period of time.

Gradually, soil develops layers called horizons. A **soil horizon** is a layer of soil that differs in color and texture from the layers above or below it.

If you dug a hole in the ground about half a meter deep, you would see the different soil horizons. Figure 8 shows how soil scientists classify the soil into three horizons. The A horizon is made up of **topsoil**, a crumbly, dark brown soil that is a mixture of humus, clay, and other minerals. The B horizon, often called **subsoil**, usually consists of clay and other particles washed down from the A horizon, but little humus. The C horizon contains only partly weathered rock.

The rate at which soil forms depends on the climate and type of rock. Remember that weathering occurs most rapidly in areas with a warm, rainy climate. As a result, soil develops more quickly in these areas. In contrast, weathering and soil formation take place slowly in areas where the climate is cold and dry.

Some types of rock weather and form soil faster than others. For example, limestone, a type of rock formed from the shells and skeletons of once-living things, weathers faster than granite. Thus, soil forms more quickly from limestone than from granite.

1 The C horizon forms as bedrock weathers and rock breaks up into soil particles.

2 The A horizon develops as plants add organic material to the soil and plant roots weather pieces of rock.

3 The B horizon develops as rainwater washes clay and minerals from the A horizon to the B horizon.

C horizon

Bedrock

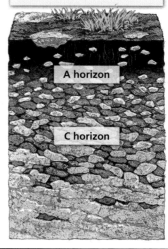

A horizon

C horizon

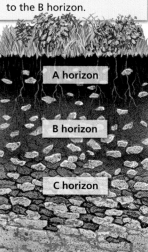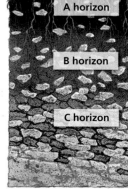

A horizon

B horizon

C horizon

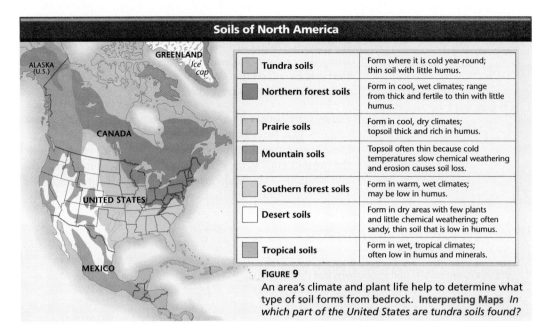

Soils of North America

	Tundra soils	Form where it is cold year-round; thin soil with little humus.
	Northern forest soils	Form in cool, wet climates; range from thick and fertile to thin with little humus.
	Prairie soils	Form in cool, dry climates; topsoil thick and rich in humus.
	Mountain soils	Topsoil often thin because cold temperatures slow chemical weathering and erosion causes soil loss.
	Southern forest soils	Form in warm, wet climates; may be low in humus.
	Desert soils	Form in dry areas with few plants and little chemical weathering; often sandy, thin soil that is low in humus.
	Tropical soils	Form in wet, tropical climates; often low in humus and minerals.

FIGURE 9
An area's climate and plant life help to determine what type of soil forms from bedrock. **Interpreting Maps** In which part of the United States are tundra soils found?

Soil Types

If you were traveling across the hills of north-central Georgia, you would see soils that seem to be made of red clay. In other parts of the country, soils can be black, brown, yellow, or gray. In the United States alone, there are thousands of different types of soil.

Scientists classify the different types of soil into major groups based on climate, plants, and soil composition. Fertile soil can form in regions with hot, wet climates, but rain may wash humus and minerals out of the A horizon. In mountains and polar regions with cold, dry climates, the soil is often very thin. The thickest, most fertile soil forms in climate regions with moderate temperatures and rainfall.

The most common plants found in a region are also used to help classify the soil. For example, grassland soils are very different from forest soils. In addition, scientists classify soil by its composition—whether it is rocky, sandy, or rich in clay. Other factors in the classification of soil include the type of bedrock and the amount of time the soil has been developing.

Major soil types found in North America include forest, prairie, desert, mountain, tundra, and tropical soils. Look at Figure 9 to see where each of the major soil types is found.

Reading Checkpoint What major soil types are found in North America?

Lab zone Try This Activity

A Square Meter of Soil

1. Outdoors, measure an area of one square meter. Mark your square with string.
2. Observe the color and texture of the soil at the surface and a few centimeters below the surface. Is it dry or moist? Does it contain sand, clay, or gravel? Are there plants, animals, or humus?
3. When you finish, leave the soil as you found it. Wash your hands.

Drawing Conclusions What can you conclude about the soil's fertility? Explain.

Lab zone Try This Activity

Skills Focus Drawing conclusions [L2]

Materials metric ruler, string, stakes, trowel, white poster board, hand lens

Time 30 minutes

Tips Provide white poster board on which students can spread out their diggings.

Expected Outcome Students may find rocks, sand, clay, silt, insects, worms, and plants. The soil's fertility is based on its composition, particularly the amount of humus.

Extend Encourage students to examine a second plot of soil in a different location. Have students compare and contrast the soils in the two locations. **learning modality: visual**

Soil Types

Teach Key Concepts [L2]
Classifying Soil

Focus Remind students that when classifying soils, people group soils that have similar properties.

Teach Ask: **What affects the type of soil that forms from bedrock in a region?** *(The region's climate and plant life)* **Why might different soils in Arctic regions have similar characteristics?** *(Because the climate and plant life are similar)*

Apply Ask: **Which soil would be similar to that in the prairie region of the U.S.—a soil in the Brazilian rain forest or a soil in the grasslands of Argentina?** *(The grassland soil in Argentina)* **learning modality: verbal**

Use Visuals: Figure 9 [L2]
Soils of North America

Focus Ask volunteers to explain how to read the figure. Check that students can correlate the groups described in the key with those shown on the map.

Teach Have students locate your state on the map. Then ask: **Which soil type exists where we live? What climate and vegetation types occur in our region?** Remind students that climate and vegetation type affect soil.

Apply Ask: **Why does soil type vary across the country?** *(Because vegetation and climate vary)* **learning modality: visual**

All in One Teaching Resources
• Transparency G15

Monitor Progress [L2]

Skills Check Have each student create a flowchart that shows the process of soil formation. Have students place their flowcharts in their portfolios.

Answers
Figure 8 The A horizon
Figure 9 Alaska

Reading Checkpoint Forest, prairie, desert, mountain, tundra, and tropical

Living Organisms in Soil

Teach Key Concepts L2
Formation of Humus

Focus Ask: **Have you ever walked through a forest and noticed the thick layer of leaves on the forest floor?** (*Many students have experienced this.*) Tell students that this material is litter and that litter is one source of organic matter for soils.

Teach Ask: **How does organic matter, like litter, become humus?** (*Bacteria and fungi feed on the organic matter. Humus forms during this process.*) **Where does most of the organic matter go?** (*Some is given off as carbon dioxide gas, and some goes into the bodies of the decomposing organisms.*) **Why does humus remain?** (*It is more resistant to being used for food than other types of organic matter.*)

Apply Ask: **Why is humus essential for plant growth?** (*Humus contains important nutrients and gives the soil an airy, open structure.*) **learning modality: logical/mathematical**

Use Visuals: Figure 10 L2
Life in Soil

Focus Have students list the different organisms shown in Figure 10.

Teach Ask: **How are the organisms in the illustration adapted to living in soil?** (*Animals such as mice and chipmunks have claws for digging. Earthworms are segmented, enabling them to burrow through the soil. Insects have mouth parts and appendages for eating and burrowing.*)

Apply Ask: **In which part of the soil would you expect to find the fewest examples of plant and animal life? Explain.** (*The C horizon—it lacks the nutrients and organic matter that occur in the upper layers. The C horizon is difficult for animals to burrow through and for plant roots to grow through.*)
learning modality: visual

All in One Teaching Resources
• Transparency G16

Living Organisms in Soil

If you look closely at soil, you can see that it is teeming with living things. **Some soil organisms make humus, the material that makes soil fertile. Other soil organisms mix the soil and make spaces in it for air and water.**

Forming Humus Plants contribute most of the organic remains that form humus. As plants shed leaves, they form a loose layer called **litter.** When plants die, their remains fall to the ground and become part of the litter. Plant roots also die and begin to decay underground. Although plant remains are full of stored nutrients, they are not yet humus.

FIGURE 10
Life in Soil

Every cubic meter of soil contains billions of organisms. All organisms that live in soil enrich humus with their remains or wastes. This illustration shows some of the organisms typically found in northern forest soil.
Relating Cause and Effect *Which organisms in the art help air and water to enter the soil?*

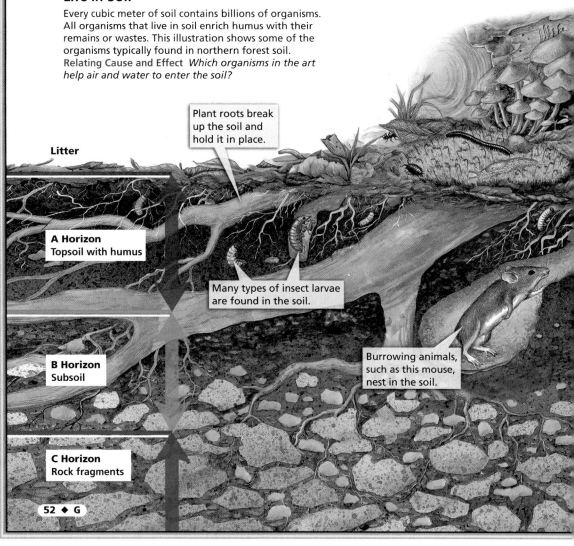

Litter

Plant roots break up the soil and hold it in place.

A Horizon
Topsoil with humus

Many types of insect larvae are found in the soil.

B Horizon
Subsoil

Burrowing animals, such as this mouse, nest in the soil.

C Horizon
Rock fragments

52 ◆ G

Humus forms in a process called decomposition. During decomposition, organisms that live in soil turn dead organic material into humus. These organisms are called decomposers. **Decomposers** are the organisms that break the remains of dead organisms into smaller pieces and digest them with chemicals.

Soil decomposers include fungi, bacteria, worms, and other organisms. Fungi are organisms such as molds and mushrooms. Fungi grow on, and digest, plant remains. Bacteria are microscopic decomposers that cause decay. Bacteria attack dead organisms and their wastes in soil. Very small animals, such as mites and worms, also decompose dead organic material and mix it with the soil.

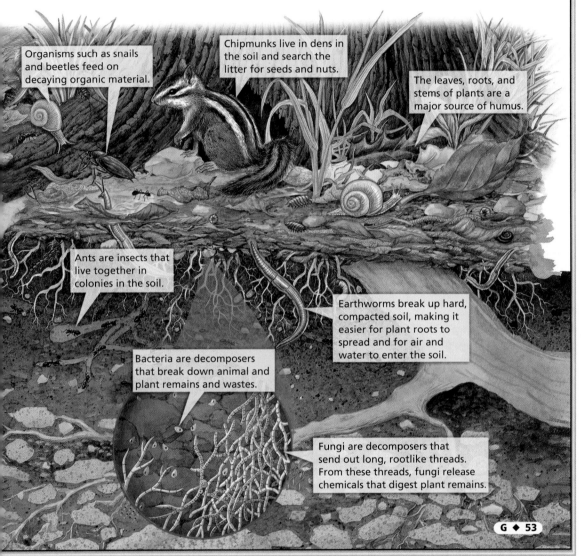

Organisms such as snails and beetles feed on decaying organic material.

Chipmunks live in dens in the soil and search the litter for seeds and nuts.

The leaves, roots, and stems of plants are a major source of humus.

Ants are insects that live together in colonies in the soil.

Earthworms break up hard, compacted soil, making it easier for plant roots to spread and for air and water to enter the soil.

Bacteria are decomposers that break down animal and plant remains and wastes.

Fungi are decomposers that send out long, rootlike threads. From these threads, fungi release chemicals that digest plant remains.

G ◆ 53

Help Students Read　　　L1
Relate Text and Visuals Have students refer to the visual as they read the captions and the text for Living Organisms in Soil. Ask students to check the visual for animals and plant roots that break up the soil and organisms that are decomposers.

Lab zone **Build Inquiry**　　　L2

The Amount of Air in Soil

Materials soil sample, 2 measuring cups, scoop or old spoon, water

Time 15 minutes

Focus Help students understand that spaces exist between soil particles and that these spaces can be filled with either air or water.

Teach Challenge small groups of students to determine the amount of air in a soil sample by adding a measured volume of soil to a measuring cup and then pouring an equal volume of water into the cup. The water will fill the spaces in the soil, so the amount of soil and water in the cup will be less than the two volumes added together. Students can find the volume of air in the original volume of soil by subtracting the final volume in the cup from the sum of the original volumes of soil and water.

Apply Ask: **Why is the combined volume of soil and water less than the original volumes?** (*The water filled the air spaces in the soil.*) **learning modality: visual**

Differentiated Instruction

Gifted and Talented　　　L3
Worm Composting Invite students to learn how to build a worm compost bin in which plant materials can be added to make fertile soil for gardens. A typical bin is a large container with drainage holes in the bottom. To prepare the bin for worms, fill it halfway with strips of newspaper and fallen leaves. Then add the worms and cover the container with plastic, allowing enough air for the worms to breathe. The worms will digest most food scraps except meat and dairy products. Red wiggler worms work best in composting bins and can be obtained from biological supply companies. **learning modality: kinesthetic**

Monitor Progress　　　L2

Oral Presentation Ask students to explain how each different kind of soil organism contributes to soil formation.

Answer
Figure 10 Earthworms and burrowing animals

Answers

Figure 11 The soil is likely to be very fertile because earthworms carry humus down to the subsoil and pass out soil as waste, which is enriched with substances plants need to grow.

 Earthworms

Assess

Reviewing Key Concepts

1. a. Rock particles, minerals, decayed organic material, air, and water **b.** Soil horizons form as bedrock weathers, and rock breaks up into soil particles. Plants weather rock mechanically and chemically and add organic material to the soil. Rainwater washes clay and minerals from topsoil to other soil horizons. **c.** Topsoil, subsoil, C horizon, bedrock

2. a. Climate, plants, and soil composition **b.** Tundra soils and desert soils would form most slowly. Tundras are cold, and deserts are dry.

3. a. Some soil organisms make humus, a material that makes soil fertile. Other soil organisms mix the soil and make spaces for air and water. **b.** Decomposers include fungi, bacteria, and worms. They digest or decompose dead organic material and mix it with the soil. **c.** The soil would become less fertile because the decomposers make humus.

Reteach L1

Have students make a concept map about soil that includes the following connecting phrases: *form when, are classified according to,* and *contain organisms that include.*

Performance Assessment

Writing Challenge students to design and write a two-page pamphlet (such as a local park might hand out) that explains the formation and composition of the local soil. The pamphlet should include drawings of soil profiles and other relevant visual aids.

All in One Teaching Resources

- Section Summary: *How Soil Forms*
- Review and Reinforce: *How Soil Forms*
- Enrich: *How Soil Forms*

FIGURE 11
Soil Mixers
Earthworms break up the soil, allowing in air and water. An earthworm eats its own weight in soil every day. **Predicting** *How fertile is soil that contains many earthworms likely to be? Explain.*

Mixing the Soil Earthworms do most of the work of mixing humus with other materials in soil. As earthworms eat their way through the soil, they carry humus down to the subsoil and subsoil up to the surface. Earthworms also pass out the soil they eat as waste. The waste soil is enriched with substances that plants need to grow, such as nitrogen.

Many burrowing mammals such as mice, moles, prairie dogs, and gophers break up hard, compacted soil and mix humus through it. These animals also add nitrogen to the soil when they produce waste. They add organic material when they die and decay.

Earthworms and burrowing animals also help to aerate, or mix air into, the soil. Plant roots need the oxygen that this process adds to the soil.

 Reading Checkpoint **Which animals are most important in mixing humus into the soil?**

Section 2 Assessment

Target Reading Skill

Building Vocabulary Use your definitions to help you answer the questions below.

Reviewing Key Concepts

1. a. Describing What five materials make up soil?
   b. Explaining How do soil horizons form?
   c. Sequencing Place these terms in the correct order starting from the surface: C horizon, subsoil, bedrock, topsoil.
2. a. Reviewing What are three main factors used to classify soils?
   b. Interpreting Maps Soil forms more rapidly in warm, wet areas than in cold, dry areas. Study the map in Figure 9. Which soil type on the map would you expect to form most slowly? Explain.

3. a. Identifying What are two main ways in which soil organisms contribute to soil formation?
   b. Describing Give examples of three types of decomposers and describe their effects on soil.
   c. Predicting What would happen to the fertility of a soil if all decomposers were removed? Explain.

Writing in Science

Product Label Write a product label for a bag of topsoil. Your label should give the soil a name that will make consumers want to buy it, state how and where the soil formed, give its composition, and suggest how it can be used.

Lab zone Chapter Project

Keep Students on Track Check that students have chosen their sample soils and growing materials. Choices include sand, vermiculite, gravel, potting soil, and local topsoil. Confirm that students have planted their bean seeds. Students can begin to make notes describing each sample, predict which material will be best for plant growth, and design a method for recording data about growth.

Writing in Science

Writing Skill Persuasion

Scoring Rubric

4 Exceeds criteria in some way; for example, by reading and appearing like an actual product label

3 Meets criteria but does not go beyond requirements

2 Includes only brief description of required elements

1 Is incorrect and incomplete

Comparing Soils

Problem

What are the characteristics of two samples of soil?

Skills Focus

observing, inferring, developing hypotheses

Materials

- 20–30 grams of local soil
- 20–30 grams of bagged topsoil
- plastic spoon • plastic dropper • toothpick
- water • stereomicroscope
- plastic petri dish or jar lid
- graph paper ruled with 1- or 2-mm spacing

Procedure

1. Obtain a sample of local soil. As you observe the sample, record your observations in your lab notebook.

2. Spread half of the sample on the graph paper. Spread the soil thinly so that you can see the lines on the paper through the soil. Using the graph paper as a background, estimate the sizes of the particles that make up the soil.

3. Place the rest of the sample in the palm of your hand, rub it between your fingers, and squeeze it. Is it soft or gritty? Does it clump together or crumble when you squeeze it?

4. Place about half the sample in a plastic petri dish. Using the dropper, add water one drop at a time. Watch how the sample changes. Does any material in the sample float? As the sample gets wet, do you notice any odor? (*Hint:* If the wet soil has an odor or contains material that floats, it is likely to contain organic material.)

5. Look at some of the soil under the stereomicroscope. (*Hint:* Use the toothpick to separate the particles in the soil.) Sketch what you see. Label the particles, such as gravel, organic matter, or strangely shaped grains.

6. Repeat Steps 1–5 with the topsoil. Be sure to record your observations.

7. Clean up and dispose of your samples as directed by your teacher. **CAUTION:** *Wash your hands when you finish handling soil.*

Analyze and Conclude

1. **Observing** Did you observe any similarities between the local soil sample and the topsoil? Any differences?

2. **Inferring** What can you infer about the composition of both types of soil from the different sizes of their particles? From your observations of texture? From how the samples changed when water was added?

3. **Inferring** Do you think that both types of soil were formed in the same way? Explain.

4. **Developing Hypotheses** Based on your observations and study of the chapter, develop a hypothesis about which soil would be better for growing flowers and vegetables.

5. **Communicating** Write a report for consumers that summarizes your analysis of the two soil samples. Be sure to describe what factors you analyzed and give a suggestion for which soil consumers should use for growing flowers and vegetables.

Design an Experiment

In Question 4 you developed a hypothesis about which soil would be better for growing flowers and vegetables. Design an experiment that would test this hypothesis. Be sure to indicate how you would control variables. *After you receive your teacher's approval, carry out your experiment.*

Comparing Soils L2

Prepare for Inquiry

Key Concept
The characteristics of soil determine its usefulness.

Skills Objectives
After this lab, students will be able to

- observe and compare two soil samples
- infer the soil's composition from their observations and infer how the soil samples formed
- develop hypotheses about which soil would be better for growing flowers and vegetables

 Prep Time 30 minutes

Class Time 40 minutes

All in One **Teaching Resources**

- Lab Worksheet: *Comparing Soils*

Advance Planning
Collect soil at least one day in advance. Make sure that it is relatively dry. Potting soil can be obtained from gardening centers. Use a balance to prepare individual samples of 20–30 grams each.

Guide Inquiry

Troubleshooting the Experiment

- Tell students to view only a small amount of soil under the microscope. Too much material will make viewing difficult.
- Caution students not to put soil in the sink, where it could clog the drain.

Expected Outcome
Specific outcomes will depend on the soil samples used. All students should be able to observe various characteristics of their samples.

Extend Inquiry

Design an Experiment Students' experiments should have the two different soil samples as the independent variable. The factors to control include the amount of sunlight, the amount of water, and the temperature. Students should develop a procedure, a list of materials, and a method of recording data.

Analyze and Conclude

1. Answers will vary, depending on the local soil samples used. Most bagged topsoil samples will have high percentages of organic materials. Most natural soils will have less organic material.

2. Students should be able to estimate what proportions of the sample are clay, silt, and sand. Organic material will float in water.

3. Students might note that the bagged topsoil contains more organic matter and formed from more plant matter than the local soil did.

4. Hypotheses will vary, depending on the soil samples. Normally, bagged topsoil is a good mix for flowers and vegetables.

5. Reports will vary. Students' suggestions should be supported by data.

Objectives

After this lesson, students will be able to

G.2.3.1 Explain why soil is a valuable resource.

G.2.3.2 List ways that soil can lose its value.

G.2.3.3 Identify ways that soil can be conserved.

Target Reading Skill 🔄

Previewing Visuals Explain that looking at the visuals before they read helps students activate prior knowledge and predict what they are about to read.

Answers

Possible answers: **Where was the Dust Bowl?** (*The Dust Bowl was in western Oklahoma and parts of the surrounding states.*) **What caused the Dust Bowl?** (*Farming practices exposed the soil so that in times of drought the topsoil quickly dried out, turned to dust, and blew away.*)

All in One Teaching Resources

• Transparency G17

Preteach

Build Background Knowledge   L1

A Small-Scale Dust Bowl

Ask students to suggest an area in your community that consists of exposed soil, such as a construction site or a plowed field. Ask: **What happens when the soil is dry and the wind blows?** (*Fine sediment is blown into the air.*) **Why isn't soil picked up when the exposed land is wet?** (*Moisture helps the soil grains stick together.*)

Section
3 Soil Conservation

Reading Preview

Key Concepts
• Why is soil a valuable resource?
• How can soil lose its value?
• What are some ways that soil can be conserved?

Key Terms
• sod • natural resource
• Dust Bowl • soil conservation
• contour plowing
• conservation plowing
• crop rotation

🔄 Target Reading Skill

Previewing Visuals Before you read, preview Figure 13, The Dust Bowl. Then write two questions that you have about the photo and map in a graphic organizer like the one below. As you read, answer your questions.

The Dust Bowl

Q.	Where was the Dust Bowl?
A.	
Q.	

Prairie grasses and wildflowers ▼

Lab zone   Discover **Activity**

How Can You Keep Soil From Washing Away?

1. Pour about 500 mL of soil into a pie plate, forming a pile.
2. Devise a way to keep the soil from washing away when water is poured over it. To protect the pile of soil, you may use craft sticks, paper clips, pebbles, modeling clay, strips of paper, or other materials approved by your teacher.
3. After arranging your materials to protect the soil, hold a container filled with 200 mL of water about 20 cm above the center of the soil. Slowly pour the water in a stream onto the pile of soil.

4. Compare your pan of soil with those of your classmates.

Think It Over

Observing Based on your observations, what do you think is the best way to prevent soil on a slope from washing away?

Suppose you were a settler traveling west in the mid 1800s. Much of your journey would have been through vast, open grasslands called prairies. After the forests and mountains of the East, the prairies were an amazing sight. Grass taller than a person rippled and flowed in the wind like a sea of green.

The prairie soil was very fertile. It was rich with humus because of the tall grass. The **sod**—the thick mass of tough roots at the surface of the soil—kept the soil in place and held onto moisture.

The prairies covered a vast area. They included Iowa and Illinois, as well as the eastern parts of Kansas, Nebraska, and North and South Dakota. Today, farms growing crops such as corn, soybeans, and wheat have replaced the prairies. But prairie soils are still among the most fertile in the world.

Lab zone   Discover **Activity**

Skills Focus Observing   L1

Materials soil, pie plate, water, container, craft sticks, paper clips, pebbles, modeling clay, paper

Time 15 minutes

Tips Provide students with soil in measured amounts, or prepare each pie plate with 500 mL of soil before class.

Encourage students to be creative in their arrangements.

Expected Outcome Students will discover a variety of ways to prevent the soil from washing away.

Think It Over Answers will vary. Typical answers might suggest ways that protect the soil or bind it together.

The Value of Soil

A **natural resource** is anything in the environment that humans use. **Soil is one of Earth's most valuable natural resources because everything that lives on land, including humans, depends directly or indirectly on soil.** Plants depend directly on the soil to live and grow. Humans and animals depend on plants—or on other animals that depend on plants—for food.

Fertile soil is valuable because there is a limited supply. Less than one eighth of the land on Earth has soils that are well suited for farming. Soil is also in limited supply because it takes a long time to form. It can take hundreds of years for just a few centimeters of soil to form. The thick, fertile soil of the prairies took many thousands of years to develop.

 Reading Checkpoint Why is fertile soil valuable?

Soil Damage and Loss

Human activities and changes in the environment can affect the soil. **The value of soil is reduced when soil loses its fertility and when topsoil is lost due to erosion.**

Loss of Fertility Soil can be damaged when it loses its fertility. Soil that has lost its fertility is said to be exhausted. This type of soil loss occurred in large parts of the South in the late 1800s. Soils in which only cotton had been grown were exhausted. Many farmers abandoned their farms. Early in the 1900s in Alabama, a scientist named George Washington Carver developed new crops and farming methods that helped to restore soil fertility in the South. Peanuts were one crop that helped make the soil fertile again. Peanut plants are legumes. Legumes have small lumps on their roots that contain nitrogen-fixing bacteria. These bacteria make nitrogen, an important nutrient, available in a form that plants can use.

Discovery CHANNEL SCHOOL

Weathering and Soil Formation

Video Preview
▶ Video Field Trip
Video Assessment

FIGURE 12
Restoring Soil Fertility
George Washington Carver (1864–1943) taught new methods of soil conservation. He also encouraged farmers to plant peanuts, which helped restore soil fertility.
Applying Concepts *What nutrient do peanut plants add to the soil?*

Chapter 2 **G ◆ 57**

The Value of Soil

Discovery CHANNEL SCHOOL
Video Field Trip

Weathering and Soil Formation

Show the Video Field Trip to help students understand weathering and soil formation. Discussion question: **How do earthworms benefit prairie soil?** (*Earthworms mix humus into the soil, carry humus to the subsoil, and excrete soil as waste, which has many nutrients.*)

Teach Key Concepts   L1

Soil Is a Natural Resource

Focus Have students suggest ways that people depend on soil. (*Answers include growing crops, lawns, trees, and flowers.*)

Teach Remind students that natural resources such as coal, oil, and natural gas are nonrenewable. Point out that Earth has a finite amount of soil, which takes time to form.

Apply Ask: **What are the consequences of losing too much topsoil?** (*The remaining soil will be less fertile and less capable of supporting plants.*) **learning modality: logical/mathematical**

Independent Practice   L2

All in One Teaching Resources

• Guided Reading and Study Worksheet: *Soil Conservation*

⊙ **Student Edition on Audio CD**

Differentiated Instruction

Less Proficient Readers   L1
Making Pictograms Read aloud the text below *Soil Loss in the Dust Bowl* on the next page as students follow along. Then, ask students to make pictograms that communicate the same information. Have students work in small groups and refer to the text as needed. **learning modality: visual**

Gifted and Talented   L3
Writing Telegrams Challenge students to write telegrams about the Dust Bowl to be sent back East. You might suggest that students role-play farmers who lived in the Dust Bowl during the 1930s. Telegrams could be addressed to family members or to government officials. **learning modality: verbal**

Monitor Progress   L2

Oral Presentation Have students explain how the planting of peanuts restored fertility to the soil.

Answers
Figure 12 Nitrogen

 Reading Checkpoint Fertile soil is valuable because there is only a limited supply of it.

Soil Damage and Loss

Teach Key Concepts L1

Soil Can Lose Fertility

Focus Review what makes soil fertile.

Teach Ask: **What might happen if plants use nutrients faster than they are replaced?** *(Soil can become exhausted.)* **How can exhausted soil be improved?** *(Sometimes plants such as legumes can restore fertility.)*

Apply Ask students to identify common legumes. *(Peanuts and alfalfa)* **learning modality: logical/mathematical**

Help Students Read L1

Summarizing Refer to the Content Refresher for guidelines on summarizing. Have students read the passage *Soil Conservation.* Then ask them to write separate sentences that explain how each method helps conserve soil.

Lab zone Build **Inquiry** L2

Reducing the Loss of Soil

Materials soil, sod, water, 2 painter's pans, 2 buckets

Time 20 minutes

Focus Have students hypothesize about the effects of vegetation on soil erosion before performing the activity.

Teach Challenge students to test their hypotheses, using the materials provided. A typical experiment might compare the difference in the amount of soil runoff when water is poured on a slope of bare soil versus a slope of soil covered by sod.

Apply Ask: **How can what you learned be used to reduce erosion on natural slopes?** *(Grass and other vegetation can be planted on slopes.)* **learning modality: kinesthetic**

FIGURE 13
The Dust Bowl
The Dust Bowl ruined farmland in western Oklahoma and parts of the surrounding states. Wind blew dry particles of soil into great clouds of dust that traveled thousands of kilometers.

Loss of Topsoil Whenever soil is exposed, water and wind can quickly erode it. Plant cover can protect soil from erosion. Plants break the force of falling rain, and plant roots hold the soil together. Wind is another cause of soil loss. Wind erosion is most likely in areas where farming methods are not suited to dry conditions. For example, wind erosion contributed to the Dust Bowl on the Great Plains.

Soil Loss in the Dust Bowl Toward the end of the 1800s, farmers settled the Great Plains. The soil of the Great Plains is fertile. But rainfall decreases steadily from east to west across the Great Plains. The region also has droughts—years when rainfall is scarce. Plowing removed the grass from the Great Plains and exposed the soil. In times of drought, the topsoil quickly dried out, turned to dust, and blew away.

By 1930, almost all of the Great Plains had been turned into farms or ranches. Then, a long drought turned the soil on parts of the Great Plains to dust. The wind blew the soil east in great, black clouds that reached Chicago and New York City. The erosion was most serious in the southern Plains states. This area, shown in Figure 13, was called the **Dust Bowl.** The Dust Bowl helped people appreciate the value of soil. With government support, farmers in the Great Plains and throughout the country began to take better care of their land. They adopted methods of farming that helped save the soil. Some methods were new. Others had been practiced for hundreds of years.

 **Reading Checkpoint** **What caused the Dust Bowl?**

Soil Conservation

Since the Dust Bowl, farmers have adopted modern methods of soil conservation. **Soil conservation** is the management of soil to prevent its destruction. **Soil can be conserved through contour plowing, conservation plowing, and crop rotation.**

In **contour plowing,** farmers plow their fields along the curves of a slope. This helps slow the runoff of excess rainfall and prevents it from washing the soil away.

In **conservation plowing,** farmers disturb the soil and its plant cover as little as possible. Dead weeds and stalks of the previous year's crop are left in the ground to help return soil nutrients, retain moisture, and hold soil in place. This method is also called low-till or no-till plowing.

In **crop rotation,** a farmer plants different crops in a field each year. Different types of plants absorb different amounts of nutrients from the soil. Some crops, such as corn and cotton, absorb large amounts of nutrients. The year after planting these crops, the farmer plants crops that use fewer soil nutrients, such as oats, barley, or rye. The year after that the farmer sows legumes such as alfalfa or beans to restore the nutrient supply.

 Reading Checkpoint How does conservation plowing help conserve soil?

FIGURE 14
Soil Conservation Methods
This farm's fields show evidence of contour plowing and crop rotation. **Predicting** *How might contour plowing affect the amount of topsoil?*

Section 3 Assessment

Target Reading Skill Previewing Visuals Compare your questions and answers about Figure 13 with those of a partner.

Reviewing Key Concepts

1. **a. Defining** What is a natural resource?
   b. Explaining Why is soil valuable as a natural resource?
2. **a. Listing** What are two ways in which the value of soil can be reduced?
   b. Explaining Explain how topsoil can be lost.
   c. Relating Cause and Effect What caused the Dust Bowl?
3. **a. Defining** What is soil conservation?
   b. Listing What are three methods by which farmers can conserve soil?
   c. Problem Solving A farmer growing corn wants to maintain soil fertility and reduce erosion. What conservation methods could the farmer try? Explain.

Writing in Science

Public Service Announcement
A severe drought in a farming region threatens to produce another Dust Bowl. Write a paragraph about soil conservation to be read as a public service announcement on radio stations. The announcement should identify the danger of soil loss due to erosion. It should also describe the steps farmers can take to conserve the soil.

Chapter 2 G ◆ 59

Soil Conservation

Teach Key Concepts L1
Comparing Conservation Techniques

Focus Remind students about the Discover Activity that they conducted at the beginning of this section. Tell them that farmers face the same problem.

Teach Ask: **In which soil conservation method are plant stalks used to protect the soil?** (*Conservation plowing*) **In which method are fields tilled across the slope to slow the flow of water?** (*Contour plowing*)

Apply Ask: **Why is so much effort used to save soil?** (*Topsoil is best for plant growth. Saving topsoil increases crop yields.*)

learning modality: logical/mathematical

Monitor Progress L2
Answers
Figure 14 It prevents excess rainfall from washing the soil away.

Reading Checkpoint A combination of overplowing and drought

Reading Checkpoint It disturbs the soil as little as possible, leaving plants in the ground to retain nutrients and moisture and to prevent erosion.

Assess

Reviewing Key Concepts

1. a. Anything in the environment that humans use **b.** All living organisms depend, either directly or indirectly, on soil to live and grow.
2. a. Loss of fertility and loss of topsoil **b.** Topsoil is lost because of erosion by wind and water. **c.** A combination of overplowing and drought turned the soil in the Great Plains to dust.
3. a. The management of soil to prevent its destruction **b.** Contour plowing, conservation plowing, and crop rotation **c.** A combination of conservation plowing to reduce erosion and crop rotation to maintain soil fertility

Reteach L1
Ask students to make a cause-and-effect chart to show what caused people to leave the Great Plains in the 1930s.

G ● 59

1 Rocks and Weathering

Key Concepts

- Weathering and erosion work together continuously to wear down and carry away the rocks at Earth's surface.

- The causes of mechanical weathering include freezing and thawing, release of pressure, plant growth, actions of animals, and abrasion.

- The causes of chemical weathering include the action of water, oxygen, carbon dioxide, living organisms, and acid rain.

- The most important factors that determine the rate at which weathering occurs are the type of rock and the climate.

Key Terms

weathering
erosion
uniformitarianism
mechanical weathering
abrasion
ice wedging
chemical weathering
oxidation
permeable

2 How Soil Forms

Key Concepts

- Soil is a mixture of rock particles, minerals, decayed organic material, water, and air.

- Soil forms as rock is broken down by weathering and mixes with other materials on the surface. Soil is constantly being formed wherever bedrock is exposed.

- Scientists classify the different types of soil into major groups based on climate, plants, and soil composition.

- Some soil organisms make humus, the material that makes soil fertile. Other soil organisms mix the soil and make spaces in it for air and water.

Key Terms

soil
bedrock
humus
fertility
loam
soil horizon
topsoil
subsoil
litter
decomposer

3 Soil Conservation

Key Concepts

- Soil is one of Earth's most valuable natural resources because everything that lives on land, including humans, depends directly or indirectly on soil.

- The value of soil is reduced when soil loses its fertility and when topsoil is lost due to erosion.

- Soil can be conserved through contour plowing, conservation plowing, and crop rotation.

Key Terms

sod
natural resource
Dust Bowl
soil conservation
contour plowing
conservation plowing
crop rotation

Help Students Read

Building Vocabulary

Word Forms Students benefit from knowing related word forms of a key word tied to lesson concepts, such as *erode* and *erosion* and *abrade* and *abrasion*. Point out that the suffix *-ion* means "the act of," so *erosion* is "the act of eroding."

Paraphrasing To help students understand vocabulary terms, paraphrase their definitions using words and phrases with which students are familiar. For example, something that is permeable, such as soil, allows fluids to pass or flow through it.

Connecting Concepts

Concept Maps Help students develop one way to show how the information in this chapter is related. The weathering of rocks is a key factor in the formation and composition of soil and relates to its fertility. Have students brainstorm to identify the key concepts, key terms, details, and examples, then write each one on a sticky note and attach it at random on chart paper or on the board.

Tell students that this concept map will be organized in hierarchical order and begin at the top with key concepts. Ask students these questions to guide them to categorize the information on the stickies: **How do mechanical and chemical weathering cause the formation of soil? What are the processes involved in the formation of soil from bedrock?**

Prompt students by using connecting words or phrases, such as "results in," "classified according to," and "is made of" to indicate the basis for the organization of the map. The phrases should form a sentence between or among a set of concepts.

Answer
Accept logical presentations by students.

All in One Teaching Resources

- Key Terms Review: *Weathering and Soil Formation*
- Connecting Concepts: *Weathering and Soil Formation*

Go Online
PHSchool.com
For: Self-Assessment
Visit: PHSchool.com
Web Code: cfa-2020

Organizing Information

Sequencing Fill in the flowchart to show how soil horizons form. (For more information on flowcharts, see the Skills Handbook.)

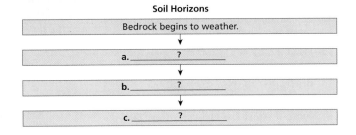

Soil Horizons

Bedrock begins to weather.

↓

a. _____ ?

↓

b. _____ ?

↓

c. _____ ?

Reviewing Key Terms

Choose the letter of the best answer.

1. The process that splits rock through freezing and thawing is called
   a. erosion.
   b. chemical weathering.
   c. ice wedging.
   d. abrasion.

2. Acid rain results in
   a. chemical weathering.
   b. abrasion.
   c. oxidation.
   d. mechanical weathering.

3. Soil that is made up of roughly equal parts of clay, sand, and silt is called
   a. sod.
   b. loam.
   c. tropical soil.
   d. subsoil.

4. The B horizon consists of
   a. subsoil.
   b. topsoil.
   c. litter.
   d. bedrock.

5. The humus in soil is produced by
   a. mechanical weathering.
   b. bedrock.
   c. chemical weathering.
   d. decomposers.

If the statement is true, write *true.* If it is false, change the underlined word or words to make the statement true.

6. <u>Mechanical weathering</u> is the removal of rock particles by gravity, wind, water, or ice.

7. Rock that is <u>permeable</u> weathers easily because it is full of tiny air spaces.

8. The decayed organic material in soil is called <u>loam</u>.

9. The layer of plant remains at the surface of the soil is called <u>litter</u>.

10. In <u>contour plowing</u>, farmers conserve soil fertility by leaving dead stalks and weeds in the ground.

Writing in Science

Journal Entry You are a farmer on the tall grass prairie in the midwestern United States. Write a journal entry describing prairie soil. Include the soil's composition, how it formed, and how animals helped it develop.

Discovery CHANNEL SCHOOL

Weathering and Soil Formation
Video Preview
Video Field Trip
▶ Video Assessment

Go Online
PHSchool.com
For: Self-Assessment
Visit: PHSchool.com
Web Code: cfa-2020

Students can take a practice test online that is automatically scored.

All in One Teaching Resources
- Transparency G18
- Chapter Test
- Performance Assessment Teacher Notes
- Performance Assessment Student Worksheet
- Performance Assessment Scoring Rubric

ExamView® Computer Test Bank CD-ROM

Organizing Information

a. The C horizon forms as bedrock breaks apart.
b. The A horizon develops from the C horizon when plants grow in it.
c. The B horizon develops as clay and minerals wash down from the A horizon.

Reviewing Key Terms

1. c **2.** a **3.** b **4.** a **5.** d
6. Erosion
7. true
8. humus
9. true
10. conservation plowing

Writing in Science

Writing Skill Description

Scoring Rubric
4 Exceeds criteria in some way; for example, by including methods the farmer might use to preserve topsoil
3 Meets criteria but does not go beyond requirements
2 Includes only brief description of required elements
1 Is incorrect and imcomplete

Discovery CHANNEL SCHOOL
Video Assessment

Weathering and Soil Formation

Show the Video Assessment to review chapter content and as a prompt for the writing assignment. Discussion questions:
Name two important prairie decomposers. *(Fungi and bacteria)* **What is the role of decomposers on the prairie?** *(They break down organic material and enrich the soil.)* **How has development by humans changed the tall grass prairie?** *(Farming interferes with the soil's natural cycle and decreases its fertility. Many farming practices favor certain plant and animal species, destroying the diversity of the grasslands.)*

Checking Concepts

11. The principle of uniformitarianism states that the same processes that operate today operated in the past.

12. Plants are an agent of mechanical weathering when their roots pry open cracks in rock. Plants are an agent of chemical weathering when their roots produce weak acids that slowly dissolve rock.

13. Oxygen combines with iron in a process called oxidation, which results in rust. Carbon dioxide dissolves in water to form carbonic acid, which weathers rock.

14. Soil forms as rock is broken down by weathering and mixes with other materials on the surface, including decayed organic material that can support plant growth.

15. Topsoil contains more humus than subsoil. Because topsoil contains more humus, it is more fertile than subsoil.

16. Earthworms do most of the work of mixing humus into soil.

17. Grass held the soil in place and provided organic matter to the soil.

18. Conservation plowing disturbs the soil and plant cover as little as possible, thus keeping soil in place, retaining moisture, and conserving soil nutrients. When using crop rotation, the farmer plants different crops each year at the same location, allowing crops to periodically restore nutrients that have been lost.

Review and Assessment

Checking Concepts

11. What is the principle of uniformitarianism?

12. Explain how plants can act as agents of both mechanical and chemical weathering.

13. What is the role of gases such as oxygen and carbon dioxide in chemical weathering?

14. Briefly describe how soil is formed.

15. Which contains more humus, topsoil or subsoil? Which has higher fertility? Explain.

16. What organism does most of the work in mixing humus into soil?

17. What role did grass play in conserving the soil of the prairies?

18. How do conservation plowing and crop rotation contribute to soil conservation?

Thinking Critically

19. Predicting If mechanical weathering breaks a rock into pieces, how would this affect the rate at which the rock weathers chemically?

20. Comparing and Contrasting Compare the layers in the diagram below in terms of their composition and humus content.

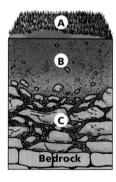

21. Classifying Classify as mechanical or chemical weathering: cracks in a sidewalk next to a tree; limestone with holes like Swiss cheese; a rock that slowly turns reddish brown.

Applying Skills

Use the following information to answer Questions 22–24.

You have two samples of soil. One is mostly sand and one is mostly clay.

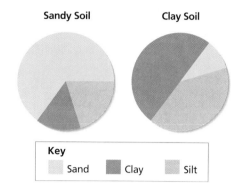

22. Developing Hypotheses Which soil sample would lose water more quickly? Why?

23. Designing Experiments Design an experiment to test how quickly water passes through each soil sample.

24. Posing Questions You are a farmer who wants to grow soybeans in one of these two soils. What questions would you need to answer before choosing where to plant your soybeans?

Lab zone Chapter **Project**

Performance Assessment You are ready to present your data and conclusions about what type of material is best for growing bean plants. How did your group's results compare with those of the other groups in your class?

In your journal, describe how well the results of your experiment matched your predictions. What have you learned from this project about soil characteristics that help plants to grow? How could you improve your experiment?

Lab zone Chapter **Project**   L3

Performance Assessment As each group presents its results to the class, have students explain the experiment that they carried out, including their descriptions of the types of soil used, explanations of the data collected, and conclusions they have drawn from their data. Students might use visual aids or graphs to help them present their research.

Ask students to compare the data and conclusions of their group with their predictions and with the data and conclusions of other groups. Have each student explain what lessons can be drawn from the project and how the project could have been carried out in a better way.

Standardized Test Prep

Choose the letter of the best answer.

1. Which of the following is a type of mechanical weathering?
  A abrasion
  B freezing and thawing
  C plant growth
  D all of the above

2. You are designing an experiment to test the resistance to weathering of various types of materials. What weathering process could be modeled using sandpaper?
  F acid rain
  G freezing and thawing
  H abrasion
  J all of the above

3. In what type of climate would soil form fastest from limestone bedrock?
  A a cold, dry climate   **B** a cold, wet climate
  C a hot, dry climate   **D** a hot, wet climate

Use the data table below and your knowledge of science to answer Questions 4–5.

Soil Erosion by State

State	Tons per Acre per Year		
	Water Erosion	Wind Erosion	Total Erosion
Montana	1.08	3.8	4.9
Wyoming	1.57	2.4	3.97
Texas	3.47	14.9	18.4
New Mexico	2.00	11.5	13.5
Colorado	2.5	8.9	11.4
Tennessee	14.12	0.0	14.12
Hawaii	13.71	0.0	13.71

4. Of the states listed in the table, which two have the greatest amount of erosion by water?
  F Texas and Tennessee
  G Texas and Hawaii
  H New Mexico and Colorado
  J Tennessee and Hawaii

5. What state in the table has the greatest soil erosion?
  A Texas
  B Hawaii
  C Tennessee
  D New Mexico

Constructed Response

6. Two rocks, each in a different location, have been weathering for the same amount of time. Mature soil has formed from one rock, but only immature soil has formed from the other. What factors might have caused this difference in rate of soil formation? In your answer, include examples of both mechanical and chemical weathering.

Thinking Critically

19. Breaking a rock into pieces increases the rate at which the rock will weather chemically because the broken rock has more surface area exposed to weathering agents.

20. **a.** The A horizon contains highly weathered rock and mineral pieces and abundant humus from the decay of organic remains. **b.** The B horizon is less weathered and contains less humus than the A horizon does. It is enriched in clay and some other minerals that were washed down from the A horizon. **c.** The C horizon is the least weathered horizon. It is similar to bedrock.

21. Mechanical; chemical; chemical

Applying Skills

22. The sandy soil would lose water more quickly because water can move through the spaces between grains easily. Clay particles hold water better.

23. Answers will vary. A typical design could include the following: use two identical flowerpots with drain holes; place gravel at the bottom of each pot, and cover with equal amounts of the sample soils; suspend the pots over two catch basins, and pour equal amounts of water into the pots. Compare how quickly water passes through the pots.

24. Answers will vary. Sample questions: In what kind of soil do soybeans grow best? What needs to be added to either type of soil to make it suitable for growing soybeans?

Standardized Test Prep

1. D **2.** H **3.** D **4.** J **5.** A
6. The rates of chemical weathering, mechanical weathering, or both might have been faster where the mature soil formed. These differences could be due to climate or vegetation differences. Tree roots might have increased mechanical weathering. High temperature and moisture might have increased acid weathering and oxidation. Also, the type of rock in the area with immature soil might have been more resistant to weathering than the other type of rock.

Chapter at a Glance

  Chapter Project *Design and Build a Dam*

PRENTICE HALL
TeacherEXPRESS™
Plan · Teach · Assess

| Technology | Local Standards |

All in One Teaching Resources
- Chapter Project Teacher Notes, pp. 158–159
- Chapter Project Student Overview, pp. 160–161
- Chapter Project Student Worksheets, pp. 162–163
- Chapter Project Scoring Rubric, p. 164

DISCOVERY
SCHOOL
Video Preview

 Section 1

Changing Earth's Surface

2–3 periods
1–1 1/2 blocks

G.3.1.1 Describe the processes that wear down and build up Earth's surface.

G.3.1.2 Identify the causes of the different types of mass movement.

Go Online
active art

Go Online
PHSchool.com

 Section 2

Water Erosion

4–5 periods
2–2 1/2 blocks

G.3.2.1 Explain how water erosion is mainly responsible for shaping the surface of the land.

G.3.2.2 Describe some of the land features that are formed by water erosion and deposition.

G.3.2.3 Describe the cause of groundwater erosion.

DISCOVERY
SCHOOL
Video Field Trip

Go Online
PHSchool.com

 Section 3

The Force of Moving Water

1–2 periods
1/2–1 block

G.3.3.1 Describe how water is able to do work.

G.3.3.2 Explain how sediment enters rivers and streams.

G.3.3.3 List the factors that affect a river's ability to erode and carry sediment.

Go Online
PHSchool.com

 Section 4

Glaciers

1–2 periods
1/2–1 block

G.3.4.1 Identify the two kinds of glaciers.

G.3.4.2 Describe how a valley glacier forms and moves.

G.3.4.3 Explain how glaciers cause erosion and deposition.

Go Online
SCi LINKS NSTA

  Section 5

Waves

1 period
1/2 block

G.3.5.1 Identify what gives ocean waves their energy.

G.3.5.2 Describe how ocean waves erode a coast.

G.3.5.3 Identify features that result from deposition by waves.

Go Online
SCi LINKS NSTA

Section 6

Wind

1 period
1/2 block

G.3.6.1 Explain how wind causes erosion.

G.3.6.2 Identify features resulting from deposition by wind.

Review and Assessment

All in One Teaching Resources
- Key Terms Review, p. 210
- Transparency G32
- Performance Assessment Teacher Notes, p. 217

- Performance Assessment Scoring Rubric, p. 218
- Performance Assessment Student Worksheet, p. 219
- Chapter Test, pp. 220–223

Go Online
PHSchool.com

DISCOVERY
SCHOOL
Video Assessment

| Test Preparation |

Test Preparation
Blackline Masters

Lab zone Chapter Activities Planner

Student Edition	Inquiry	Time	Materials	Skills	Resources
Chapter Project, p. 65	Open-Ended	Ongoing (2 to 3 weeks)	**All in One** Teaching Resources See p. 158	Designing an experiment, making models	Lab zone Easy Planner **All in One** Teaching Resources Support pp. 158–159
Section 1					
Discover Activity, p. 66	Guided	15 minutes	Small board, marble, block of wood, sandpaper	Developing hypotheses	**Lab zone Easy Planner**
Skills Activity, p. 67	Open-Ended	40 minutes	Possible materials: plastic tub, sand, soil, pebbles, clay, water	Making models	**Lab zone Easy Planner**
Skills Lab, pp. 70–71	Guided	Prep 40 minutes; Class 40 minutes	Dry sand (500 mL), cardboard tube, tray, wooden barbecue skewer, masking tape, spoon, ruler, pencil or crayon, white paper	Developing hypotheses, interpreting data, predicting	**Lab zone Easy Planner** **Lab Activity Video** **All in One** Teaching Resources Skills Lab: *Sand Hills*, pp. 171–172
Section 2					
Discover Activity, p. 72	Directed	15 minutes	2 bars of soap, cold-water faucet, watch or clock with second hand	Predicting	**Lab zone Easy Planner**
Try This Activity, p. 74	Directed	15 minutes	Petri dish, fine-textured soil, newspaper, plastic dropper, water, meter stick	Drawing conclusions	**Lab zone Easy Planner**
Skills Lab, pp. 82–83	Guided	Prep 15 minutes; Class 40 minutes	Diatomaceous earth, plastic measuring cup, spray bottle, hand lens, watch or clock, water, 1 metal spoon, plastic foam cup, blue food coloring, liquid detergent, scissors, 2 wood blocks, bucket, plastic stirrers, 13–15 cm of 20-gauge wire	Making models, observing	**Lab zone Easy Planner** **Lab Activity Video** **All in One** Teaching Resources Skills Lab: *Streams in Action*, pp. 181–183
Section 3					
Discover Activity, p. 86	Directed	20 minutes	Clear plastic jar or bottle with top, water, plastic beaker, fine and coarse sand, soil, clay, small pebbles	Inferring	**Lab zone Easy Planner**
Skills Activity, p. 87	Open-Ended	5 minutes	None	Developing hypotheses	**Lab zone Easy Planner**
Section 4					
Discover Activity, p. 91	Directed	Prep 1 day; 10 minutes	Sand, small plastic container, water, freezer, paper towel, bar of soap	Inferring	**Lab zone Easy Planner**
Section 5					
Discover Activity, p. 96	Guided	15 minutes	Sand from 2 beaches, hand lens	Posing questions	**Lab zone Easy Planner**
Skills Activity, p. 99	Directed	15 minutes	Calculator	Calculating	**Lab zone Easy Planner**
Section 6					
Discover Activity, p. 101	Guided	10 minutes	Shallow pan, cornmeal, straw	Observing	**Lab zone Easy Planner**

Section 1 Changing Earth's Surface

 *2–3 periods, 1–1 1/2 blocks*

ABILITY LEVELS
L1 Basic to Average
L2 For All Students
L3 Average to Advanced

Objectives

G.3.1.1 Describe the processes that wear down and build up Earth's surface.

G.3.1.2 Identify the causes of the different types of mass movement.

Key Terms

• erosion • sediment • deposition • mass movement

Local Standards

Preteach

Build Background Knowledge

Recall experiences on a slope and connect the experiences with mass movement.

Lab zone Discover Activity *How Does Gravity Affect Materials on a Slope?* **L1**

Targeted Print and Technology Resources

All in One Teaching Resources

L2 Reading Strategy Transparency G19: *Comparing and Contrasting*

○ **PresentationExpress™ CD-ROM**

Instruct

Wearing Down and Building Up Consider erosion and deposition as part of a never-ending cycle.

Mass Movement Consider why landslides occur.

Lab zone Skills Lab *Sand Hills* **L2**

Targeted Print and Technology Resources

All in One Teaching Resources

L2 Guided Reading, pp. 167–168
Transparency G20

L2 Skills Lab: *Sand Hills,* pp. 171–172

Lab Activity Video/DVD
Skills Lab: *Sand Hills*

PHSchool.com Web Code: cfp-2031

PHSchool.com Web Code: cfd-2031

○ **Student Edition on Audio CD**

Assess

Section Assessment Questions

Have students use their completed comparing and contrasting graphic organizers to answer the questions.

Reteach

Make a chart that includes the four types of mass movement.

Targeted Print and Technology Resources

All in One Teaching Resources

• Section Summary, p. 166

L1 Review and Reinforce, p. 169

L3 Enrich, p. 170

Section 2 Water Erosion

4–5 periods, 2–2 1/2 blocks

Objectives

G.3.2.1 Explain how water erosion is mainly responsible for shaping the surface of the land.

G.3.2.2 Describe some of the land features that are formed by water erosion and deposition.

G.3.2.3 Describe the cause of groundwater erosion.

Key Terms

• runoff • rill • gully • stream • tributary • flood plain • meander
• oxbow lake • alluvial fan • delta • groundwater • stalactite • stalagmite
• karst topography

Local Standards

Preteach

Build Background Knowledge

Describe the source of a river's water.

 **Discover Activity** *How Does Moving Water Wear Away Rocks?* **L1**

Targeted Print and Technology Resources

All in One Teaching Resources

L2 Reading Strategy Transparency G21: *Previewing Visuals*

◉ **PresentationExpress™ CD-ROM**

Instruct

Runoff and Erosion Explain how water can erode the land.

Erosion by Rivers Describe waterfalls and explain how erosion can cause them to move.

Deposits by Rivers Describe features that form where rivers deposit sediment.

Groundwater Erosion Explain how caves form.

 Skills Lab *Streams in Action* **L2**

Targeted Print and Technology Resources

All in One Teaching Resources

L2 Guided Reading, pp. 175–178
L2 Transparencies G22, G23
L2 Skills Lab: *Streams in Action,* pp. 181–183

📼 **Lab Activity Video/DVD**
Skills Lab: *Streams in Action*

PHSchool.com Web Code: cfd-2032

DISCOVERY CHANNEL SCHOOL
Video Field Trip

PHSchool.com Web Code: cfh-2030

◉ **Student Edition on Audio CD**

Assess

Section Assessment Questions

🔄 Have students use their previewing visuals graphic organizers to help them answer the questions.

Reteach

Compare and contrast features formed by groundwater erosion with those formed by groundwater deposition.

Targeted Print and Technology Resources

All in One Teaching Resources

• Section Summary, p. 174
L1 Review and Reinforce, p. 179
L3 Enrich, p. 180

Section 3 The Force of Moving Water

ABILITY LEVELS
L1 Basic to Average
L2 For All Students
L3 Average to Advanced

🕐 *1–2 periods, 1/2–1 block*

Objectives

G.3.3.1 Describe how water is able to do work.

G.3.3.2 Explain how sediment enters rivers and streams.

G.3.3.3 List the factors that affect a river's ability to erode and carry sediment.

Key Terms

• energy • potential energy • kinetic energy • abrasion • load • friction
• turbulence

Local Standards

Preteach

Build Background Knowledge

Describe how fast water flows in different streams.

 **Discover Activity** *How Are Sediments Deposited?*   L2

Targeted Print and Technology Resources

 Teaching Resources

L2   Reading Strategy:
Building Vocabulary

⊙ **PresentationExpress™ CD-ROM**

Instruct

Work and Energy Contrast potential and kinetic energy.

How Water Erodes Explain how streams move sediment.

Erosion and Sediment Load Describe factors that affect how fast a stream flows.

Targeted Print and Technology Resources

All in One Teaching Resources

L2   Guided Reading, pp. 186–188

L2   Transparency G24

PHSchool.com Web Code: cfd-2033

⊙ **Student Edition on Audio CD**

Assess

Section Assessment Questions

 Have students use their definitions of key terms to help them answer the questions.

Reteach

List ways that sediment enters a river.

Targeted Print and Technology Resources

All in One Teaching Resources

• Section Summary, p. 185

L1   Review and Reinforce, p. 189

L3   Enrich, p. 190

Section 4 Glaciers

⏱ *1–2 periods, 1/2–1 block*

ABILITY LEVELS
L1 Basic to Average
L2 For All Students
L3 Average to Advanced

Objectives

G.3.4.1 Identify the two kinds of glaciers.
G.3.4.2 Describe how a valley glacier forms and moves.
G.3.4.3 Explain how glaciers cause erosion and deposition.

Local Standards

Key Terms

• glacier • continental glacier • ice age • valley glacier • plucking • till
• moraine • kettle

Preteach

Build Background Knowledge

Describe how snow changes after it has fallen.

 **Discover Activity** *How Do Glaciers Change the Land?* **L1**

Targeted Print and Technology Resources

All in One Teaching Resources

L2 Reading Strategy Transparency G25:
Asking Questions

💿 **PresentationExpress™ CD-ROM**

Instruct

How Glaciers Form and Move Explain how glaciers
form and flow.

How Glaciers Shape the Land Explain glacial erosion
and deposition.

Targeted Print and Technology Resources

All in One Teaching Resources

L2 Guided Reading, pp. 193–195
L2 Transparencies G26, G27

www.SciLinks.org Web Code: scn-0734

💿 **Student Edition on Audio CD**

Assess

Section Assessment Questions

 Have students use their graphic organizers to help them
answer the questions.

Reteach

Define valley glacier, continental glacier, plucking, till,
moraine, and kettle.

Targeted Print and Technology Resources

All in One Teaching Resources

• Section Summary, p. 192
L1 Review and Reinforce, p. 196
L3 Enrich, p. 197

Section 5 Waves

 1 period, 1/2 block

Objectives

G.3.5.1 Identify what gives ocean waves their energy.

G.3.5.2 Describe how ocean waves erode a coast.

G.3.5.3 Identify features that result from deposition by waves.

Key Terms

• headland • beach • longshore drift • spit

Local Standards

Preteach

Build Background Knowledge

Describe beaches and beach sand.

Lab zone Discover Activity *What Is Sand Made Of?* L1

Targeted Print and Technology Resources

All in One Teaching Resources

L2 Reading Strategy Transparency G28: *Identifying Main Ideas*

◎ **PresentationExpress™ CD-ROM**

Instruct

How Waves Form Infer the source of energy for waves and explain how the energy is transferred.

Erosion by Waves Describe rocky coastlines and explain their features.

Deposits by Waves Explain longshore drift and the formation of spits.

Targeted Print and Technology Resources

All in One Teaching Resources

L2 Guided Reading, pp. 200–201

L2 Transparency G29

www.SciLinks.org Web Code: scn-0735

◎ **Student Edition on Audio CD**

Assess

Section Assessment Questions

↻ Have students use their identifying main ideas graphic organizers to help them answer the questions.

Reteach

Compare landforms formed by wave erosion with those formed by wave deposition.

Targeted Print and Technology Resources

All in One Teaching Resources

• Section Summary, p. 199

L1 Review and Reinforce, p. 202

L3 Enrich, p. 203

Section 6 Wind

1 period, 1/2 block

ABILITY LEVELS
L1 Basic to Average
L2 For All Students
L3 Average to Advanced

Objectives
G.3.6.1 Explain how wind causes erosion.
G.3.6.2 Identify features resulting from deposition by wind.

Key Terms
• sand dune • deflation • loess

Local Standards

Preteach

Build Background Knowledge
Describe deserts and sand dunes.

 **Discover Activity** *How Does Moving Air Affect Sediment?*
L1

Targeted Print and Technology Resources

 Teaching Resources
L2 Reading Strategy Transparency G30: *Sequencing*

 PresentationExpress™ CD-ROM

Instruct

How Wind Causes Erosion Explain how wind moves sediment.

Wind Deposition Describe the formation of sand dunes and loess deposits.

Targeted Print and Technology Resources

 Teaching Resources
L2 Guided Reading, pp. 206–207
L2 Transparency G31

 Student Edition on Audio CD

Assess

Section Assessment Questions
Have students use their sequencing graphic organizers to help them answer the questions.

Reteach
Explain how wind transports grains of various sizes.

Targeted Print and Technology Resources

 Teaching Resources
• Section Summary, p. 205
L1 Review and Reinforce, p. 208
L3 Enrich, p. 209

Go Online

NSTA–PDi LINKS

For: Professional development support
Visit: www.SciLinks.org/PDLinks
Web Code: scf-0730

Professional Development

Section 1 Changing Earth's Surface

Landslides and Mudflows Gravity causes mass movement, but water almost always has a major role. Water reduces friction between rock layers. During a wet season, rocks that were stable can suddenly slide over other rock layers. In sand or clay, some water might increase stability, but too much water causes flow.

A lahar is a dangerous type of mudflow that occurs on the flanks of volcanoes. Lahars can form when snow and ice melt rapidly during volcanic activity. They also might form after loose volcanic ash is soaked by heavy rains. Lahars generally have a high water content. They flow quickly down steep volcano slopes and are capable of transporting large amounts of debris.

A lahar is a mudflow formed from a mixture of volcanic ash and water.

Section 2 Water Erosion

Two Models of Stream Erosion Traditionally, many geologists used the terms *youth, maturity, old age,* and *rejuvenation* to describe stages in the development of landscapes eroded by rivers and streams. William Morris Davis, a nineteenth-century American geomorphologist, pioneered the use of these terms to describe stream erosion.

In *youth,* a stream flows down steep slopes at high velocity, but carries relatively little sediment. The valley through which a youthful stream flows has a V-shaped profile. In *maturity,* a stream has a moderate slope and a rounded valley profile. A mature stream moves more slowly and carries more sediment. In *old age,* a stream flows slowly through a wide, gently sloping valley. Meanders and oxbow lakes form. The stream carries a heavy load of sediment that may be deposited along its banks,

forming natural levees or a delta. According to Davis's theory, erosion could continue until the land surface is a featureless plain. In fact, however, *rejuvenation* occurs. That is, tectonic forces uplift the land, causing the cycle of erosion to begin again.

Today, geologists have modified this traditional view of stream erosion. They have also discarded Davis's terminology. Instead, geologists now view stream erosion as a dynamic process in which a system—made up of a stream, its sediment load, and the land surface—tends toward equilibrium. As a stream erodes the land, it gradually reduces the slope of the land until the stream's speed and sediment load are in equilibrium with the slope of the land surface. Any change disturbs the equilibrium and leads to changes in other parts of the system. For example, if a stream's volume increases because of heavy rainfall, then erosion along the stream's banks and bed also increases. Uplift of the land surface caused by movement along a fault would increase the stream's slope. This, in turn, increases the stream's speed and its downcutting into its bed. Viewed from a systems-equilibrium perspective, stream erosion becomes a process with no specific beginning or idealized end.

United States Cave Systems Just south of the town of Benson, Kartchner Caverns is a living cave system in Arizona. It contains many large rooms and an abundance of cave formations, such as cave pearls, draperies, and pillars.

Living cave systems are fragile environments that can be damaged easily. To avoid harming the natural environment within Kartchner Caverns, detailed environmental studies were conducted before the caverns were made ready for the public. Variables such as relative humidity, water influx, and air exchange all were measured to establish baseline cavern conditions. Even small changes from the natural average relative humidity of 99.4% could increase evaporation rates and cause the cave to dry. This would prevent or slow the precipitation of calcium carbonate and consequent growth of cave formations.

Address Misconceptions

Many students believe that all or most groundwater consists of rivers or lakes beneath Earth's surface. However, while underground caves may contain streams and lakes, almost all groundwater is in small pores in cracks in rocks. For a strategy for overcoming this misconception, see **Address Misconceptions** in the section *Water Erosion.*

Section 3 The Force of Moving Water

Sediment Transport Sediment transport in rivers varies. In many rivers, most of the sediment load is suspended load. These rivers often appear murky and have muddy bottoms along much of their course. In other streams, coarser sediment is abundant and bedload transport is more important. Such rivers might have large sand dunes moving along their beds. These dunes can be several meters high in some streams. All streams transport significant amounts of dissolved load. Runoff into streams contributes dissolved load, but groundwater is a more important source of dissolved material.

Section 4 Glaciers

Glacier Movement Glaciers move by two different processes: ice flow and basal sliding. When the glacial ice becomes thick enough, the force of gravity causes flow to occur. The mechanism by which ice flows is complex. Bonds within the ice crystals break, movement of planes of molecules occurs, and the bonds re-form. Although movement is slow, this process can transport huge amounts of ice. The ice moves from the zone of accumulation, where snowfall exceeds melting, to the zone of ablation, where melting exceeds snowfall. Basal sliding occurs when a glacier slides over its substrate. Although there may be some exceptions, most basal sliding occurs beneath warm-base glaciers. These glaciers have basal temperatures high enough to allow some melting at their base. Cold-base glaciers often are frozen to the substrate below. Glacier surges are examples of rapid basal sliding.

Glacial Movement

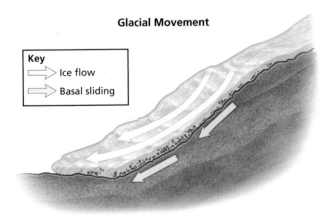

Key
→ Ice flow
→ Basal sliding

Section 5 Waves

Coastlines One difference between rocky coastlines and sandy coastlines is the amount of sediment available. A beach forms where sediment is abundant. The sand often originates far from the beach. Much of the sand on North Carolina's Cape Hatteras, for example, originally came from the Hudson River, Long Island, and southern New England.

Section 6 Wind

Loess There are two major sources of the wind-deposited clay and silt that form loess: deserts and the flood plains of glacial streams. The loess of the U.S. Midwest formed as a result of deflation at the end of the last ice age. Many meltwater streams flowed away from the glaciers. High winds blew silt and clay from the flood plains of these streams and deposited it on higher ground. Loess blown great distances from desert regions blankets large regions of China.

Help Students Read

Outlining
Understanding Text Structure

Strategy Help students focus on the text rather than simply skimming it. Outlining is a good strategy to apply to an entire section, if it is not excessively long, using the headings as major divisions. Outlining is best applied to sections in which the headings are parallel, and in which there are main headings and subheadings. Before you begin, choose a section for students to read and outline.

Example
1. Before students read, have them preview the section's title and headings. Demonstrate and display how to make a skeleton outline for the section. Have students list the section title at the top level, the main headings as major divisions, and the subheadings at the next level.
I. Section Title
  A. Main heading
    1. Subheading
      a. Detail
      b. Detail
      c. Detail
2. Have students copy the skeleton outline as they read, filling in details under each main heading and subheading of the outline.
3. Tell students not to outline sections that focus on the details of cycles or processes. Students can represent these with diagrams and flowcharts rather than by outlining.
4. After reading, have students review the entire section and their outlines to make sure they have included all vocabulary definitions and key concepts as main ideas or details under the appropriate levels of their outlines.

Interactive Textbook

- Complete student edition
- Video and audio
- Simulations and activities
- Section and chapter activities

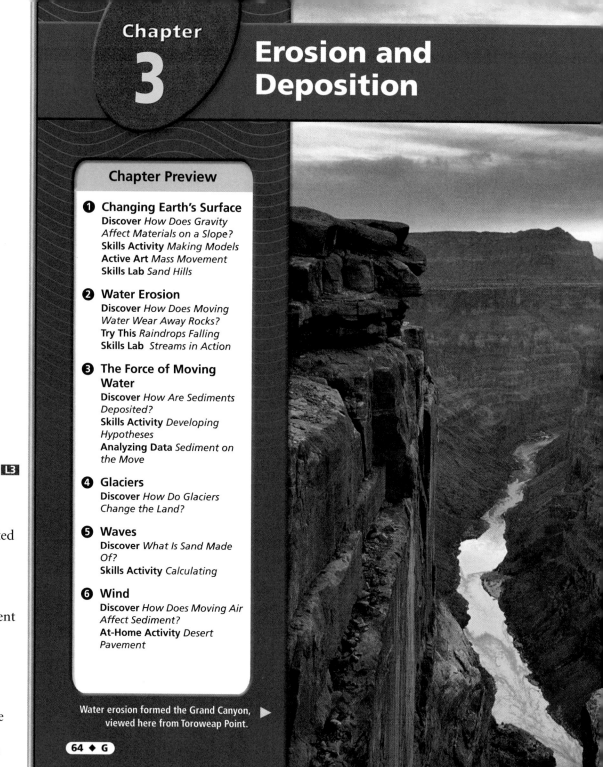

Chapter 3

Erosion and Deposition

Chapter Preview

❶ Changing Earth's Surface
Discover *How Does Gravity Affect Materials on a Slope?*
Skills Activity *Making Models*
Active Art *Mass Movement*
Skills Lab *Sand Hills*

❷ Water Erosion
Discover *How Does Moving Water Wear Away Rocks?*
Try This *Raindrops Falling*
Skills Lab *Streams in Action*

❸ The Force of Moving Water
Discover *How Are Sediments Deposited?*
Skills Activity *Developing Hypotheses*
Analyzing Data *Sediment on the Move*

❹ Glaciers
Discover *How Do Glaciers Change the Land?*

❺ Waves
Discover *What Is Sand Made Of?*
Skills Activity *Calculating*

❻ Wind
Discover *How Does Moving Air Affect Sediment?*
At-Home Activity *Desert Pavement*

Water erosion formed the Grand Canyon, viewed here from Toroweap Point. ▶

Chapter Project

Objectives

This project will enhance students' understanding of how dams are constructed and which soils are most effective for holding back water. After this Chapter Project, students will be able to

- Design and conduct an experiment to determine the permeability of the different grain sizes of soil
- Evaluate how readily the different grain sizes are eroded when water passes over them
- Design and build a dam
- Apply concepts from the text to evaluate and improve the model
- Communicate the features of their dam

Skills Focus

Designing an experiment, interpreting data, making models, applying concepts, communicating

Project Time Line 2 to 3 weeks

All in One Teaching Resources

- Chapter Project Teacher Notes
- Chapter Project Overview
- Chapter Project Worksheet 1
- Chapter Project Worksheet 2
- Chapter Project Scoring Rubric

Developing a Plan

Give students three different types of soil: silt, sand, and gravel. They will begin by designing and conducting an experiment to investigate the permeability of the different soils. Students can design their dams and construct them using multiple layers of soil. Allow students time and opportunity to test and redesign their dams.

Possible Materials

- The types of soil students use should consist of three different grain sizes, such as silt, sand, and gravel. If silt is difficult to obtain, cornstarch can be used as a substitute. Aquarium gravel can be used.
- The dam can be constructed inside a large foil roasting pan. Water can be poured into one half of the pan, and students can time how long it takes for the water to penetrate the dam.

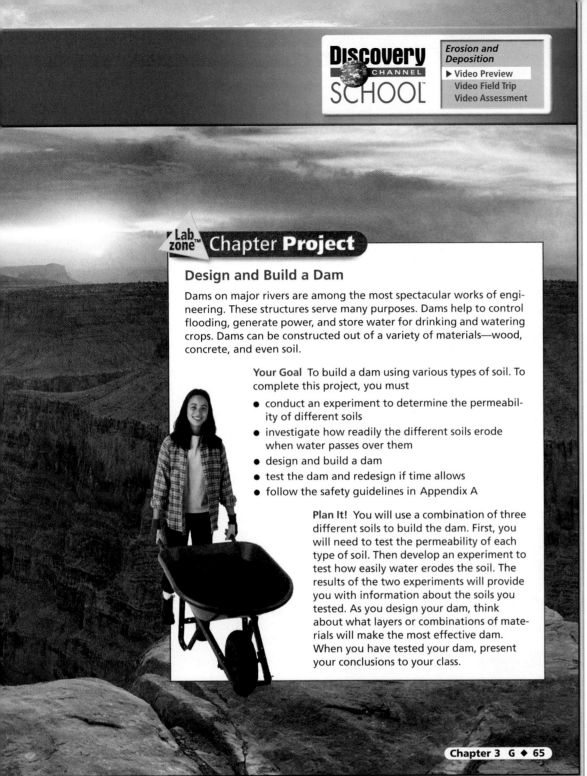

Lab zone™ Chapter Project

Design and Build a Dam

Dams on major rivers are among the most spectacular works of engineering. These structures serve many purposes. Dams help to control flooding, generate power, and store water for drinking and watering crops. Dams can be constructed out of a variety of materials—wood, concrete, and even soil.

Your Goal To build a dam using various types of soil. To complete this project, you must

- conduct an experiment to determine the permeability of different soils
- investigate how readily the different soils erode when water passes over them
- design and build a dam
- test the dam and redesign if time allows
- follow the safety guidelines in Appendix A

Plan It! You will use a combination of three different soils to build the dam. First, you will need to test the permeability of each type of soil. Then develop an experiment to test how easily water erodes the soil. The results of the two experiments will provide you with information about the soils you tested. As you design your dam, think about what layers or combinations of materials will make the most effective dam. When you have tested your dam, present your conclusions to your class.

Chapter 3 G ◆ 65

Erosion and Deposition

Show the Video Preview to introduce the Chapter Project and overview the chapter content. Discussion question: **Why are ancient artifacts so well preserved in a cave environment?** (*Unlike the outside world, caves have almost no variation in humidity or temperature. As a result, even fragile materials such as wood are preserved for centuries.*)

Performance Assessment

The Chapter Project Scoring Rubric will help you evaluate how well students complete the Chapter Project. You may want to share the rubric with your students so they know what is expected. Students will be assessed on

- Experimental design of soil permeability and ability to withstand erosion tests
- Design and construction of the dam
- Presentation of the results to the class
- Group participation, if they worked in groups

Possible Shortcuts

- Streamline the project by conducting a permeability experiment for the class.
- Assign different tasks to different student groups. For example, have one group be responsible for testing permeability and another group for testing how easily the soil is eroded.

Launching the Project

Show a picture of an earthen dam. Ask: **What is unique about this dam?** (*The dam is made from soil.*) **What characteristics of the materials used to construct this dam are important?** (*Possible answers: strength, ability to hold back water, ability to resist erosion*) Tell students that in this project, they will make a dam from soil.

Objectives

After this lesson, students will be able to

G.3.1.1 Describe the processes that wear down and build up Earth's surface.

G.3.1.2 Identify the causes of the different types of mass movement.

Target Reading Skill

Comparing and Contrasting Explain that comparing and contrasting information shows how ideas, facts, and events are similar and different. The results of comparison can have importance.

Answers

One way that students might organize the information is as follows:

Landslide	rapid	steep
Mudflow	rapid	gentle to steep
Slump	rapid	steep
Creep	slow	gentle to steep

All in One Teaching Resources

• Transparency G19

Preteach

Build Background Knowledge L1

Slopes

Encourage students to discuss their experiences on a steep path on a hill or mountain. Ask: **What happens when you step on loose rock or dirt?** (*You slip, and the rock or dirt falls downward.*) **What natural events could cause movement of sediment downhill?** (*Students might suggest a heavy storm or an earthquake.*)

Section 1
Changing Earth's Surface

Reading Preview

Key Concepts

• What processes wear down and build up Earth's surface?

• What causes the different types of mass movement?

Key Terms

• erosion • sediment
• deposition • gravity
• mass movement

Target Reading Skill

Comparing and Contrasting As you read, compare and contrast the different types of mass movement by completing a table like the one below.

Mass Movement

Type of Mass Movement	Speed	Slope
Landslide		

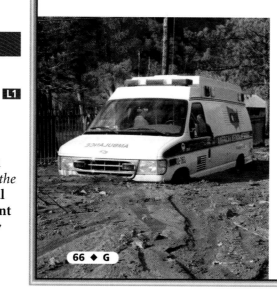

66 ◆ G

Lab zone Discover Activity

How Does Gravity Affect Materials on a Slope?

1. Place a small board flat on your desk. Place a marble on the board and slowly tip one end of the board up slightly. Observe what happens.

2. Place a block of wood on the board. Slowly lift one end of the board and observe the result.

3. Next, cover the board and the wood block with sandpaper and repeat Step 2.

Think It Over

Developing Hypotheses How do the results of each step compare? Develop a hypothesis to explain the differences in your observations.

The ground you stand on is solid. But under certain conditions, solid earth can quickly change to thick, soupy mud. For example, high rains soaked into the soil and triggered the devastating mudflow in Figure 1. A river of mud raced down the mountainside, burying homes and cars. Several lives were lost. In moments, the mudflow moved a huge volume of soil mixed with water and rock downhill.

Wearing Down and Building Up

A mudflow is a spectacular example of erosion. **Erosion** is the process by which natural forces move weathered rock and soil from one place to another. You may have seen water carrying soil and gravel down a driveway after it rains. That's an example of erosion. A mudflow is a very rapid type of erosion. Other types of erosion move soil and rock more slowly. Gravity, running water, glaciers, waves, and wind are all causes, or agents, of erosion. In geology, an agent is a force or material that causes a change in Earth's surface.

FIGURE 1
Mudflow
A mudflow caused by heavy rains in San Bernardino, California, brought this ambulance to a stop.

Lab zone Discover Activity

Skills Focus Developing hypotheses L1

Materials small board, marble, block of wood, sandpaper

Time 15 minutes

Tips Precut sandpaper to sizes that can be wrapped around the board and the block of wood. The block of wood should be completely wrapped in sandpaper. The board does not have to be completely covered if there is enough overlap.

Expected Outcome Upon tipping the board, the marble will immediately roll down the slope, but the block of wood will slide down only when the board is tipped higher. When the block of wood and board are covered with sandpaper, the block will not move unless the board is tipped up almost to vertical.

Think It Over Hypotheses will vary. A typical hypothesis might suggest that downward movement depends on the slope angle and on the frictional resistance.

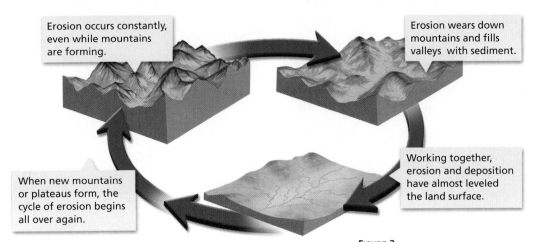

Erosion occurs constantly, even while mountains are forming.

Erosion wears down mountains and fills valleys with sediment.

Working together, erosion and deposition have almost leveled the land surface.

When new mountains or plateaus form, the cycle of erosion begins all over again.

FIGURE 2
Cycle of Erosion and Deposition
Over millions of years, erosion gradually wears away mountains while deposition fills in valleys with sediment.
Predicting *What would happen to the surface of the land if uplift did not occur?*

The material moved by erosion is **sediment.** Sediment may consist of pieces of rock or soil or the remains of plants and animals. Both weathering and erosion produce sediment. **Deposition** occurs where the agents of erosion, deposit, or lay down, sediment. Deposition changes the shape of the land. You may have watched a playing child who picked up several toys, carried them across a room, and then put them down. This child was acting something like an agent of erosion and deposition.

Weathering, erosion, and deposition act together in a cycle that wears down and builds up Earth's surface. Erosion and deposition are at work everywhere on Earth. As a mountain wears down in one place, new landforms build up in other places. The cycle of erosion and deposition is never-ending.

 Reading Checkpoint What is sediment?

Mass Movement

Imagine that you are sitting on a bicycle at the top of a hill. With only a slight push, you can coast down the hill. If the slope of the hill is very steep, you will reach a high speed before reaching the bottom. The force that pulls you and your bicycle downward is gravity. Gravity pulls everything toward the center of Earth.

Gravity is the force that moves rock and other materials downhill. Gravity causes **mass movement,** any one of several processes that move sediment downhill. **The different types of mass movement include landslides, mudflows, slump, and creep.** Mass movement can be rapid or slow.

 Lab zone Skills Activity

Making Models
You can make a model of mass movement. Design a plan to model one of the types of mass movement using sand, pebbles, and water. With your teacher's approval, make and test your model.

How well did your model represent the type of mass movement you chose? How could you improve your model?

Chapter 3 G ◆ 67

Lab zone Skills Activity

Skills Focus Making models [L2]

Materials possible materials: plastic tub, sand, soil, pebbles, clay, water

Time 40 minutes

Tips Encourage students to use materials of their choice. Approve students' designs before allowing them to make and test their models.

Expected Outcome Students' models and outcomes will vary. Students might suggest improvements that include changing the slope angle, sediment size, or amount of water.

Extend Have students suggest ways to prevent or reduce the risk of the type of mass movement that was modeled.
learning modality: kinesthetic

Teach Key Concepts [L1]
The Cycle of Erosion and Deposition

Focus Help students understand the concept of a cycle. Ask: **What is a cycle?** (*A sequence of repeating events*) **What are some natural cycles?** (*Cycle of day and night, water cycle, oxygen-carbon dioxide cycle*) Remind students that a cycle has no beginning and no end.

Teach Ask: **Why are erosion and deposition part of a cycle?** (*These processes occur again and again.*) **What part of this cycle wears down Earth's surface?** (*Erosion*) **What part builds up Earth's surface?** (*Deposition*)

Apply Have students identify features on Earth's surface that formed by erosion and features that formed by deposition. (*Erosion: scar on slope, river valley, mountain bowl; Deposition: river delta, sand dune, sand bar*) **learning modality: logical/mathematical**

Independent Practice [L2]

All in One Teaching Resources
• Guided Reading and Study Worksheet: *Changing Earth's Surface*

◉ Student Edition on Audio CD

Monitor Progress [L2]

Writing Have students use the section key terms in sentences.

Answers
Figure 2 The land surface would become flat and featureless.

Reading Checkpoint Loose pieces of rock, soil, or animal and plant remains that can be moved by erosion

Mass Movement

Teach Key Concepts　L2
Landslides and Slope

Focus Point out that a steep slope is necessary for a landslide to occur. Ask: **What force causes movement down a slope?** *(Gravity)*

Teach Have students speculate about what might trigger a landslide. Remind them that landslides often occur after large storms or earthquakes. *(Water can reduce friction, and shaking often triggers movement.)*

Apply Ask: **What damage might be caused by landslides?** *(Homes destroyed, roadways covered, people injured or killed)* **learning modality: verbal**

All in One Teaching Resources
• Transparency G20

Help Students Read　L1
Preview Before students read about the types of mass movement, have them preview the subheadings in bold. Ask students to write down what they already know before reading the selection.

Modeling Mass Movement　L1

Materials soil, large plastic tub, water, watering can

Time 15 minutes

Focus Review with students the different types of mass movement.

Teach Using soil, build a model mountain in the plastic tub. Then, as students observe, shake the tub. Ask: **What does the shaking model?** *(An earthquake)* **What does the model earthquake cause?** *(A landslide)* Rebuild the mountain. Use the watering can to "rain" on the model. Continue adding water until some movement of wet sediment occurs. Ask: **What did the "rainfall" cause?** *(A mudflow)*

Apply Ask: **Can mass movement occur without an earthquake or storm occurring?** *(Yes. Mass movement can occur at any time, but it is frequently triggered by storms and earthquakes.)* **learning modality: visual**

FIGURE 3
Mass Movement
In addition to mudflows, types of mass movement include landslides, slump, and creep.
Making Judgments *Which form of mass movement produces the most drastic change in the surface?*

Landslides The most destructive kind of mass movement is a landslide, which occurs when rock and soil slide quickly down a steep slope. Some landslides contain huge masses of rock. But many landslides contain only a small amount of rock and soil. Some landslides occur where road builders have cut highways through hills or mountains. Figure 3 shows an example of a landslide.

Mudflows A mudflow is the rapid downhill movement of a mixture of water, rock, and soil. The amount of water in a mudflow can be as high as 60 percent. Mudflows often occur after heavy rains in a normally dry area. In clay soils with a high water content, mudflows may occur even on very gentle slopes. Under certain conditions, clay soils suddenly turn to liquid and begin to flow. An earthquake can trigger both mudflows and landslides. Mudflows can be very dangerous.

Slump If you slump your shoulders, the entire upper part of your body drops down. In the type of mass movement known as slump, a mass of rock and soil suddenly slips down a slope. Unlike a landslide, the material in a slump moves down in one large mass. It looks as if someone pulled the bottom out from under part of the slope. A slump often occurs when water soaks the bottom of soil that is rich in clay.

Differentiated Instruction

Less Proficient Readers　L1
Listing Details Have students make three lists: one about erosion, another about deposition, and a third about mass movement. Ask students to write details in each list. Suggest that students use their lists as a study guide for the section. **learning modality: verbal**

Special Needs　L1
Clarifying Slope Explain that in common speech, a *slope* means the side of a hill or a mountain or any sloping surface. In this chapter, the term *slope* means the amount of an incline. Sketch some hills with slopes of different inclines and use the term, for example, "This hill has an angle of slope that is 45 degrees." **learning modality: verbal**

Creep

Creep Creep is the very slow downhill movement of rock and soil. It can even occur on gentle slopes. Creep often results from the freezing and thawing of water in cracked layers of rock beneath the soil. Like the movement of an hour hand on a clock, creep is so slow you can barely notice it. But you can see the effects of creep in objects such as telephone poles, gravestones, and fenceposts. Creep may tilt these objects at spooky angles. Landscapes affected by creep may have the eerie, out-of-kilter look of a funhouse in an amusement park.

 Reading Checkpoint What is the main difference between a slump and a landslide?

Section 1 Assessment

Target Reading Skill Comparing and Contrasting Use the information in your table to help you answer Question 2 below.

Reviewing Key Concepts

1. **a. Listing** What are five agents of erosion?
   b. Defining In your own words, write a definition of *deposition*.
   c. Predicting Over time, how will erosion and deposition affect a mountain range? Explain.
2. **a. Listing** What are the four types of mass movement?
   b. Relating Cause and Effect What force causes all types of mass movement?
   c. Inferring A fence runs across a steep hillside. The fence is tilted downhill and forms a curve rather than a straight line. What can you infer happened to the fence? Explain.

Lab zone At-Home **Activity**

Evidence of Erosion After a rainstorm, take a walk with an adult family member around your neighborhood. Look for evidence of erosion. Try to find areas where there is loose soil, sand, gravel, or rock. **CAUTION:** *Stay away from any large pile of loose sand or soil—it may slide without warning.* Which areas have the most erosion? The least erosion? How does the slope of the ground affect the amount of erosion? Sketch or take photographs of the areas showing evidence of erosion.

Monitor Progress

Answers
Figure 3 Landslide

Reading Checkpoint The main difference between slump and landslide is that the material in a slump moves as one large mass.

Assess

Reviewing Key Concepts

1. **a.** Five agents of erosion are gravity, running water, glaciers, waves, and wind.
   b. Deposition is a process that occurs when agents of erosion lay down sediment, which changes the shape of the land. **c.** Erosion will gradually wear away the mountain range. Deposition will fill valleys with sediment.
2. **a.** Four types of mass movement are landslide, mudflow, slump, and creep.
   b. Gravity causes all types of mass movement. **c.** The fence moved as a result of creep.

Reteach

Have students make a chart listing the characteristics of the four types of mass movement.

Performance Assessment

Skills Check Have students make a concept map about mass movements, starting with the word *gravity*.

All in One Teaching Resources

- Section Summary: *Changing Earth's Surface*
- Review and Reinforce: *Changing Earth's Surface*
- Enrich: *Changing Earth's Surface*

Lab zone At-Home **Activity**

Evidence of Erosion Encourage students to make the erosion survey around their neighborhood. Advise them to look for evidence of sediment that has moved downhill because of gravity. Students can bring their drawings or photos to class and show interesting examples to others.

Lab zone Chapter **Project**

Keep Students on Track Check that students have designed an experiment for testing permeability of the soil samples. Encourage students to record data and draw conclusions from their data.

Sand Hills

Prepare for Inquiry

Key Concept
The steepness of most hills depends on the material from which the hills are made.

Skills Objectives
After this lab, students will be able to
- Develop hypotheses about how the height and width of a sand hill are related
- Interpret data by making a graph
- Predict what would happen if more data were obtained

 **Prep Time** 40 minutes
Class Time 40 minutes

All in One Teaching Resources
- Lab Worksheet: *Sand Hills*

Advance Planning
Collect in advance cardboard box tops or plastic trays. Make sure that the sand is dry.

Alternative Materials
Fine aquarium gravel can be used instead of sand. Butcher-block paper cut to fit the tray bottom can be used instead of taping smaller sheets together.

Guide Inquiry

Invitation
Focus on the skill developing hypotheses by asking: **What is a hypothesis?** (*A hypothesis is a proposed explanation or answer to a question.*) **What do scientists do to support or disprove a hypothesis?** (*They test the hypothesis through experimentation.*)

Introduce the Procedure
Give students time to read through the procedure, and then ask: **What are some possible relationships between the width of the sand hill and the height of the sand hill?** (*The width could be greater than the height, or vice versa. The ratio between width and height*

Sand Hills

Problem
What is the relationship between the height and width of a sand hill?

Skills
developing hypotheses, interpreting data, predicting

Materials
- dry sand, 500 mL • cardboard tube
- tray (about 15 cm × 45 cm × 60 cm)
- wooden barbecue skewer • masking tape
- spoon • ruler • pencil or crayon
- several sheets of white paper

Procedure
1. Begin by observing how gravity causes mass movement. To start, place the cardboard tube vertically in the center of the tray.
2. Using the spoon, fill the cardboard tube with the dry sand. Take care not to spill the sand around the outside of the tube.
3. Carefully lift the sand-filled tube straight up so that all the sand flows out. As you lift the tube, observe the sand's movement.

How to Measure a Sand Hill
1. Cover the bottom of the tray with unlined white paper and tape it firmly in place.
2. Mark off points 0.5 cm apart along one side of the paper in the tray.
3. Carefully draw the sand hill's outline on the paper. The line should go completely around the base of the hill.
4. Now measure the width of the hill against the marks you made along the edge of the paper.

4. Develop a hypothesis explaining how you think the width of the sand pile is related to its height for different amounts of sand.
5. Empty the sand in the tray back into a container. Then set up your system for measuring the sand hill.
6. Copy the data table into your lab notebook.
7. Following Steps 1 through 3, make a new sand hill.

Data Table					
Test	1	2	3	4	5
Width					
Height					

8. Measure and record the sand hill's height and width for Test 1. (See the instructions on the bottom of the page to help you accurately measure the height and width.)

5. Measure the sand hill's height by inserting a barbecue skewer through its center. Make a mark on the skewer at the top of the hill.
6. Remove the skewer and use the ruler to measure how much of the skewer was buried in the hill. Try not to disturb the sand.

---

might be the same for all sizes of piles, or it might differ.*) Guide students to develop a specific hypothesis that can be tested. A testable hypothesis might be that the ratio of the sand hill's width to its height always remains the same. Allow students to test any reasonable hypotheses.

Troubleshooting the Experiment
- Tell students to fill the cardboard tube carefully so that they don't spill sand outside the tube onto the hill.
- Caution students not to touch the sand hill, but to allow the sand hill to form as sand falls from the tube.

Go Online
PHSchool.com

For: Data sharing
Visit: PHSchool.com
Web Code: cfd-2031

Go Online
PHSchool.com

For: Data Sharing
Visit: PHSchool.com
Web Code: cfd-2031

Students can share data from this experiment online.

9. Now test what happens when you add more sand to the sand hill. Place your cardboard tube vertically at the center of the sand hill. Be careful not to push the tube down into the sand hill! Using the spoon, fill the tube with sand as before.

10. Carefully raise the tube and observe the sand's movement.

11. Measure and record the sand hill's height and width for Test 2.

12. Repeat Steps 9 through 11 at least three more times. After each test, record your results. Be sure to number each test.

Analyze and Conclude

1. **Graphing** Make a graph showing how the sand hill's height and width changed with each test. (Hint: Use the x-axis of the graph for height. Use the y-axis of the graph for width.)

2. **Interpreting Data** What does your graph show about the relationship between the sand hill's height and width?

3. **Drawing Conclusions** Does your graph support your hypothesis about the sand hill's height and width? Why or why not?

4. **Developing Hypotheses** How would you revise your original hypothesis after examining your data? Give reasons for your answer.

5. **Predicting** Predict what would happen if you continued the experiment for five more tests. Extend your graph with a dashed line to show your prediction. How could you test your prediction?

6. **Communicating** Write a paragraph in which you discuss how you measured your sand hill. Did any problems you had in making your measurements affect your results? How did you adjust your measurement technique to solve these problems?

Design an Experiment

Do you think the use of different materials, such as wet sand or gravel, would produce different results from those using dry sand? Make a new hypothesis about the relationship between slope and width in hills made of materials other than dry sand. Design an experiment in which you test how these different materials form hills. *Obtain your teacher's approval before you try the experiment.*

Chapter 3 G ◆ 71

Expected Outcome
Both the height and the width of the sand hill increase as more sand is added. Repeated tests show that the ratio between the sand hill's width and height remains constant (that is, the points form approximately a straight line on the graph). The value of this ratio can vary. It depends mostly on the characteristics of the sand grains (size, shape) and the amount of moisture in the sand.

Analyze and Conclude

1. A typical graph should show a line rising from left to right. If height is on the x-axis and width on the y-axis, the slope of the line should be about 3. However, this value can vary slightly.

2. The ratio between height and width remains the same.

3. Answers will vary, depending on students' hypotheses. Students should compare their original hypotheses with the data they collected.

4. Advise students who proposed a hypothesis that was not supported to develop a new hypothesis that is consistent with the data collected.

5. Students extend the line on the graph with a dashed line to indicate that the ratio between width and height will continue to remain the same. Students could test this prediction by trying to form sand hills of appropriate size.

6. Students' answers will vary. Students might mention that disturbing the sand hills while taking measurements affected results.

Extend Inquiry

Design an Experiment Hypotheses will vary. Using wet sand will produce hills that stand at a higher angle (lower width-to-height ratio). Using larger sediment, such as gravel, also will produce hills that stand at a higher angle.

Objectives
After this lesson, students will be able to
G.3.2.1 Explain how water erosion is mainly responsible for shaping the surface of the land.
G.3.2.2 Describe some of the land features that are formed by water erosion and deposition.
G.3.2.3 Describe the cause of groundwater erosion.

Target Reading Skill 🔄

Previewing Visuals Explain that looking at the visuals before they read helps students activate prior knowledge and predict what they are about to read.

Answers
Q. What features does a river produce by erosion?
A. V-shaped valley, bluffs
Q. What feature does a river produce by deposition?
A. Delta

All in One Teaching Resources
• Transparency G21

Preteach

Build Background Knowledge   **L1**

Rivers
Ask students to describe a major river in your county or state. Ask: **Where does the river get its water?** (*From smaller rivers and streams*) **Where does this water ultimately come from?** (*Precipitation*)

Section
2 Water Erosion

Reading Preview

Key Concepts
• What process is mainly responsible for shaping the surface of the land?
• What features are formed by water erosion and deposition?
• What causes groundwater erosion?

Key Terms
• runoff • rill • gully • stream
• tributary • flood plain
• meander • oxbow lake
• alluvial fan • delta
• groundwater • stalactite
• stalagmite • karst topography

🔄 Target Reading Skill
Previewing Visuals Before you read, preview Figure 10. Then write two questions that you have about the illustration in a graphic organizer like the one below. As you read, answer your questions.

The Course of a River

Q.	What features does a river produce by erosion?
A.	
Q.	

Lab zone   Discover **Activity**

How Does Moving Water Wear Away Rocks?
1. Obtain two bars of soap that are the same size and brand.
2. Open a faucet just enough to let the water drip out very slowly. How many drops of water does the faucet release per minute?
3. Place one bar of soap in a dry place. Place the other bar of soap under the faucet. Predict the effect of the dripping water droplets on the soap.
4. Let the faucet drip for 10 minutes.
5. Turn off the faucet and observe both bars of soap. What difference do you observe between them?

Think It Over
Predicting What would the bar of soap under the dripping faucet look like if you left it there for another 10 minutes? For an hour? How could you speed up the process? Slow it down?

Walking in the woods in summer, you can hear the racing water of a stream before you see the stream itself. The water roars as it foams over rock ledges and boulders. When you reach the stream, you see water rushing by. Sand and pebbles tumble along the bottom of the stream. As it swirls downstream, the water also carries twigs, leaves, and bits of soil. In sheltered pools, insects such as water striders skim the water's calm surface. Beneath the surface, a rainbow trout swims in the clear water.

In winter, the stream freezes. Chunks of ice scrape and grind away at the stream's bed and banks. In spring, the stream floods. Then the flow of water may be strong enough to move large rocks. But throughout the year, the stream continues to erode its small part of Earth's surface.

▼ A stream in summer

Lab zone   Discover **Activity**

Skills Focus Predicting

Materials 2 bars of soap, cold-water faucet, watch or clock with second hand

Time 15 minutes

Tips Before students conduct the experiment, have them read the procedure and identify the variable that is being tested (dripping water) and the control (the bar in the dry place).

L1 Expected Outcome The dripping water will wear a depression in the bar of soap.

Think It Over Predictions will vary. Typical predictions might suggest that the depression would be larger after another 10 minutes and larger still after an hour. Increasing the flow would speed up the process; decreasing the flow would slow it down.

Runoff and Erosion

Moving water is the major agent of the erosion that has shaped Earth's land surface. Erosion by water begins with the splash of rain. Some rainfall sinks into the ground. Some evaporates or is taken up by plants. The force of a falling raindrop can loosen and pick up soil particles. As water moves over the land, it carries these particles with it. This moving water is called runoff. **Runoff** is water that moves over Earth's surface. When runoff flows in a thin layer over the land, it may cause a type of erosion called sheet erosion.

Amount of Runoff The amount of runoff in an area depends on five main factors. The first factor is the amount of rain an area receives. A second factor is vegetation. Grasses, shrubs, and trees reduce runoff by absorbing water and holding soil in place. A third factor is the type of soil. Some types of soils absorb more water than others. A fourth factor is the shape of the land. Land that is steeply sloped has more runoff than flatter land. Finally, a fifth factor is how people use the land. For instance, a paved parking lot absorbs no water, so all the rain that falls on it becomes runoff. Runoff also increases when a farmer cuts down crops, since this removes vegetation from the land.

Generally, more runoff means more erosion. In contrast, factors that reduce runoff will reduce erosion. Even though deserts have little rainfall, they often have high runoff and erosion because they have few plants. In wet areas, runoff and erosion may be low because there are more plants to protect the soil.

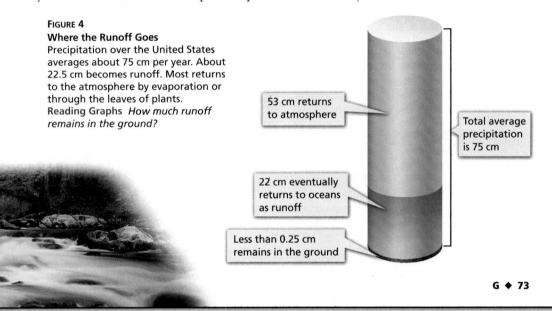

FIGURE 4
Where the Runoff Goes
Precipitation over the United States averages about 75 cm per year. About 22.5 cm becomes runoff. Most returns to the atmosphere by evaporation or through the leaves of plants.
Reading Graphs *How much runoff remains in the ground?*

53 cm returns to atmosphere

Total average precipitation is 75 cm

22 cm eventually returns to oceans as runoff

Less than 0.25 cm remains in the ground

G ◆ 73

Differentiated Instruction

Gifted and Talented 〔L3〕
Have students make sketches that show how urban areas could be designed to reduce the amount of runoff into streets and local streams. *(Possible solutions: include open areas for water absorption, include retention structures, plant appropriate vegetation)* **learning modality: logical/mathematical**

Less Proficient Readers 〔L1〕
The Meaning of "Agent" Point out that an "agent" of erosion means a "force or substance that causes change," not a representative, such as in "insurance agent," or a spy, such as in "secret agent." **learning modality: verbal**

Instruct

Runoff and Erosion

Teach Key Concepts 〔L1〕
Effect of Water on Earth's Surface

Focus Have students explain how people shape Earth's surface. *(They dig soil from one place and dump it at another place.)* Tell them that water also picks up soil at one place and deposits it at another and that water moves much more soil than people do.

Teach Ask: **How can water move soil and sediment?** *(By flowing over Earth's surface)* **In what ways does this water flow?** *(As a sheet, in rills, in gullies, in streams)*

Apply Ask: **What evidence have you seen of the effects of water on Earth's surface?** *(Encourage students to consider large features, such as canyons and deltas, and small features, such as rills.)* **learning modality: verbal**

All in One Teaching Resources
- Transparency G22

Independent Practice 〔L2〕
All in One Teaching Resources
- Guided Reading and Study Worksheet: *Water Erosion*

⊙ **Student Edition on Audio CD**

Monitor Progress _____ 〔L2〕
Writing Have students explain how runoff causes erosion.

Answer
Figure 4 Less than 0.25 cm

Help Students Read L1

Outlining Refer to the Content Refresher for guidelines on outlining. Have students read the section. Then have students use the headings and subheadings as the major divisions and subdivisions in an outline. Allow students to refer to their outlines when answering the questions in the Section Assessment.

Build Inquiry L2

Identifying Tributaries

Materials map of the United States that shows drainage patterns, tracing paper, pencil

Time 30 minutes

Focus Remind students that major rivers have many tributaries. Ask: **What is a tributary?** *(A smaller stream that flows into a larger stream or river)*

Teach Challenge students to identify and trace all of the tributaries of a major U.S. river. They might choose the Mississippi, Columbia, or Susquehanna. Also ask students to identify and draw the major river's drainage basin.

Apply Ask: **How can you identify tributaries on the map?** *(The tributaries flow into the larger river.)* **What general shape is the river pattern that you traced?** *(Answers will vary. One common pattern resembles a tree trunk with branches.)* **learning modality: visual**

Try This Activity

Raindrops Falling

Find out how the force of falling raindrops affects soil.

1. Fill a petri dish with fine-textured soil to a depth of about 1 cm. Make sure the soil has a smooth flat surface, but do not pack it firmly in the dish.
2. Place the dish in the center of a newspaper.
3. Fill a dropper with water. Squeeze a large water drop from a height of 1 m onto the surface of the soil. Repeat 4 times.
4. Use a meter stick to measure the distance the soil splashed from the dish. Record your observations.
5. Repeat Steps 1 through 4, this time from a height of 2 m.

Drawing Conclusions Which test produced the greater amount of erosion? Why?

FIGURE 5
Runoff, Rills, and Gullies
Water flowing across the land runs together to form rills, gullies, and streams.
Predicting What will happen to the land between the gullies as they grow wider?

74 ◆ G

Rills and Gullies Because of gravity, runoff and the material it contains move downhill. As runoff travels, it forms tiny grooves in the soil called **rills.** As many rills flow into one another, they grow larger, forming gullies. A **gully** is a large groove, or channel, in the soil that carries runoff after a rainstorm. As water flows through gullies, it moves soil and rocks with it, thus enlarging the gullies through erosion. Gullies contain water only after it rains.

Streams and Rivers Gullies join together to form a larger channel called a stream. A **stream** is a channel along which water is continually flowing down a slope. Unlike gullies, streams rarely dry up. Small streams are also called creeks or brooks. As streams flow together, they form larger and larger bodies of flowing water. A large stream is often called a river.

Tributaries A stream grows into a larger stream or river by receiving water from tributaries. A **tributary** is a stream or river that flows into a larger river. For example, the Missouri and Ohio rivers are tributaries of the Mississippi River. A drainage basin, or watershed, is the area from which a river and its tributaries collect their water.

 Reading Checkpoint **What is a tributary?**

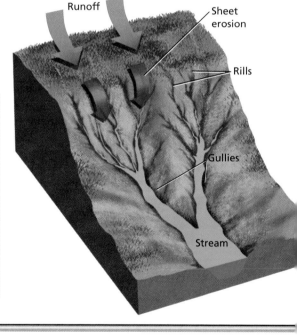

Runoff

Sheet erosion

Rills

Gullies

Stream

Try This Activity

Skills Focus Drawing conclusions L2

Materials petri dish, fine-textured soil, newspaper, plastic dropper, water, meter stick

Time 15 minutes

Tips To drop water from a height of 2 m, students will have to place the petri dish on the floor and hold the dropper above their heads. An alternative is to reduce the distances to 0.5 m in the first trials and then 1 m in the second trials.

Expected Outcome The drops from 2 m will cause splashes that travel farther than the splashes from the 1 m drops. Because the drops move sediment when they hit the soil, the 2 m drops will cause more erosion. The 2 m drops have more kinetic energy because the water falls from a greater distance.

Extend Encourage students to try the same procedure with different materials in the dish, including sand, clayey soil, and gravel, and then compare results.
learning modality: kinesthetic

Erosion by Rivers

As a river flows from the mountains to the sea, the river forms a variety of features. **Through erosion, a river creates valleys, waterfalls, flood plains, meanders, and oxbow lakes.**

Rivers often form on steep mountain slopes. Near its source, a river is often fast flowing and generally follows a straight, narrow course. The steep slopes along the river erode rapidly. The result is a deep, V-shaped valley.

Waterfalls Waterfalls may occur where a river meets an area of rock that is very hard and erodes slowly. The river flows over this rock and then flows over softer rock downstream. As you can see in Figure 6, the softer rock wears away faster than the harder rock. Eventually a waterfall develops where the softer rock was removed. Areas of rough water called rapids also occur where a river tumbles over hard rock.

Flood Plain Lower down on its course, a river usually flows over more gently sloping land. The river spreads out and erodes the land, forming a wide river valley. The flat, wide area of land along a river is a **flood plain.** A river often covers its flood plain when it overflows its banks during floods. On a wide flood plain, the valley walls may be kilometers away from the river itself.

Go Online
PLANET DIARY

For: More on floods
Visit: PHSchool.com
Web Code: cfd-2032

FIGURE 6
How a Waterfall Forms
A waterfall forms where a flat layer of tough rock lies over a layer of softer rock that erodes easily. When the softer rock erodes, pieces of the harder rock above break off, creating the waterfall's sharp drop.

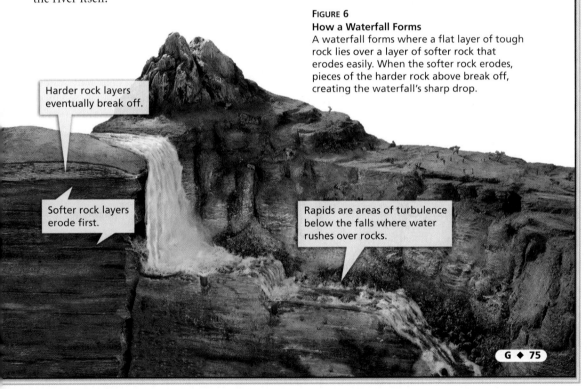

Harder rock layers eventually break off.

Softer rock layers erode first.

Rapids are areas of turbulence below the falls where water rushes over rocks.

Erosion by Rivers

Go Online
PLANET DIARY

For: More on floods
Visit: PHSchool.com
Web Code: cfd-2032

Teach Key Concepts L1
Waterfall Formation

Focus Have students examine the figure and the caption.

Teach Ask: **Why would the top of a layer of hard rock be higher than the top of a layer of soft rock?** *(The hard rock resists erosion, so it doesn't wear down as much.)* **Why might the waterfall move upstream through time?** *(Rock breaks from the cliff at the waterfall and the cliff moves backward.)*

Apply Ask: **If a person wanted to visit Niagara Falls in 5,000 years, would it be at the same location?** *(No. Niagara Falls would be farther upstream.)* **learning modality: logical/mathematical**

Help Students Read L1
Monitor Understanding After students read *Erosion by Rivers,* ask them to stop and monitor their understanding. Have students quiz each other about the topics in the headings and write any questions that they cannot answer. Then challenge students to find the answers to these questions in the text.

Monitor Progress _____ L2

Oral Presentation Call on students to explain how a flood plain forms.

Answers
Figure 5 The land between the gullies will become narrower as the sides of the gullies erode.

Reading Checkpoint A stream or river that flows into a larger river

Meanders and Oxbow Lakes

Focus Have students describe the shape of the oxbow lake in the figure. *(U-shaped)* Tell them that an oxbow is a U-shaped collar that is placed around an ox's neck.

Teach Make certain that students understand that meanders form because sediment is eroded on the outside bank of a river and deposited on the inside. Ask: **Where on a meander does erosion occur?** *(The outside)* **What happens on the inside of a meander?** *(Sediment is deposited there until the river channel is filled.)* **When might the meander become an oxbow lake?** *(When the river floods, and the water finds a more direct route downstream)*

Apply Give each student a copy of a map or an aerial photograph of a land area that has several prominent meanders and oxbow lakes. (A good choice would be eastern Louisiana, where the lower Mississippi River has formed wide loops and several large oxbow lakes on its flat flood plain.) Have each student locate these two features and circle them in different colors. **learning modality: visual**

All in One Teaching Resources

• Transparency G23

Lab zone Build Inquiry **L2**

Comparing and Contrasting Deltas

Materials atlas or encyclopedia

Time 15 minutes

Focus Review the definition of a delta.

Teach Have pairs of students find maps or aerial photographs in an atlas or encyclopedia that show the deltas of these major world rivers: Nile River (Egypt), Niger River (Nigeria), Ganges River (Bangladesh), Mekong River (Vietnam), Mississippi River (Louisiana), Columbia River (Oregon/Washington). Have students make drawings and write descriptions of each delta. Call on students to compare and contrast the deltas.

Apply Ask: **Why do you think the Columbia River has no delta at its end?** *(The currents of the Pacific Ocean move the sediments away, preventing development of a delta.)* **learning modality: visual**

FIGURE 7

Meanders and Oxbow Lakes
Erosion often forms meanders and oxbow lakes where a river winds across its floodplain.

1 A small obstacle creates a slight bend in the river.

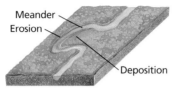

Meander
Erosion
Deposition

2 As water erodes the outer edge of a meander, the bend becomes bigger. Deposition occurs along the inner edge.

3 Gradually, the meander becomes more curved. The river breaks through and takes a new course.

Oxbow lake

4 An oxbow lake remains.

Meanders A river often develops meanders where it flows through easily eroded rock or sediment. A **meander** is a loop-like bend in the course of a river. As the river winds from side to side, it tends to erode the outer bank and deposit sediment on the inner bank of a bend. Over time, the meander becomes more and more curved.

Because of the sediment a river carries, it can erode a very wide flood plain. Along this part of a river's course, its channel is deep and wide. Meanders are common. The southern stretch of the Mississippi River is one example of a river that meanders on a wide, gently sloping flood plain.

Oxbow Lakes Sometimes a meandering river forms a feature called an oxbow lake. As Figure 7 shows, an **oxbow lake** is a meander that has been cut off from the river. An oxbow lake may form when a river floods. During the flood, high water finds a straighter route downstream. As the flood waters fall, sediments dam up the ends of a meander. The meander has become an oxbow lake.

Reading Checkpoint How does an oxbow lake form?

Deposits by Rivers

As water moves, it carries sediments with it. Any time moving water slows down, it drops, or deposits, some of the sediment. As the water slows down, fine particles fall to the river's bed. Larger stones quit rolling and sliding. **Deposition creates landforms such as alluvial fans and deltas. It can also add soil to a river's flood plain.** In Figure 10, you can see these and other features shaped by rivers and streams.

Alluvial Fans Where a stream flows out of a steep, narrow mountain valley, the stream suddenly becomes wider and shallower. The water slows down. Here sediments are deposited in an alluvial fan. An **alluvial fan** is a wide, sloping deposit of sediment formed where a stream leaves a mountain range. As its name suggests, this deposit is shaped like a fan. You can see an alluvial fan in Figure 8.

Deltas A river ends its journey when it flows into a still body of water, such as an ocean or a lake. Because the river water is no longer flowing downhill, the water slows down. At this point, the sediment in the water drops to the bottom. Sediment deposited where a river flows into an ocean or lake builds up a landform called a **delta**. Deltas can be a variety of shapes. Some are arc shaped, others are triangle shaped. The delta of the Mississippi River, shown in Figure 9, is an example of a type of delta called a "bird's foot" delta.

Soil on Flood Plains Deposition can also occur during floods. Then heavy rains or melting snow cause a river to rise above its banks and spread out over its flood plain. When the flood water finally retreats, it deposits sediment as new soil. Deposition of new soil over a flood plain is what makes a river valley fertile. Dense forests can grow in the rich soil of a flood plain. The soil is also perfect for growing crops.

 Reading Checkpoint How can a flood be beneficial?

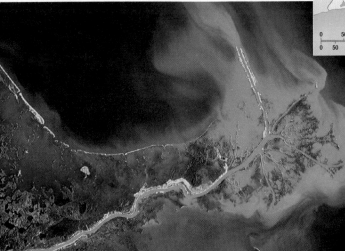

FIGURE 8
Alluvial Fan
This alluvial fan in Death Valley, California, was formed from deposits by streams from the mountains.

FIGURE 9
Mississippi Delta
This satellite image shows the part of the Mississippi River delta where the river empties into the Gulf of Mexico.
Observing *What happens to the Mississippi River as it flows through its delta? Can you find the river's main channel?*

Chapter 3 G ◆ 77

Deposits by Rivers

Teach Key Concepts
Features Formed by River Deposition

Focus Remind students that deposition occurs where the flow of river water slows.

Teach Ask: **What features form because of deposition by rivers?** *(Deltas, alluvial fans, soil on flood plains)* **Where do deltas form?** *(Deltas form where a river enters an ocean or a lake and its water stops flowing.)* **Alluvial fans?** *(Alluvial fans form where a river flows onto a flat valley floor and the river's water slows.)* **Why is sediment deposited on flood plains?** *(As flood waters expand onto the flood plain, the water flows more slowly.)*

Apply Ask: **Where in the United States is an example of a delta?** *(The mouth of the Mississippi River, among others)* **Where could you see an alluvial fan?** *(In the desert southwest, such as in Death Valley, California)* **learning modality: verbal**

Monitor Progress

Skills Check Have students make two flowcharts, one for the process that results in an alluvial fan and the other for the process that results in a delta. Have students place their flowcharts in their portfolios.

Answers
Figure 9 The water in the river slows down and deposits sediment in the delta. The river's main channel flows almost to the tip of the delta, where it divides into several channels to form the "bird foot."

✓ Reading Checkpoint An oxbow lake forms when a meander is cut off from the river.

✓ Reading Checkpoint The sediment that is deposited by a flood becomes fertile soil.

Differentiated Instruction

English Learners/Beginning L1
Vocabulary: Link to Visual Explain and clarify the meaning of *meanders, erosion, deposition,* and *oxbow lakes* by discussing the diagrams in Figure 7. Have students use tracing paper to make a labeled diagram of each stage. **learning modality: visual**

English Learners/Intermediate L2
Vocabulary: Link to Visual Have students do the *Beginning* activity. Then have them write sentences using the words *meander, erosion, deposition,* and *oxbow lake.* **learning modality: visual**

Use Visuals: Figure 10 L2
The Course of a River

Focus Help students understand that the figure begins at a river's head and ends at the river's mouth.

Teach After students have examined the figure, call on volunteers to read the figure's captions. Have them begin at the river's head. Ask: **Why would a river in the mountains have rapids, waterfalls, and a V-shaped valley?** *(In mountains, the slopes are steep. This causes rivers to have many rapids and to erode narrow valleys. Rivers in mountains commonly flow over cliffs to form waterfalls.)* Have students continue reading the captions. Question them at each step.

Apply Ask students to summarize how the river changes from its head to its mouth. **learning modality: visual**

Illustrating River Environments

Materials nature magazines, poster board, scissors, tape or glue

Time 90 minutes

Focus Refer students to the figure on this page. Remind them that rivers have a variety of environments from head to mouth.

Teach Have students sketch a river from its head to its mouth on poster board. Then, ask students to find photographs of river environments in magazines or online. Have students tape or glue the photographs at appropriate locations on their drawings.

Apply Ask: **Which part of a river might be best for whitewater rafting?** *(Areas near the head)* **Which part would have a wide flood plain?** *(Areas closer to the mouth)* **Where along a river is new land being formed?** *(At the delta)* **learning modality: kinesthetic**

Waterfalls and Rapids
Waterfalls and rapids are common where the river passes over harder rock.

V-Shaped Valley
Near its source, the river flows through a deep, V-shaped valley. As the river flows, it cuts the valley deeper.

Flood Plain
A flood plain forms where the river's power of erosion widens its valley rather than deepening it.

Meanders
Where the river flows across easily eroded sediment, its channel bends from side to side in a series of meanders.

Beaches
Sand carried downstream by the river spreads along the coast to form beaches.

78 ◆ G

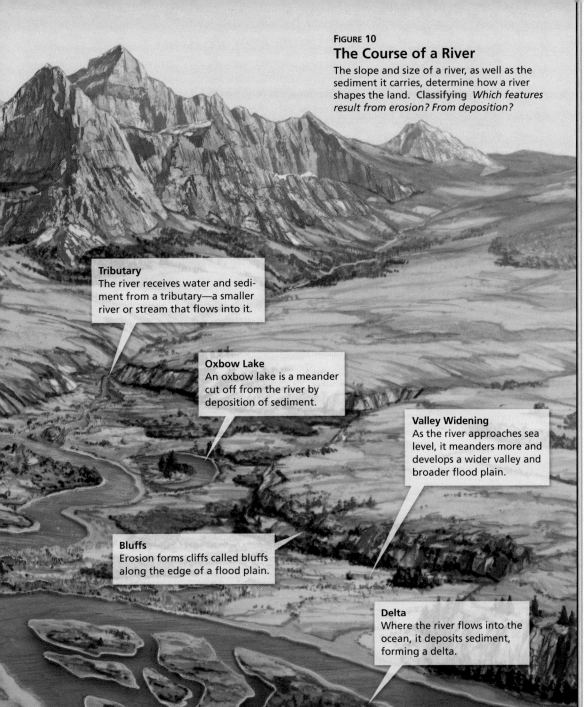

FIGURE 10

The Course of a River

The slope and size of a river, as well as the sediment it carries, determine how a river shapes the land. **Classifying** *Which features result from erosion? From deposition?*

Tributary
The river receives water and sediment from a tributary—a smaller river or stream that flows into it.

Oxbow Lake
An oxbow lake is a meander cut off from the river by deposition of sediment.

Valley Widening
As the river approaches sea level, it meanders more and develops a wider valley and broader flood plain.

Bluffs
Erosion forms cliffs called bluffs along the edge of a flood plain.

Delta
Where the river flows into the ocean, it deposits sediment, forming a delta.

G ◆ 79

Tributaries and Distributary Channels

Materials chalkboard and chalk or blank overhead transparency and marker

Time 10 minutes

Focus Ask: **What happens when rivers or streams merge?** *(A larger river or stream forms.)* **What happens when a river or stream divides?** *(Smaller streams form.)*

Teach Draw a river with several tributaries on the board or blank transparency. Include arrows to show in which direction the water flows. Tell students that rivers merge to form larger streams along most of a river's course. Now draw a main river splitting into several smaller channels (called distributary channels) at a delta. Include arrows to show the direction of the water's flow. Tell students that river channels often divide on a delta.

Apply Have students compare and contrast the two drawings and relate them to river features. **learning modality: visual**

Differentiated Instruction

Gifted and Talented   L3
A Travel Journal Provide maps of your state for students to examine. Then challenge students to suppose that they are boating along one of your state's major rivers. Ask them to write a travel journal that summarizes their observations and experiences. **learning modality: verbal**

Special Needs   L1
Matching Titles Make a copy of the figure *The Course of a River*. On the copy, remove the titles of the annotations, leaving only the definitions and descriptions. Write the annotation titles on small tags. Have students match the titles to their descriptions. **learning modality: visual**

Monitor Progress _____ L2

Skills Check Call on students to describe a river environment. Then, reverse the procedure by having students identify a river environment from a description.

Answer
Figure 10 Erosion: waterfalls, V-shaped valleys, flood plain, meanders, oxbow lake, bluffs; Deposition: beaches, delta

Erosion and Deposition

Show the Video Field Trip to let students learn more about erosion and deposition. Discussion question: **In what kind of rock are caves like Mammoth Cave found?** (*Limestone*)

Groundwater Erosion

Teach Key Concepts   L1

Caves and Caverns

Focus Tell students that carbonated beverages are acidic. Carbon dioxide also makes groundwater acidic.

Teach As a class, summarize the sequence of events that results in a cave: a limestone layer that has cracks in it is partially filled with groundwater, the groundwater dissolves limestone below the water table, caves eventually form in the limestone, the water table drops, and the caves are filled with air.

Apply Ask: **When do stalactites and stalagmites form in a cave?** (*After the water table has lowered and the cave is filled with air*) **learning modality: logical/mathematical**

Lab zone   Teacher **Demo**   L3

Modeling How Carbonic Acid Forms

Materials beaker, water, pH paper or pH probe, drinking staw

Time 10 minutes

Focus Ask: **Which gas is more abundant in the air that we exhale than in the air that we inhale?** (*Carbon dioxide*)

Teach Fill a beaker halfway with distilled water. Determine the pH of the water. Record this value on the board. Using a drinking straw, exhale into the water in the beaker for several minutes. Determine the pH again, and write this value on the board. The second pH value should be lower than the first because the exhaled carbon dioxide combined with water to form carbonic acid.

DISCOVERY
CHANNEL
SCHOOL
Erosion and Deposition
Video Preview
▶ Video Field Trip
Video Assessment

Groundwater Erosion

When rain falls and snow melts, not all of the water evaporates or becomes runoff. Some water soaks into the ground. There it fills the openings in the soil and trickles into cracks and spaces in layers of rock. **Groundwater** is the term geologists use for this underground water. Like running water on the surface, groundwater affects the shape of the land.

Groundwater can cause erosion through a process of chemical weathering. When water sinks into the ground, it combines with carbon dioxide to form a weak acid, called carbonic acid. Carbonic acid can break down limestone. Groundwater containing carbonic acid flows into any cracks in the limestone. Then some of the limestone changes chemically and is carried away in a solution of water. This process gradually hollows out pockets in the rock. Over time, these pockets develop into large holes underground, called caves or caverns.

Cave Formations The action of carbonic acid on limestone can also result in deposition. Inside limestone caves, deposits called stalactites and stalagmites often form. Water containing carbonic acid and calcium from limestone drips from a cave's roof. Carbon dioxide is released from the solution, leaving behind a deposit of calcite. A deposit that hangs like an icicle from the roof of a cave is known as a **stalactite** (stuh LAK tyt). Slow dripping builds up a cone-shaped **stalagmite** (stuh LAG myt) from the cave floor.

Karst Topography in the United States

FIGURE 11
Karst topography is found in many parts of the United States where the bedrock is made up of thick layers of limestone.

Key
Areas of karst topography

80 ◆ G

Karst Topography In rainy regions where there is a layer of limestone near the surface, groundwater erosion can significantly change the shape of the land. Streams are rare, because water easily sinks down into the weathered limestone. Deep valleys and caverns are common. If the roof of a cave collapses because of the erosion of the underlying limestone, the result is a depression called a sinkhole. This type of landscape is called **karst topography** after a region in Eastern Europe. In the United States, regions of karst topography are found in Florida, Texas, and many other states.

Reading Checkpoint   **How does deposition occur in a limestone cave?**

Apply Ask: **How is this similar to the way carbonic acid forms in soil?** (*Respiration by plant roots and microorganisms in soil produces carbon dioxide. The carbon dioxide combines with water to form carbonic acid.*) **learning modality: visual**

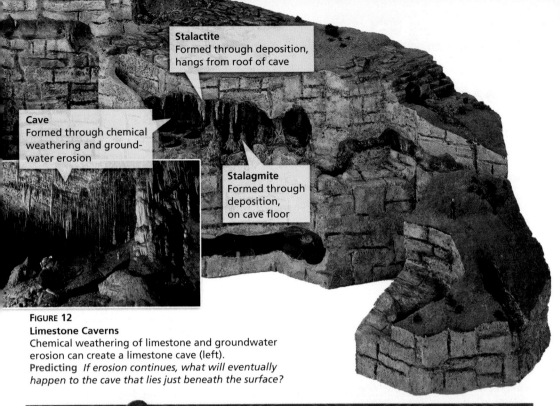

Stalactite
Formed through deposition, hangs from roof of cave

Cave
Formed through chemical weathering and ground-water erosion

Stalagmite
Formed through deposition, on cave floor

FIGURE 12
Limestone Caverns
Chemical weathering of limestone and groundwater erosion can create a limestone cave (left).
Predicting If erosion continues, what will eventually happen to the cave that lies just beneath the surface?

Section 2 Assessment

Target Reading Skill Previewing Visuals Refer to your questions and answers about Figure 10 to help you answer Question 2 below.

Reviewing Key Concepts

1. **a. Reviewing** What is the major agent of erosion on Earth's surface?
   b. Sequencing List these in order of size: tributary, stream, rill, gully, runoff, river.
   c. Predicting Where would gullies be more likely to form: a field with plowed soil and no plants, or a field covered with thick grass? Explain.

2. **a. Listing** What are five features that erosion forms along a river?
   b. Listing What are three features that result from deposition along a river?
   c. Relating Cause and Effect Why does a delta often form where a river empties into the ocean?

3. **a. Identifying** What process is the cause of groundwater erosion?
   b. Explaining How do groundwater erosion and deposition produce a limestone cave?

Lab zone At-Home **Activity**

Erosion Cube In a small dish, build a cube out of 27 small sugar cubes. Your cube should be three sugar cubes on a side. Fold a square piece of paper towel to fit the top of the cube. Wet the paper towel, place it on the cube, and let it stand for 15 or 20 minutes. Every few minutes, sprinkle a few drops of water on the paper towel to keep it wet. Then remove the paper towel. What happened to your cube? How is the effect of water on a sugar cube similar to groundwater eroding limestone? How is it different?

Lab zone At-Home **Activity**

Erosion Cube L2 Students will find that some of the sugar of the large cube dissolves in water from the paper towel, which leaves the cube smaller and misshapen. The purpose of building a large cube with smaller ones is to form cracks for water to seep through. This is analogous to water seeping through cracks in limestone, eroding the rock, and then carrying the material away in solution.

Underground Streams and Lakes

Focus Many students believe that all or most groundwater is held in rivers or lakes beneath Earth's surface. Ask: **How does groundwater exist beneath Earth's surface?** *(Accept all answers at this time.)*

Teach Point out that underground caves do sometimes contain streams and lakes but that this is the exception rather than the rule. Almost all groundwater exists in small pores in rock or in cracks in rock.

Apply Have students compare groundwater in rock to the water held in an old, cracked sponge. **learning modality: verbal**

Monitor Progress ____ L2

Answers
Figure 12 The cave's roof will collapse to form a sinkhole.

✓ **Reading Checkpoint** Water that contains calcium and carbonic acid drips into a cave. When carbon dioxide leaves the solution, a deposit of calcite is left behind.

Assess

Reviewing Key Concepts

1. **a.** Moving water **b.** Runoff, rill, gully, stream, tributary, river **c.** A field with plowed soil and no plants—there would not be anything to hold the soil in place.
2. **a.** Valleys, waterfalls, flood plains, meanders, and oxbow lakes **b.** Alluvial fans, river deltas, and soil on flood plains **c.** The flowing water of the river slows down and deposits its sediment.
3. **a.** Chemical weathering **b.** Carbonic acid in groundwater breaks down limestone, which is carried away in solution by the water. Eventually a cave forms. If the level of groundwater lowers, the cave becomes filled with air. Stalactites and stalagmites can form when water that contains carbonic acid and calcium drips into the cave.

Reteach L1

As a class, make a table to compare and contrast the features formed by groundwater erosion with the features formed by groundwater deposition.

All in One Teaching Resources

• Section Summary: *Water Erosion*
• Review and Reinforce: *Water Erosion*
• Enrich: *Water Erosion*

Streams in Action L2

Prepare for Inquiry

Key Concept
As water moves over land, it erodes soil and rock to form a channel.

Skills Objectives
After this lab, students will be able to
- Make a model of a stream
- Observe how time and angle of slope affect erosion of the land

 **Prep Time** 15 minutes
Class Time 40 minutes

All in One Teaching Resources
- Lab Worksheet: *Streams in Action*

Advance Planning
Diatomaceous earth is a silica material that works well in stream tables. It is available at many aquarium and pet stores. Scoop diatomaceous earth from the bag into each container. Use caution to avoid inhaling the material. Place about 1 kg of diatomaceous earth into each tub. Spray water on the diatomaceous earth until it is moist throughout. Stir the sediment slowly to expose all of the diatomaceous earth to the water. Drain off any excess water. While wearing gloves, form a hill at one end of the tub, and slope the diatomaceous earth from the hill to the bottom of the tub. Leave about one third of the tub free of the material.

Alternative Materials
Local topsoil or commercial soil can be used instead of diatomaceous earth.

Safety
Caution students to wear goggles while using diatomaceous earth. The silica particles can irritate the eyes. Advise students to wear lab aprons and to be careful with the scissors and wire. Review the safety guidelines in Appendix A.

Streams in Action

Problem
How do rivers and streams erode the land?

Skills Focus
making models, observing

Materials
- diatomaceous earth • plastic measuring cup
- spray bottle
- hand lens
- watch or clock
- water
- 1 metal spoon
- plastic foam cup
- blue food coloring
- liquid detergent
- scissors
- 2 wood blocks about 2.5 cm thick
- bucket to hold 2–3 L of water or a source of tap water
- plastic stirrers, 10–12 cm long, with two small holes each
- wire, 13–15 cm long, 20 gauge

Making the Dripper
1. Insert the wire into one of the two holes in a plastic stirrer. The ends of the wire should protrude from the stirrer.
2. Gently bend the stirrer into a **U** shape. Be careful not to make any sharp bends. This is the dripper.
3. With scissors, carefully cut two small notches on opposite sides of the top of the foam cup.
4. Fill the cup to just below the notches with water colored with two drops of blue food coloring. Add more food coloring later as you add more water to the cup.

5. Add one drop of detergent to keep air bubbles out of the dripper and increase flow.
6. To start the dripper, fill it with water. Then quickly tip it and place it in one of the notches in the cup, as shown at left.

Procedure

PART 1 Creating Streams Over Time

1. Your teacher will give you a plastic tub containing diatomaceous earth that has been soaked with water. Place the tub on a level surface. **CAUTION:** *Dry diatomaceous earth produces dust that may be irritating if inhaled.* To keep the diatomaceous earth from drying out, spray it lightly with water.
2. One end of the tub will contain more diatomaceous earth. Use a block of wood to raise this end of the tub 2.5 cm.
3. Place the cup at the upper end of the slope with the notches pointing to the left and right.
4. Press the cup firmly down into the earth to secure its position.
5. Start the dripper (see Step 6 in the box below). Allow the water to drip to the right onto the diatomaceous earth.
6. Allow the dripper to drip for 5 minutes. (*Hint:* When you need to add more water, be careful not to disturb the dripper.)

7. Adjust the flow rate of the dripper to about 2 drips per 1 second. (*Hint:* Bend the dripper into more of a **U** shape to increase flow. Lessen the curve to reduce flow.)

Guide Inquiry

Invitation
Ask: **What is the major agent of erosion that shapes Earth's surface?** *(Moving water)* **How does water cause erosion?** *(Moving water picks up and moves soil and rock particles.)* **What factors affect how much sediment a river can erode?** *(Factors include a river's slope and volume of flow.)*

Introduce the Procedure
Give students time to read through the whole procedure, and then ask: **What factor are you changing in Part 1?** *(The amount of time that the water drips)* **What factor are you changing in Part 2?** *(The angle of slope)*

5. Replace the cup and restart the dripper, placing it in the notch on the left side of the cup. Allow the dripper to drip for 5 minutes. Notice any changes in the new stream bed.

6. At the end of 5 minutes, remove the dripper.

7. Draw the new stream bed in your lab notebook. Label it "Increased Angle."

8. Follow your teacher's instructions for cleanup after this activity. Wash your hands when you have finished.

Analyze and Conclude

1. **Observing** Compare the 5-minute stream with the 10-minute stream. How did the length of time that the water flowed affect erosion along the stream bed?

2. **Drawing Conclusions** Were your predictions about the effects of increasing the angle of slope correct? Explain your answer.

3. **Observing** What happened to the eroded material that was carried downstream?

4. **Making Models** What features of streams were you able to observe using your model? How could you modify the model to observe additional features?

5. **Controlling Variables** What other variables besides time and angle of slope might affect the way rivers and streams erode the land?

6. **Communicating** Describe an example of water erosion that you have seen, such as water flowing down a hillside or street after a heavy rain. Include in your answer details such as the slope of the land, the color of the water, and the effects of the erosion.

Design an Experiment

Design an experiment in which you use your model to measure how the amount of sediment carried by a river changes as the volume of flow of the river increases. *Obtain your teacher's approval before you try the experiment.*

7. Observe the flow of water and the changes it makes. Use the hand lens to look closely at the stream bed.

8. After 5 minutes, remove the dripper.

9. In your lab notebook, draw a picture of the resulting stream and label it "5 minutes."

10. Now switch the dripper to the left side of the cup. Restart the dripper and allow it to drip for 10 minutes. Then remove the dripper.

11. Draw a picture and label it "10 minutes."

PART 2 **Changing the Angle of Slope**

1. Remove the cup from the stream table.

2. Save the stream bed on the right side of the tub. Using the bowl of the spoon, smooth out the diatomaceous earth on the left side.

3. To increase the angle of slope of your stream table, raise the end of the tub another 2.5 cm.

4. In your lab notebook, predict the effects of increasing the angle of slope.

Troubleshooting the Experiment

After starting the dripper, a stream of water will form as the drops accumulate on the diatomaceous earth. If it does not, the dripper needs to be adjusted to increase the flow.

Expected Outcome

In Part 1, the water erodes the diatomaceous earth. The dripped water will form a channel; the 10-minute drip will cause a deeper channel than the 5-minute drip. In Part 2, increasing the angle of slope will produce a deeper channel and cause more erosion.

Analyze and Conclude

1. The 10-minute stream should have a deeper channel than the 5-minute stream. The longer the water flowed, the more erosion occurred along the stream bed.

2. Most students will have predicted that increasing the angle of slope would result in a deeper channel and more erosion; their results should confirm this prediction.

3. The eroded material moved down the slope until it was deposited.

4. Students observed a channel that is more deeply incised at its head. Other features, such as meanders, might have been observed away from the stream's head. Students might suggest that allowing the drip to continue for a longer time will allow more features to develop.

5. The characteristics of the sediment or bedrock, the amount and type of vegetation, the frequency and intensity of floods

6. Answers will vary. Make certain that students include details about the erosion event that they describe.

Extend Inquiry

Design an Experiment Designs will vary. Students might suggest dripping water onto opposite sides of the slope at two different rates and measuring the erosion caused by each stream. After reviewing the designs, encourage students to conduct their experiments.

Science and Society

Protecting Homes in Flood Plains

Key Concept
Students discuss issues related to flooding and its effect on homes in flood plains.

Build Background Knowledge
Point out that a flood plain might be thought of as a natural safety valve for times when a river's channel cannot hold all of the runoff. Geologists try to estimate the risk of major floods by using the past to calculate a probability. A "50-year flood," for example, is one that occurs once in 50 years, on average. However, such a flood can occur in any year and even in two consecutive years.

Introduce the Role-Play
In this activity, students will role-play a town meeting that takes place after a major flood destroys homes and businesses in a river's flood plain. If there is a major river in your area, students could predict what would be damaged if it flooded and then use those predictions in the role-play. You could also develop a flood scenario for any river and give students copies.

Facilitate the Role-Play
Organize the class into three groups. Students in one group will role-play public officials, including a mayor, a congressperson, the head of a federal agency for flood relief, and so on. This group will run the town meeting. Students in a second group will role-play people affected by the flood. Students in a third group will role-play citizens who oppose spending public money for rebuilding in the flood plain. Give each group 10 to 15 minutes to discuss positions and arguments to take in the town meeting. Then hold the town meeting according to rules set by the officials' group. Encourage students to assert their positions respectfully but with conviction.

Protecting Homes in Flood Plains

At least ten million American households are located in flood plains. Living near a river is tempting. Riverside land is often flat and easy to build on. Because so many people now live in flood plains, the cost of flood damage has been growing. Communities along rivers want to limit the cost of flooding. They want to know how they can protect the people and buildings already in flood plains. They also want to know how to discourage more people from moving into flood plains.

The Issues

Should the Government Insure People Against Flood Damage?

The United States government offers insurance to households in flood plains. The insurance pays part of the cost of repairs after a flood. Government flood insurance is available only to towns and cities that take steps to reduce flood damage. Cities must allow new building only on high ground. The insurance will not pay to rebuild homes that are badly damaged by flood water. Instead, these people must use the money to find a home somewhere else.

Critics say that insurance just encourages development in areas that flood. Another problem with the insurance is cost. It is very expensive. Most people who live in flood plains don't buy the government insurance. Supporters say insurance rewards towns and cities that make rules to control building on flood plains. Over time, this approach would mean fewer homes and other buildings on flood plains—and less damage from flooding.

▼ Flooded homes in Davenport, Iowa.

84 ◆ G

Background

Facts and Figures
The Federal Emergency Management Agency (FEMA) is the agency of the United States government that is responsible for providing flood insurance. To make decisions about flood risk, FEMA develops and updates flood-risk maps for the United States. Most of this information is acquired through the use of satellite technology combined with digital (computer) mapping techniques. Flood-risk maps are available to the public through FEMA's online resources (HazardMaps.gov).

Floodwater Rising
Rain from Hurricane Isabel caused this flooding in Alexandria, Virginia in 2003.

How Much of the Flood Plain Should Be Protected?

Government flood insurance is available only in areas where scientists expect flooding at least once in 100 years. But such figures are just estimates. Three floods occurred in only 12 years in a government flood insurance area near Sacramento, California.

Should the Government Tell People Where They Can Live?

Some programs of flood control forbid all new building. Other programs may also encourage people to move to safer areas. The 1997 flood on the Red River in Grand Forks, North Dakota, is one example. After the flood, the city of Grand Forks offered to buy all the damaged buildings near the river. The city wants to build high walls of earth to protect the rest of the town.

The Grand Forks plan might prevent future damage, but is it fair? Supporters say that since the government has to pay for flood damage, it has the right to make people leave flood plains. Critics of such plans say that people should be free to live where they want, even in risky areas.

Who should decide in which neighborhood no new houses can be built? Who decides which people should be asked to move away from a flood plain? Experts disagree over whether local, state, or United States government officials should decide which areas to include. Some believe scientists should make the decision.

You Decide

1. Identify the Problem
In your own words, describe the controversy surrounding flood plains and housing.

2. Analyze the Options
List several steps that could be taken to reduce the damage done to buildings in flood plains. For each step, include who would benefit from the step and who would pay the costs.

3. Find a Solution
Your town has to decide what to do about a neighborhood damaged by the worst flood in 50 years. Write a speech that argues for your solution.

For: More on protecting homes in flood plains
Visit: PHSchool.com
Web Code: cfh-2030

G ◆ 85

Weigh the Impact

1. Students' answers will vary. Possible answer: Houses and other buildings on flood plains can be damaged by floods. Some people think that the government should spend money to help rebuild houses and other buildings that are damaged during floods. Other people think that those who live in these houses and operate these businesses should relocate to higher ground.

2. Possible answers: Build levees or flood walls along the stream, residents of flood plain would benefit, government would pay the costs; dams could be built upstream, residents would benefit, government would pay cost; relocate those at highest risk, government would benefit through reduced expenditures, government would pay relocation costs

3. Encourage students to support their arguments with damage assessments, statements about the value of the affected area, and statements about the feasibility of possible solutions.

Go Online
PHSchool.com
For: More on protecting homes in flood plains
Visit: PHSchool.com
Web Code: cfh-2030

Students can research this issue online.

Extend

The 1997 Red River flood was a 500-year flood caused by an ice block to the north that prevented runoff from heavy snows and rains from flowing downstream (north into Canada). Flood waters spread out over the flood plain, causing catastrophic damage. Encourage students to find out what happened in Grand Forks after the 1997 Red River flood. With real data, students can realistically assess positions taken during the role-play.

Objectives

After this lesson, students will be able to
G.3.3.1 Describe how water is able to do work.
G.3.3.2 Explain how sediment enters rivers and streams.
G.3.3.3 List the factors that affect a river's ability to erode and carry sediment.

Target Reading Skill 🔄

Building Vocabulary Explain that knowing the definitions of key concept words helps students understand what they read.

Answers

As students read each passage that contains a key term, remind them to write a sentence in their own words. Encourage students to write one or two descriptive phrases to help them remember the key term. Call on students to share their definitions.

All in One Teaching Resources

• Guided Reading and Study Worksheet: *The Force of Moving Waters, Use Target Reading Skills*

Preteach

Build Background Knowledge   L1

Rivers and Moving Water
Encourage students to describe the size and speed of different rivers that they have seen. Then ask: **In which river does water move faster—a narrow mountain river or a wide river that flows smoothly through its floodplain?** (*Most students will say that water in the narrow mountain river moves faster.*) Suggest that they might want to revise their predictions after reading the section.

The Force of Moving Water

Reading Preview

Key Concepts
• What enables water to do work?
• How does sediment enter rivers and streams?
• What factors affect a river's ability to erode and carry sediment?

Key Terms
• energy • potential energy
• kinetic energy • abrasion
• load • friction • turbulence

🔄 Target Reading Skill

Building Vocabulary A definition states the meaning of a word or phrase by telling about its most important feature or function. Carefully read the definition of each Key Term and also read the neighboring sentences. Then write a definition of each Key Term in your own words.

FIGURE 13
Water Power
Dams like this one on the Merrimack River in Lowell, Massachusetts, help to harness the power of flowing water.

86 ◆ G

Lab zone   Discover **Activity**

How Are Sediments Deposited?

1. Put on your goggles.
2. Obtain a clear plastic jar or bottle with a top. Fill the jar about two-thirds full with water.
3. Fill a plastic beaker with 200 mL of fine and coarse sand, soil, clay, and small pebbles.
4. Pour the mixture into the jar of water. Screw on the top tightly and shake for two minutes. Be sure to hold onto the jar firmly.
5. Set the jar down and observe it for 10 to 15 minutes.

Think It Over
Inferring In what order are the sediments in the jar deposited? What do you think causes this pattern?

The Merrimack River in New Hampshire and Massachusetts is only 180 kilometers long. But the Merrimack does a great deal of work as it runs from the mountains to the sea. The river's waters fall 82 meters through many rapids and waterfalls. During the 1800s, people harnessed this falling water to run machines that could spin thread and weave cloth.

Work and Energy

A river's water has energy. **Energy** is the ability to do work or cause change. There are two kinds of energy. **Potential energy** is energy that is stored and waiting to be used later. The Merrimack's waters begin with potential energy due to their position above sea level. **Kinetic energy** is the energy an object has due to its motion. **As gravity pulls water down a slope, the water's potential energy changes to kinetic energy that can do work.**

When energy does work, the energy is transferred from one object to another. Along the Merrimack River, the kinetic energy of the moving water was transferred to the spinning machines. It became mechanical energy harnessed for making cloth. But all along a river, moving water has other effects. A river is always moving sediment from the mountains to the sea. At the same time, a river is also eroding its banks and valley.

Lab zone   Discover **Activity**

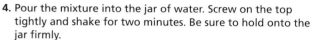

Skills Focus Inferring   L2

Materials clear plastic jar or bottle with top, water, plastic beaker, fine and coarse sand, soil, clay, small pebbles

Time 20 minutes

Tips To simplify the activity, make the sediment mixtures in advance.

Expected Outcome Students will observe the settling of the sediments.

The larger particles will settle first, and the smaller grains will settle last. After 10 to 15 minutes, most of the particles will have settled, but the water will remain cloudy because of the continued suspension of fine clay particles.

Think It Over The particles are deposited according to size. Gravity acting on the different sizes of grains causes the pattern.

How Water Erodes

Gravity causes the movement of water across Earth's land surface. But how does water cause erosion? In the process of water erosion, water picks up and moves sediment. Sediment includes soil, rock, clay, and sand. Sediment can enter rivers and streams in a number of ways. **Most sediment washes or falls into a river as a result of mass movement and runoff. Other sediment erodes from the bottom or sides of the river.** Wind may also drop sediment into the water.

Abrasion is another process by which a river obtains sediment. **Abrasion** is the wearing away of rock by a grinding action. Abrasion occurs when particles of sediment in flowing water bump into the streambed again and again. Abrasion grinds down sediment particles. For example, boulders become smaller as they are moved down a streambed. Sediments also grind and chip away at the rock of the streambed, deepening and widening the stream's channel.

The amount of sediment that a river carries is its **load.** Gravity and the force of the moving water cause the sediment load to move downstream. Most large sediment falls to the bottom and moves by rolling and sliding. Fast-moving water actually lifts sand and other, smaller sediment and carries it downstream. Water dissolves some sediment completely. The river carries these dissolved sediments in solution. Figure 14 shows other ways in which water can carry sediment. For example, grains of sand or small stones can move by bouncing.

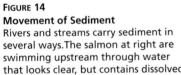 **Reading Checkpoint** What causes the sediment in a river to move downstream?

Lab zone | Skills Activity

Developing Hypotheses

A geologist is comparing alluvial fans. One alluvial fan is composed of gravel and small boulders. The other fan is composed of sand and silt. Propose a hypothesis to explain the difference in the size of the particles in the two fans. (*Hint:* Think of the characteristics of the streams that formed each alluvial fan.)

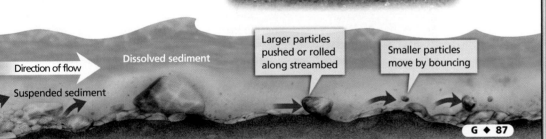

FIGURE 14
Movement of Sediment
Rivers and streams carry sediment in several ways. The salmon at right are swimming upstream through water that looks clear, but contains dissolved sediment. *Predicting How would a boulder in a stream be likely to move?*

Direction of flow

Dissolved sediment

Suspended sediment

Larger particles pushed or rolled along streambed

Smaller particles move by bouncing

G ◆ 87

Lab zone | Skills Activity

Skills Focus Developing hypotheses **L3**

Materials none

Time 5 minutes

Tips Have students review the description in the previous section of an alluvial fan and how it forms.

Expected Outcome A typical hypothesis might suggest that the river that produced the gravel-boulder alluvial fan had a greater slope and volume of flow than the river that produced the sand-silt fan.

Extend Challenge students to design an experiment to test their hypotheses using a stream table. **learning modality: logical/mathematical**

Erosion and Sediment Load

Teach Key Concepts L2

Speed of a River

Focus Review with students the meanings of the words *slope* and *volume*.

Teach Ask: **Does a sled move faster over a steep hill or a gentle hill?** (*Steep hill*) **If everything else were equal, would water flow faster over a steep slope?** (*Yes. If everything else were the same, water would flow faster over a steep slope.*) **What can slow the flow of water?** (*Friction with the bottom of the stream*) **Which kinds of stream bottoms would cause the most friction?** (*Rough, rocky stream bottoms*) **Why might more volume of water reduce friction with the bottom and increase speed of flow?** (*The stream is deeper, so less water is close to the bottom.*)

Apply Ask students to recall the predictions they made in Building Background Knowledge at the beginning of this section. Ask them whether they would like to reconsider their predictions. (*In general, steep mountain streams flow more slowly than larger rivers that flow over gentle slopes. This is true because the friction with the bottom is much less in large rivers. The water in a mountain river moves turbulently, but it moves downhill more slowly than the water in most other rivers.*) **learning modality: logical/mathematical**

FIGURE 15
The Slope of a River
A river's slope is usually greatest near the river's source. As a river approaches its mouth, its slope lessens. *Inferring Where would you expect the water in this river to have the greatest amount of potential energy?*

Erosion and Sediment Load

The power of a river to cause erosion and carry sediment depends on several factors. **A river's slope, volume of flow, and the shape of its streambed all affect how fast the river flows and how much sediment it can erode.**

A fast-flowing river carries more and larger particles of sediment. When a river slows down, it drops its sediment load. The larger particles of sediment are deposited first.

Slope Generally, if a river's slope increases, the water's speed also increases. A river's slope is the amount the river drops toward sea level over a given distance. If a river's speed increases, its sediment load and power to erode may increase. But other factors are also important in determining how much sediment the river erodes and carries.

Volume of Flow A river's flow is the volume of water that moves past a point on the river in a given time. As more water flows through a river, its speed increases. During a flood, the increased volume of water helps the river to cut more deeply into its banks and bed. When a river floods, its power to erode may increase by a hundredfold. A flooding river can carry huge amounts of sand, soil, and other sediments. It may move giant boulders as if they were pebbles.

 Reading Checkpoint How does a river's slope affect its speed?

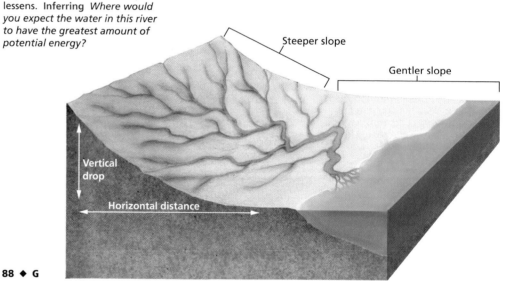

Steeper slope

Gentler slope

Vertical drop

Horizontal distance

Differentiated Instruction

Less Proficient Readers L1
Writing Questions Have students rewrite the section heads and subheads as questions such as the following: *What is sediment load? How is it related to erosion? How does slope affect speed and erosion? How does volume of flow affect speed and erosion? How does stream bed shape affect speed and erosion?* Suggest that students write the answers to each question and use their questions and answers as a study guide. **learning modality: logical/mathematical**

Streambed Shape A streambed's shape affects the amount of friction between the water and the streambed. **Friction** is the force that opposes the motion of one surface as it moves across another surface. Friction, in turn, affects a river's speed. Where a river is deep, less water comes in contact with the streambed. The reduced friction allows the river to flow faster. In a shallow river, much of the water comes in contact with the streambed. Therefore friction increases, reducing the river's speed.

A streambed is often full of boulders and other obstacles. This roughness prevents the water from flowing smoothly. Roughness thus increases friction and reduces the river's speed. Instead of moving downstream, the water moves every which way in a type of movement called **turbulence.** For example, a stream on a steep slope may flow at a slower speed than a large river on a gentle slope. Friction and turbulence slow the stream's flow. But a turbulent stream or river may have great power to erode.

FIGURE 16
Turbulence
The turbulent flow of this stream increases the stream's power to cause erosion.

Math ▶ Analyzing Data

Sediment on the Move

The speed, or velocity, of a stream affects the size of the sediment particles the stream can carry. Study the graph, then answer the questions below.

1. **Reading Graphs** What variable is shown on the *x*-axis of the graph?

2. **Reading Graphs** What variable is shown on the *y*-axis of the graph?

3. **Interpreting Data** What is the speed at which a stream can move coarse sand? Small pebbles? Large boulders?

4. **Predicting** A stream's speed increases to about 600 cm per second during a flood. What are the largest particles the stream can move?

5. **Developing Hypotheses** Write a hypothesis that states the relationship between the speed of a stream and the size of the sediment particles it can move.

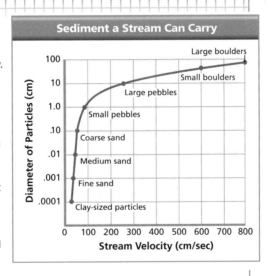

Sediment a Stream Can Carry

Diameter of Particles (cm) vs. Stream Velocity (cm/sec)

- Large boulders
- Small boulders
- Large pebbles
- Small pebbles
- Coarse sand
- Medium sand
- Fine sand
- Clay-sized particles

Lab zone Build **Inquiry** L3

Modeling River Speed

Materials stream table, clay, pebbles, small rocks, large rocks, water

Time 20 minutes

Focus Ask: **What factors affect the speed of flowing water?** (*Slope, volume of water, friction with bottom*)

Teach Set up a stream table, and have students use clay, pebbles, and small rocks to create a stream bed. Change the angle of the slope by propping one end higher than the other end. Change the volume of flow by allowing different amounts of water to move down the slope. Have students experiment with different factors and record their observations.

Apply Ask: **How do different factors affect the speed of water?** (*An increase in slope, an increase in volume, and a decrease in bottom roughness will increase the speed of water in a stream.*) **learning modality: kinesthetic**

Math ▶ Analyzing Data

Math Skill Making and interpreting graphs

Focus Point out that line graphs show how variables are related.

Teach Ask: **How can a line be drawn on a graph like this one?** (*Data are measured, and points are plotted on the graph. The points can be connected to make the line.*)

Answers

1. Stream velocity

2. Diameter of sediment particles

3. About 50 cm/s; about 90 cm/s; about 800 cm/s

4. Small boulders

5. Possible answer: The faster the speed of the flowing water, the larger the particles the stream is able to move.

Differentiated Instruction

English Learners/Beginning L1
Comprehension: Key Concept On the board, rewrite the boldfaced sentence under *Erosion and Sediment Load* into individual sentences that explain how each factor affects how fast a river flows and how much sediment it erodes. Then, help students construct a concept map that illustrates these relationships. **learning modality: verbal**

English Learners/Intermediate L2
Comprehension: Key Concept Have these students write the individual sentences themselves. Provide help as needed. **learning modality: verbal**

Monitor Progress _____ L2

Drawing Have students draw sketches that show why stream bed shape affects the way a river flows.

Answer
Figure 15 At the highest point

Use Visuals: Figure 17

Stream Erosion and Deposition

Focus Direct students' attention to the figure and the meaning of the symbols in the key.

Teach Ask: **Where does the river erode its bank, at point A or point B?** *(At point B, on the outside of the curve)* **Where is sediment deposited?** *(At point A, on the inside of the curve)*

Apply Ask: **As this process of erosion and deposition continues, what will happen to the meander?** *(It will become more curved.)* **learning modality: visual**

Monitor Progress _____ L2

Answer

Figure 17 The water speed is slowest there.

✓ **Reading Checkpoint** On the outside of the curve

Assess

Reviewing Key Concepts

1. a. The ability to do work or to cause change **b.** Gravity causes river water to move down a slope. As the water flows, its potential energy changes into kinetic energy. **c.** Erosion and deposition

2. a. Mass movement and runoff **b.** Sand and other sediment grains can strike the rock of the stream's bed and wear it away. This process is called abrasion. **c.** The piece of rock will become smaller and more rounded as it bounces or rolls along the stream bed. This occurs because pieces get broken off the rock. Jagged corners are more easily broken, so the rock becomes rounded.

3. a. Slope, volume of flow, and shape of the stream bed **b.** The river's bank will eventually erode, and the curve will become larger.

Reteach L1

As a class, make a list of ways that a river acquires sediment.

All in One Teaching Resources

- Section Summary: *The Force of Moving Water*
- Review and Reinforce: *The Force of Moving Water*
- Enrich: *The Force of Moving Water*

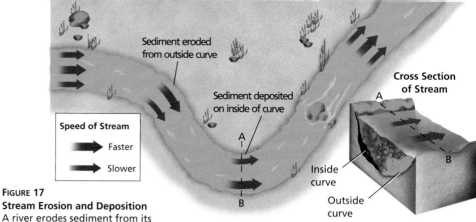

FIGURE 17
Stream Erosion and Deposition
A river erodes sediment from its banks on the outside curve and deposits sediment on the inside curve.
Relating Cause and Effect Why does a river deposit sediment on the inside of a curve?

Factors Affecting Erosion and Deposition Whether a river flows in a straight line or a curved line affects the way it erodes and deposits sediment. Where a river flows in a straight line, the water flows faster near the center of the river than along its sides. Deposition occurs along the sides of the river, where the water moves more slowly.

If a river curves, the water moves fastest along the outside of the curve. There, the river tends to cut into its bank, causing erosion. Sediment is deposited on the inside curve, where the water speed is slowest. You can see this process in Figure 17.

✓ **Reading Checkpoint** Where a stream curves, in what part of the stream does the water flow fastest?

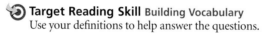

Section 3 Assessment

🔄 **Target Reading Skill** Building Vocabulary
Use your definitions to help answer the questions.

Reviewing Key Concepts

1. a. Defining What is energy?
   b. Explaining How is a river's potential energy changed into kinetic energy?
   c. Relating Cause and Effect What are two effects produced by flowing water in a river?
2. a. Reviewing What are two main sources of the sediment that rivers and streams carry?
   b. Describing Describe a process by which a stream can erode its streambed.
   c. Predicting Near a stream's source, a stream erodes a piece of rock from its streambed. As the rock is carried down the stream, how will its size and shape change? Explain.

3. a. Identifying What three factors affect how fast a river flows?
   b. Interpreting Diagrams Study Figure 17 above. Over time, what will happen to the river's bank at B? Why?

Writing in Science

Comparison Paragraph A river transports different types of sediment particles from its source to its mouth: tiny clay particles, grains of sand, pebbles, and boulders. Write a paragraph that compares clay particles and pebbles in terms of how they move, how fast they travel, and how their potential energy changes during the journey.

Writing in Science

Writing Mode Description

Scoring Rubric

4 Exceeds criteria in some way, for example, explaining how the particles cause erosion of the stream bed

3 Meets criteria but does not go beyond requirements

2 Includes only brief description of required elements

1 Is incorrect and incomplete

Lab zone Chapter **Project**

Keep Students on Track Check that students have conducted their investigations about soil permeability and have determined which of the materials will work best for holding back water. Advise students to begin to use the data that they have gathered about the soil samples to design the model dams.

Reading Preview

Key Concepts
- What are the two kinds of glaciers?
- How does a valley glacier form and move?
- How do glaciers cause erosion and deposition?

Key Terms
- glacier • continental glacier
- ice age• valley glacier
- plucking • till • moraine • kettle

Target Reading Skill

Asking Questions Before you read, preview the red headings. In a graphic organizer like the one below, ask a *what, how,* or *where* question for each heading. As you read, answer your questions.

Glaciers

Question	Answer
What kinds of glaciers are there?	Valley glaciers and . . .

▼ The Hubbard Glacier in Alaska

How Do Glaciers Change the Land?

1. Put some sand in a small plastic container.
2. Fill the container with water and place the container in a freezer until the water turns to ice.
3. Remove the block of ice from the container. Hold the ice with a paper towel.
4. Rub the ice, sand side down, over a bar of soap. Observe what happens to the surface of the soap.

Think It Over

Inferring Based on your observations, how do you think moving ice could change the surface of the land?

You are on a boat trip near the coast of Alaska. You sail by vast evergreen forests and snow-capped mountains. Then, as your boat rounds a point of land, you see an amazing sight. A great mass of ice winds like a river between rows of mountains. Suddenly you hear a noise like thunder. Where the ice meets the sea, a giant chunk of ice breaks off and plunges into the water. Carefully, the pilot steers your boat around the iceberg and toward the mass of ice. It towers over your boat. You see that it is made up of solid ice that is deep blue and green as well as white. What is this river of ice?

Objectives
After this lesson, students will be able to

G.3.4.1 Identify the two kinds of glaciers.
G.3.4.2 Describe how a valley glacier forms and moves.
G.3.4.3 Explain how glaciers cause erosion and deposition.

Target Reading Skill

Asking Questions Explain that changing a heading into a question helps students anticipate the ideas, facts, and events they are about to read.

Answers
Q. What kinds of glaciers are there?
A. Valley glaciers and continental glaciers
Q. How do glaciers shape the land?
A. By erosion and deposition

All in One **Teaching Resources**
- Transparency G25

Preteach

Build Background Knowledge **L1**

Snow and Glaciers
Encourage students to recall their experiences with snow. Ask: **Is there a difference between snow that has just fallen and snow that has been on the ground for a long time?** (*The snow that has just fallen is fluffier; the old snow is granular.*) Tell students that what they observed is similar to how snow starts to become ice in a glacier. If snow is uncommon in your area, explain that snow that has been on the ground a long time becomes coarsely crystalline and granular.

Skills Focus Inferring   **L1**

Materials sand, small plastic container, water, freezer, paper towel, bar of soap

Time Prep 1 day; 10 minutes second day

Tips Make sure that the containers are kept in the freezer long enough for the water to freeze completely.

Expected Outcome The sand should have frozen into the bottom of the ice. Rubbing the sand side of the ice block over soap will produce grooves and striations.

Think It Over Answers will vary. A typical answer might suggest that the sediment in ice changes the land by scratching and scraping the underlying rock.

How Glaciers Form and Move

Teach Key Concepts [L1]
Glacier Movement

Focus Ask: What would happen if each year more snow fell than melted? (*Snow would accumulate and become thicker each year.*) Tell students that this is how glaciers begin.

Teach Ask: Why does pancake batter spread out in a pan? (*Gravity pulls on the batter and makes the pile thinner.*) Is it possible for solid ice to flow like pancake batter? Convince students that it is possible if the ice becomes thick enough. Also tell them that ice flows much more slowly than pancake batter does. Why do glaciers flow? (*Gravity pulls on the ice and makes the pile thinner.*)

Apply Ask: If snow accumulates in some places and glacier ice flows outward, why hasn't ice covered most of the land? (*The ice eventually melts as it flows into warmer areas.*) **learning modality: logical/mathematical**

Help Students Read [L1]
Summarizing Tell students that summarizing the material in this section will help them understand the main ideas. Allow students to choose whether they would like to present a verbal, written, or pictorial summary.

Independent Practice [L1]
All in One Teaching Resources
- Guided Reading and Study Worksheet: *Glaciers*

Student Edition on Audio CD

Huge icebergs form where Antarctica's continental glacier meets the ocean.

FIGURE 18
Continental Glaciers
Today, huge icebergs form where a continental glacier (above) meets the ocean. During the last ice age (below), a continental glacier covered most of northern North America.

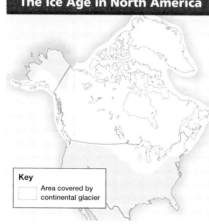

The Ice Age in North America

Key
Area covered by continental glacier

How Glaciers Form and Move

Geologists define a **glacier** as any large mass of ice that moves slowly over land. **There are two kinds of glaciers—continental glaciers and valley glaciers.**

Continental Glaciers A **continental glacier** is a glacier that covers much of a continent or large island. They can spread out over millions of square kilometers. Today, continental glaciers cover about 10 percent of Earth's land. They cover Antarctica and most of Greenland. In places, the glacier covering Antarctica is over 3 kilometers thick. Continental glaciers can flow in all directions as they move. Continental glaciers spread out much as pancake batter spreads out in a frying pan.

Many times in the past, continental glaciers have covered larger parts of Earth's surface. These times are known as **ice ages.** For example, beginning about 2.5 million years ago, continental glaciers covered about one third of Earth's land. The glaciers advanced and retreated, or melted back, several times. They finally retreated about 10,000 years ago.

Valley Glaciers A **valley glacier** is a long, narrow glacier that forms when snow and ice build up high in a mountain valley. The sides of mountains keep these glaciers from spreading out in all directions. Instead, they usually move down valleys that have already been cut by rivers. Valley glaciers are found on many high mountains. Although they are much smaller than continental glaciers, valley glaciers can be tens of kilometers long.

High in mountain valleys, temperatures seldom rise above freezing. Snow builds up year after year. The weight of more and more snow compacts the snow at the bottom into ice. **Glaciers can form only in an area where more snow falls than melts. Once the depth of snow and ice reaches more than 30 to 40 meters, gravity begins to pull the glacier downhill.**

Valley glaciers flow at a rate of a few centimeters to a few meters per day. But sometimes a valley glacier slides down more quickly in what is called a surge. A surging glacier can flow as much as 6 kilometers a year.

 Reading Checkpoint On what type of landform are valley glaciers found?

How Glaciers Shape the Land

The movement of a glacier changes the land beneath it. Although glaciers work slowly, they are a major force of erosion. **The two processes by which glaciers erode the land are plucking and abrasion.**

Glacial Erosion As a glacier flows over the land, it picks up rocks in a process called **plucking.** Beneath a glacier, the weight of the ice can break rocks apart. These rock fragments freeze to the bottom of the glacier. When the glacier moves, it carries the rocks with it. Figure 19 shows plucking by a glacier. Plucking can move even huge boulders.

Many rocks remain on the bottom of the glacier, and the glacier drags them across the land. This process, called abrasion, gouges and scratches the bedrock. You can see the results of erosion by glaciers in Figure 19.

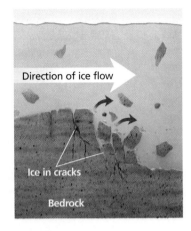

Direction of ice flow

Ice in cracks

Bedrock

FIGURE 19
Glacial Erosion
As a glacier moves (above), plucking breaks pieces of bedrock from the ground. Erosion by glaciers (below) can carve a mountain peak into a sharp horn and grind out a **V**-shaped valley to form a **U**-shaped valley.
Observing *What other changes did the glacier produce in this landscape?*

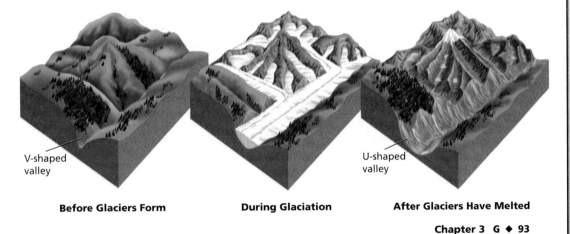

V-shaped valley

U-shaped valley

Before Glaciers Form   **During Glaciation**   **After Glaciers Have Melted**

Chapter 3   G ◆ 93

How Glaciers Shape the Land

Teach Key Concepts L2
Glacier Erosion and Deposition

Focus Review with students the meanings of *erosion* and *deposition*.

Teach Ask: **How can pieces of rock get into the bottom of a glacier?** (*The pieces are pulled loose, and then water freezes around the pieces.*) Tell students that some melting and refreezing occurs at the bases of many glaciers. **How can rock and sediment that is in glacier ice get deposited?** (*The rock and sediment are deposited when the ice melts.*)

Apply Ask: **How is a glacier similar to a conveyor belt?** (*Rock and sediment are added to the glacier, carried to its edge, and then dropped.*) **learning modality: logical/mathematical**

All in One Teaching Resources
• Transparencies G26 and G27

 **Lab zone Teacher Demo** L1

Surging Glaciers

Materials hard-surface floor, plastic lid, water

Time 5 minutes

Focus Ask: **Why are floors slippery when wet?** (*Water reduces friction between the bottom of your shoe and the floor.*)

Teach Invite a student volunteer to push a dry plastic lid across the floor. Then put some water on the floor, and ask the student to try again. It is much easier to push the lid across a wet floor.

Apply Tell students that glaciers surge for the same reason—a layer of water or wet mud gets between the glacier ice and the rock below. **learning modality: visual**

Monitor Progress L2

Writing Have students write a paragraph that addresses what a glacier is, how it forms, and how it moves.

Answers
Figure 19 Sharp ridges called arêtes and valleys that hang above a lower valley

 Reading Checkpoint Mountain valleys that were formed originally by rivers

G ● 93

Teacher Demo L2

Modeling Valleys

Materials stream table, soil, water, ice

Time 30 minutes

Focus Have students speculate about how valleys formed by ice and water differ. *(Accept all responses at this time.)*

Teach As students observe, set up a stream table with a steady trickle of water. After 5 to 10 minutes, discontinue the water. Have students examine the resulting valley and sketch what they observe. Then place an ice cube at the top of the stream-formed valley. Move the cube down the valley. Again, have students examine the valley and sketch what they see.

Apply Ask: **What shape do stream-formed valleys have?** *(V-shape)* **What shape do glacier-formed valleys have?** *(U-shape)* **learning modality: visual**

Use Visuals: Figure 20
Glacial Landforms

Focus Invite volunteers to read the captions for each of the glacial landforms in the figure.

Teach Ask: **How is the mountain valley shown here different from the valley shown in the diagram of the course of a river in a previous section?** *(A river makes a V-shaped valley; a glacier makes a U-shaped valley.)* Explain that through erosion, a glacier widens, depends, and straightens a river-cut valley. Where there was once a narrow valley, there is now a trough, or U-shaped valley.

Apply Ask: **Why does a valley glacier create different features than a continental glacier?** *(A continental glacier tends to smooth the landscape, whereas a valley glacier cuts a more rugged topography.)* **learning modality: visual**

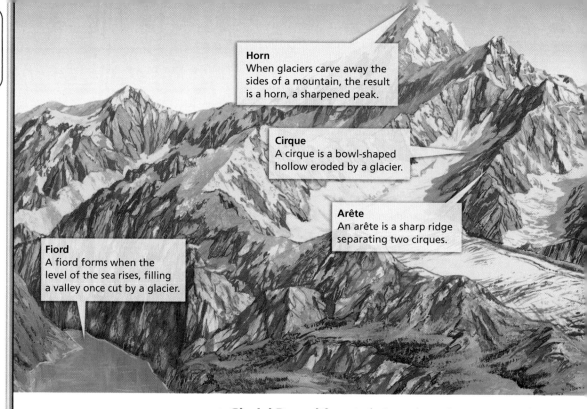

Horn
When glaciers carve away the sides of a mountain, the result is a horn, a sharpened peak.

Cirque
A cirque is a bowl-shaped hollow eroded by a glacier.

Arête
An arête is a sharp ridge separating two cirques.

Fiord
A fiord forms when the level of the sea rises, filling a valley once cut by a glacier.

FIGURE 20
Glacial Landforms
As glaciers advance and retreat, they sculpt the landscape by erosion and deposition.
Classifying *Classify these glacial features according to whether they result from erosion or deposition: drumlin, horn, cirque, moraine, U-shaped valley.*

Glacial Deposition A glacier gathers a huge amount of rock and soil as it erodes the land in its path. **When a glacier melts, it deposits the sediment it eroded from the land, creating various landforms.** These landforms remain for thousands of years after the glacier has melted. The mixture of sediments that a glacier deposits directly on the surface is called **till.** Till is made up of particles of many different sizes. Clay, silt, sand, gravel, and boulders can all be found in till.

The till deposited at the edges of a glacier forms a ridge called a **moraine.** A terminal moraine is the ridge of till at the farthest point reached by a glacier. Long Island in New York is a terminal moraine from the continental glaciers of the last ice age.

Retreating glaciers also create features called kettles. A **kettle** is a small depression that forms when a chunk of ice is left in glacial till. When the ice melts, the kettle remains. The continental glacier of the last ice age left behind many kettles. Kettles often fill with water, forming small ponds or lakes called kettle lakes. Such lakes are common in areas, such as Minnesota, that were covered with ice.

 Reading Checkpoint What is a terminal moraine?

Differentiated Instruction

Less Proficient Readers L1
Identifying Landforms Photocopy Figure 20, and replace each boldface term and annotation with lines for students to write on. Give each student a copy of the modified figure. Provide a list of the terms, and have students fill in the blanks with the correct terms. **learning modality: visual**

Special Needs L1
Modeling Glacial Landforms Have students use modeling clay to model a formerly glaciated region. Students might choose to model an alpine region or a continental region. After student models are complete, have students identify and describe each feature. **learning modality: kinesthetic**

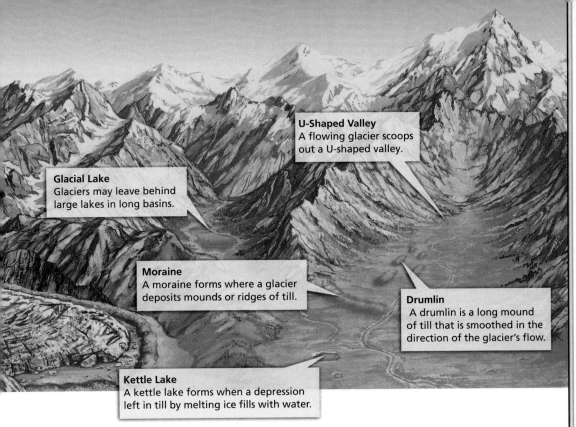

U-Shaped Valley
A flowing glacier scoops out a U-shaped valley.

Glacial Lake
Glaciers may leave behind large lakes in long basins.

Moraine
A moraine forms where a glacier deposits mounds or ridges of till.

Drumlin
A drumlin is a long mound of till that is smoothed in the direction of the glacier's flow.

Kettle Lake
A kettle lake forms when a depression left in till by melting ice fills with water.

Section 4 Assessment

🎯 **Target Reading Skill** Asking Questions Use the answers to the questions you wrote about the headings to help you answer the questions below.

Reviewing Key Concepts

1. a. Defining What is a continental glacier?
b. Defining What is a valley glacier?
c. Comparing and Contrasting How are the two types of glaciers similar? How are they different?

2. a. Reviewing What condition is necessary for a glacier to form?
b. Explaining How does a glacier move?
c. Relating Cause and Effect Why does the snow that forms a glacier change to ice?

3. a. Identifying What are two ways in which glaciers erode Earth's surface?
b. Describing How does glacial deposition occur?

Writing in Science

Travel Brochure A travel agency wants people to go on a tour of a mountain region with many glaciers. Write a paragraph for a travel brochure describing what people will see on the tour. In your answer, include features formed by glacial erosion and deposition.

Writing in Science

Writing Mode Persuasion

Scoring Rubric
4 Exceeds criteria in some way, for example, using vivid descriptions and engaging the reader
3 Meets criteria but does not go beyond requirements
2 Includes only brief description of required elements
1 Is incorrect and incomplete

Monitor Progress _____ L2

Answers
Figure 20 Drumlin, deposition; horn, erosion; cirque, erosion; moraine, deposition; U-shaped valley, erosion

✓ **Reading Checkpoint** A terminal moraine is a ridge of till deposited at the farthest point reached by a glacier.

Assess

Reviewing Key Concepts

1. a. A continental glacier is a glacier that covers much of a continent or large island.
b. A valley glacier is a long, narrow glacier in a mountain valley. **c.** Both types of glaciers are large masses of ice that move over land. Valley glaciers are long and narrow—the sides of the valley keep them from spreading. Continental glaciers spread out over a large area of land.
2. a. Glaciers form in areas where more snow falls than melts. **b.** Glaciers flow downhill because of the force of gravity.
c. Snow changes to ice as it is compacted by overlying snow.
3. a. Plucking and abrasion **b.** Deposition occurs when the glacier melts and leaves rock and sediment on the land.

Reteach L1

List *valley glacier, continental glacier, plucking, till, moraine,* and *kettle* on the board. Have students write a definition of each.

Performance Assessment L2

Skills Check Have students make a table that compares and contrasts the features formed by glacial erosion and glacial deposition. The table should include a description of each feature and an explanation of how it forms.

All in One Teaching Resources
• Section Summary: *Glaciers*
• Review and Reinforce: *Glaciers*
• Enrich: *Glaciers*

Section
5 Waves

Objectives

After this lesson, students will be able to

G.3.5.1 Identify what gives ocean waves their energy.

G.3.5.2 Describe how ocean waves erode a coast.

G.3.5.3 Identify features that result from deposition by waves.

Target Reading Skill

Identifying Main Ideas Explain that identifying main ideas and details helps students sort the facts from the information into groups. Each group can have a main topic, subtopics, and details.

Answers

Detail: Energy in waves breaks apart rocks.
Detail: Sediment wears away rock.
Detail: Landforms are created.

All in One Teaching Resources

• Transparency G28

Preteach

Build Background Knowledge   L1

Waves and Beaches

Encourage students who have been to beaches to share their experiences of the sand on the beaches and the waves that flow over the beaches. Elicit descriptions of the color and texture of the sand, and note any differences among the beaches. Then ask: **How do you think waves affect beaches?** *(Accept all reasonable responses.)* **How do you think beaches form?** *(Accept all reasonable responses.)* Record students' responses on the board, and have them refer to the responses at the end of the section.

Reading Preview

Key Concepts

• What gives waves their energy?
• How do waves erode a coast?
• What features result from deposition by waves?

Key Terms

• headland • beach
• longshore drift • spit

Target Reading Skill

Identifying Main Ideas As you read Erosion by Waves, write the main idea in a graphic organizer like the one below. Then write three supporting details that further explain the main idea.

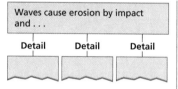

Main Idea

Waves cause erosion by impact and . . .

Detail	Detail	Detail

▼ Waves on the Oregon coast

96 ◆ G

Lab zone Discover **Activity**

What Is Sand Made Of?

1. Collect a spoonful of sand from each of two different beaches.
2. Examine the first sample of beach sand with a hand lens.
3. Record the properties of the sand grains, for example, color and shape. Are the grains smooth and rounded or angular and rough?
4. Examine the second sample and repeat Step 3. How do the two samples compare?

Think It Over

Posing Questions What questions do you need to answer to understand beach sand? Use what you know about erosion and deposition to help you think of questions.

Ocean waves contain energy—sometimes a great deal of energy. Created by ocean winds, they carry energy vast distances across the Pacific Ocean. Acting like drills or buzz saws, the waves erode the solid rock of the coast into cliffs and caves. Waves also carry sediment that forms features such as beaches.

How Waves Form

The energy in waves comes from wind that blows across the water's surface. As the wind makes contact with the water, some of its energy transfers to the water. Large ocean waves are the result of powerful storms far out at sea. But ordinary breezes can produce waves in lakes or small ponds.

The energy that water picks up from the wind causes water particles to move up and down as the wave goes by. But the water particles themselves don't move forward.

A wave changes as it approaches land. In deep water, a wave only affects the water near the surface. But as it approaches shallow water, the wave begins to drag on the bottom. The friction between the wave and the bottom causes the wave to slow down. Now the water actually does move forward with the wave. This forward-moving water provides the force that shapes the land along the shoreline.

Lab zone Discover **Activity**

Skills Focus Posing questions   L1

Materials sand from 2 beaches, hand lens

Time 15 minutes

Tips If sand is not available locally from either a nearby lake or ocean, obtain two different kinds of commercial sand. Suggest that students avoid mixing the two samples by completely removing the first sample before examining the second.

Expected Outcome Students probably will observe differences between the two samples. Differences might include grain shape, size, or color.

Think It Over Questions will vary. Possible questions: *Is beach sand a result of erosion? How is beach sand deposited? What causes differences in beach sand at different places?*

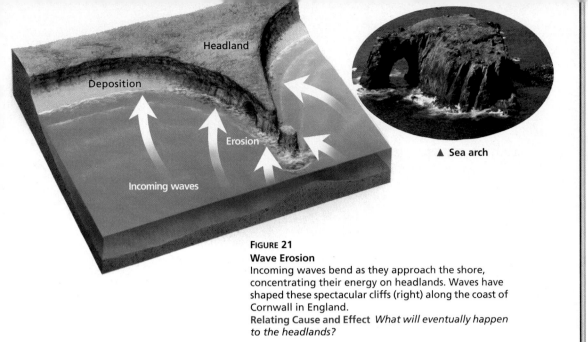

Headland

Deposition

Erosion

Incoming waves

▲ Sea arch

FIGURE 21
Wave Erosion
Incoming waves bend as they approach the shore, concentrating their energy on headlands. Waves have shaped these spectacular cliffs (right) along the coast of Cornwall in England.
Relating Cause and Effect *What will eventually happen to the headlands?*

Erosion by Waves

Waves are the major force of erosion along coasts. **Waves shape the coast through erosion by breaking down rock and transporting sand and other sediment.**

How Waves Erode One way waves erode the land is by impact. Large waves can hit rocks along the shore with great force. This energy in waves can break apart rocks. Over time, waves can make small cracks larger. Eventually, the waves cause pieces of rock to break off.

Waves also erode by abrasion. As a wave approaches shallow water, it picks up sediment, including sand and gravel. This sediment is carried forward by the wave. When the wave hits land, the sediment wears away rock like sandpaper wearing away wood.

Waves coming to shore gradually change direction. The change in direction occurs as different parts of a wave begin to drag on the bottom. Notice how the waves in Figure 21 change direction as they approach the shore. The energy of these waves is concentrated on headlands. A **headland** is a part of the shore that sticks out into the ocean. Headlands stand out from the coast because they are made of harder rock that resists erosion by the waves. But, over time, waves erode the headlands and even out the shoreline.

For: Links on waves
Visit: www.SciLinks.org
Web Code: scn-0735

Chapter 3 G ◆ 97

Instruct

How Waves Form

Teach Key Concepts   L2
Energy and Waves

Focus Remind students of the power of giant waves crashing onto shore.

Teach Ask: **How can wind transfer energy to water?** *(By blowing over the water's surface)* **What effect does this energy cause?** *(Water waves)* **What moves forward in water waves?** *(Energy)* **Does water move forward?** *(No, except on the beach)*

Apply Ask: **Why are waves near a hurricane much higher than normal waves?** *(Wind blows much faster around a hurricane, so more energy is transferred to water waves.)* **learning modality: logical/ mathematical**

Independent Practice   L2

All in One Teaching Resources

• Guided Reading and Study Worksheet: *Waves*

◉ Student Edition on Audio CD

Monitor Progress _____ L2

Writing Have students explain how energy travels along a wave.

Answer
Figure 21 The headlands will erode, and the shoreline will be straighter.

Differentiated Instruction

Gifted and Talented   L3
Investigating Beach Erosion Many coastal communities that experience severe beach erosion during storms are using modern technology to rebuild and protect their beaches from continued erosion. Invite students to find out about this technology and report their findings to the class. **learning modality: verbal**

Less Proficient Readers   L1
Making Concept Maps As students read through this section, have them make a concept map of Waves that is divided into *Wave Formation*, *Wave Erosion*, and *Wave Deposition*. Help students start the map, and make sure they include linking words between circled words. **learning modality: visual**

G ● 97

Erosion by Waves

Teach Key Concepts   L2

Landforms Formed by Wave Erosion

Focus Refer students to Figures 21 and 22.

Teach Ask: **Where will an incoming wave first touch the bottom as it approaches the shore?** *(Directly in front of the headland)* **What happens when a wave touches the bottom?** *(It slows down.)* Point out the arrows in the figure. Ask: **What do these arrows show?** *(The arrows show the wave bending around the headland and being concentrated on it.)* **How do the features along rocky coastlines form?** *(The features form because of erosion by waves.)* **What feature might form where erosion occurs at the base of a cliff?** *(A sea cave)* **How could an arch change into a stack?** *(The arch could collapse.)*

Apply Ask: **What is the overall effect of erosion along rocky shorelines?** *(The sea cliffs retreat through time.)* **learning modality: logical/mathematical**

 **Teaching Resources**

• Transparency G29

 Teacher Demo   L2

Modeling Wave Refraction

Materials chain of students, gymnasium

Time 15 minutes

Focus Remind students that wave energy is concentrated along rocky headlands.

Teach Have a group of at least 15 students join hands and stand side-by-side. Instruct them to start walking forward at the same rate. Now tell students in the middle of the chain that they are approaching a headland and will have to walk more slowly. Tell the students on the ends to continue walking at the faster rate. Make sure that students continue to hold hands.

Apply Ask: **What happened to the ends of the chain when the middle slowed down?** *(The ends curved toward the headland.)* **Why is more wave energy concentrated on headlands?** *(Just as more people walked into the headlands, more wave energy is directed onto headlands.)* **learning modality: kinesthetic**

Erosional Features

Wave-cut cliff

Sea cave Formed as wave action hollows out the cliff

Headland

Sea arch Formed when sea caves on either side of a headland join

Sea stack Left standing when a sea arch collapses

FIGURE 22
The Changing Coast

Erosion and deposition create a variety of features along a coast. **Predicting** *What will eventually happen to the sea arch?*

Landforms Created by Wave Erosion When waves hit a steep, rocky coast, they strike the area again and again. Think of an ax striking the trunk of a tree. The cut gets bigger and deeper with each strike of the blade. Finally the tree falls. In a similar way, ocean waves erode the base of the land along a steep coast. Where the rock is softer, the waves erode the land faster. Over time the waves may erode a hollow area in the rock called a sea cave.

Eventually, waves may erode the base of a cliff so much that the rock above collapses. The result is a wave-cut cliff. You can see an example of such a cliff in Figure 22.

Another feature created by wave erosion is a sea arch. A sea arch forms when waves erode a layer of softer rock that underlies a layer of harder rock. If an arch collapses, the result might be a sea stack, a pillar of rock rising above the water.

Reading Checkpoint   Over a long period of time, what effect do waves have on a steep, rocky coast?

Differentiated Instruction

Special Needs   L1
Classifying Landforms Have students divide a piece of poster board into several sections and title each section with the name of one coastline feature. For example, titles might include *sea arch, sea stack, spit,* and so on. Students then collect photographs of each landform, and mount them in the appropriate sections. Have students include a short caption and labels with each photo. **learning modality: visual**

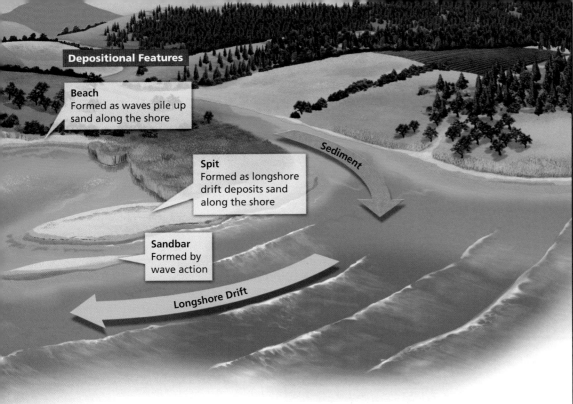

Depositional Features

Beach
Formed as waves pile up sand along the shore

Spit
Formed as longshore drift deposits sand along the shore

Sandbar
Formed by wave action

Sediment

Longshore Drift

Deposits by Waves

Waves shape a coast when they deposit sediment, forming coastal features such as beaches, spits, and barrier beaches. Deposition occurs when waves slow down, causing the water to drop its sediment. This process is similar to the deposition that occurs on a river delta when the river slows down and drops its sediment load.

Beaches As waves reach the shore, they drop the sediment they carry, forming a beach. A **beach** is an area of wave-washed sediment along a coast. The sediment deposited on beaches is usually sand. Most sand comes from rivers that carry eroded particles of rock into the ocean. But not all beaches are made of sand. Some beaches are made of small fragments of coral or sea shells piled up by wave action. Florida has many such beaches.

The sediment on a beach usually moves down the beach after it has been deposited. Waves usually hit the beach at an angle instead of straight on. These angled waves create a current that runs parallel to the coastline. As waves repeatedly hit the beach, some of the beach sediment moves down the beach with the current, in a process called **longshore drift.**

Lab zone Skills Activity

Calculating A sandy coast erodes at a rate of 1.25 m per year. But a severe storm can erode an additional 3.75 m from the shore. If 12 severe storms occur during a 50-year period, how much will the coast erode? If you wish, you may use an electronic calculator to find the answer.

Deposits by Waves

Teach Key Concepts L2
Wave Deposition

Focus Have students describe the way waves lap up onto a beach. Encourage students to mention the thin wash of water that moves up and then back down the beach.

Teach Ask: **Why might waves approach a beach at an angle?** (*Wind causes waves to come from that particular direction.*) **After waves lap up onto the beach, what causes the water to move back into the ocean?** (*Gravity*) **In which direction does gravity pull the water?** (*Straight down the slope of the beach*) **If a sand grain were moving along with this water, what path would it have?** (*A zigzag path along the beach*) Tell students that they have just explained longshore drift.

Apply Ask: **Why might a spit form where a beach curves sharply?** (*The longshore current moves sand out into the water.*) **learning modality: logical/mathematical**

Lab zone Skills Activity

Skills Focus Calculating

Materials calculator

Time 15 minutes

Tips Remind students that severe storm erosion occurs in addition to the 1.25 m/yr rate.

Expected Outcome Students set up and solve an equation to find the total erosion.

L2

Total Erosion = (1.25 m/yr)(50 yr) + (3.75 m/storm)(12 storms) = 107.5 meters

Extend Have students perform the same calculation if 25 severe storms occurred during a 50-year period. **learning modality: logical/mathematical**

Monitor Progress L2

Writing Have students explain in their own words how waves erode the land. Students can place their paragraphs in their portfolios.

Portfolio

Answers
Figure 22 The sea arch eventually will collapse because of continued erosion.

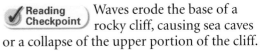
Reading Checkpoint Waves erode the base of a rocky cliff, causing sea caves or a collapse of the upper portion of the cliff.

✓ **Reading Checkpoint** Barrier beaches form when storm waves pile sand above sea level parallel to the shoreline.

Assess

Reviewing Key Concepts

1. a. Energy is transferred to ocean waves from wind. **b.** An ocean wave begins to drag at the bottom as it enters shallow water. The wave slows, and the water moves forward with the wave. **c.** Both; Ocean waves have potential because they have height. Waves have kinetic energy because they move.
2. a. Possible answers: sea cave, wave-cut cliff, sea arch, sea stack **b.** Waves erode rock by impact and abrasion. **c.** Cliff, headland, sea cave, sea arch, sea stack
3. a. Possible answers: beach, spit, barrier beach **b.** Most sand enters oceans from rivers. Spits form as a result of sand deposition by longshore drift where the coast turns abruptly.

Reteach   L1

Have students make a compare-and-contrast chart using the landforms that form by wave erosion and those that form by wave deposition.

Performance Assessment   L2

Drawing Have students make a labeled drawing of the landforms created by erosion and deposition.

All in One Teaching Resources

• Section Summary: *Waves*
• Review and Reinforce: *Waves*
• Enrich: *Waves*

FIGURE 23
Spits
This aerial photograph shows how longshore drift can carry sand and deposit it to form a spit.
Observing *How many spits can you find in this image?*

Spits One result of longshore drift is the formation of a spit. A **spit** is a beach that projects like a finger out into the water. Spits form as a result of deposition by longshore drift. Spits occur where a headland or other obstacle interrupts longshore drift, or where the coast turns abruptly.

Sandbars and Barrier Beaches Incoming waves carrying sand may build up sandbars, long ridges of sand parallel to the shore. A barrier beach is similar to a sandbar. A barrier beach forms when storm waves pile up large amounts of sand above sea level forming a long, narrow island parallel to the coast. Barrier beaches are found in many places along the Atlantic coast of the United States, such as the Outer Banks of North Carolina. People have built homes on many of these barrier beaches. But the storm waves that build up the beaches can also wash them away. Barrier beach communities must be prepared for the damage that hurricanes and other storms can bring.

✓ **Reading Checkpoint** How does a barrier beach form?

Section 5 Assessment

🔄 **Target Reading Skill** Identifying Main Ideas Use your graphic organizer to help you answer Question 2 below.

Reviewing Key Concepts

1. a. Explaining What is the source of the energy in ocean waves?
   b. Describing How does an ocean wave change when it reaches shallow water?
   c. Inferring Does an ocean wave possess potential energy or kinetic energy? Explain.
2. a. Identifying What are two results of wave erosion along a coast?
   b. Describing What are two ways in which waves erode rock?
   c. Sequencing Place these features in the order in which they would probably form: sea stack, sea cave, headland, cliff, sea arch.

3. a. Listing What are three features formed by wave deposition?
   b. Relating Cause and Effect Beginning with the source of sand, explain the process by which a spit forms.

Writing in Science

Explaining a Process Suppose that you live in a coastal area that has a barrier beach. Write a paragraph in which you explain the processes that formed the barrier beach. Also describe how the forces might change it over time.

Writing in Science

Writing Mode Exposition Cause and Effect
Scoring Rubric
4 Exceeds criteria in some way, for example, explaining the risk of building a home on a barrier beach
3 Meets criteria but does not go beyond requirements
2 Includes only brief description of required elements
1 Is incorrect and incomplete

Lab zone Chapter Project

Keep Students on Track Check that students have completed their designs for building their model dams. Encourage students to begin building and testing the dams. Have them record their observations.

Reading Preview

Key Concepts
- How does wind cause erosion?
- What features result from deposition by wind?

Key Terms
- sand dune
- deflation
- loess

 Target Reading Skill

Sequencing As you read, make a flowchart like the one below that shows the process of wind erosion and deposition. Write each step of the process in a separate box in the flowchart in the order in which it occurs.

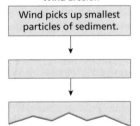

Wind Erosion

Wind picks up smallest particles of sediment.

↓

↓

Wind erosion constantly shapes the giant sand dunes in the Namib Desert of southwestern Africa. ▼

Lab zone Discover **Activity**

How Does Moving Air Affect Sediment?

1. Cover the bottom of a pan with a flat layer of cornmeal 1–2 cm deep.
2. Gently blow over the layer of cornmeal using a straw to direct your breath. Observe what happens. **CAUTION:** *Do not blow the cornmeal in the direction of another student.*

Think It Over

Observing What changes did the wind you created make in the flat layer of cornmeal?

Imagine a landscape made almost entirely of sand. One such place is the Namib Desert. The desert stretches 1,900 kilometers along the coast of Namibia in Africa. In the southern half of the Namib are rows of giant sand dunes. A **sand dune** is a deposit of wind-blown sand. Some sand dunes in the Namib are more than 200 meters high and 15 kilometers long. Much of the sand in the dunes originally came from the nearby Orange River. Over thousands of years, wind has swept the sand across the desert, piling up huge, ever-changing dunes.

How Wind Causes Erosion

Wind by itself is the weakest agent of erosion. Water, waves, moving ice, and even mass movement have more effect on the land. Yet wind can be a powerful force in shaping the land in areas where there are few plants to hold the soil in place. For example, few plants grow in deserts, so wind can easily move the grains of dry sand. **Wind causes erosion by deflation and abrasion.**

G ◆ 101

Lab zone Discover **Activity**

Skills Focus Observing   **L1**

Materials shallow pan, cornmeal, straw

Time 10 minutes

Tips Caution students to avoid blowing the cornmeal in the direction of another student. Have each student clean up any cornmeal he or she blows out of the pan. Remind students to blow gently through the straw.

Think It Over Students will observe that blowing gently through the straw eroded cornmeal from some places.

Objectives

After this lesson, students will be able to
G.3.6.1 Explain how wind causes erosion.
G.3.6.2 Identify features resulting from deposition by wind.

Target Reading Skill

Sequencing Explain that organizing information from beginning to end helps students understand a step-by-step process.

Answers

Wind picks up smallest particles of sediment. Fine particles are carried through the air. Medium-sized particles skip and bounce. Larger particles slide or roll.

All in One Teaching Resources
- Transparency G30

Preteach

Build Background Knowledge   L1

Deserts and Sandy Areas

Encourage students who have visited a desert or have seen deserts in films to describe what they saw. Ask: **Are there any natural landforms that are common in a sandy desert?** (*Most students will know about sand dunes.*) Have students speculate about how sand dunes form. Then ask: **Are there any other places where you might expect to see sand dunes?** (*Beaches*) **What characteristics do these places have in common?** (*Both have little vegetation and abundant loose sand and are often windy.*)

How Wind Causes Erosion

Teach Key Concepts ⬛L2

Deflation and Abrasion

Focus Ask students to describe being in a sandstorm or being hit by blowing sand.

Teach Ask: **How does sediment that is blown by the wind get into the air?** (*It is picked up from the ground at some locations.*) **Which sizes of sediment would be picked up?** (*Mostly the finer grains, such as clay, silt, and sand*) **Which sizes would remain on the ground?** (*Mostly the coarser grains, such as pebbles*)

Apply Ask: **What effect might abrasion have on rock surfaces?** (*It can make smooth, polished rock surfaces.*) **learning modality: verbal**

All in One Teaching Resources

• Transparency G31

Wind Deposition

Teach Key Concepts ⬛L2

Sand Dunes and Loess Deposits

Focus Tell students that grains of silt are barely visible to the unaided eye. Grains of sand are easily seen.

Teach Ask: **Which size of sediment makes up dunes?** (*Sand*) **How high does sand blow?** (*Not very*) **How does sand move across a desert landscape?** (*The sand in dunes blows, and the dunes move slowly across the land.*) **How high do you think silt can blow?** (*Silt often blows high into the atmosphere.*) **Do you think that silt would form dunes when it comes down?** (*No. Silt falls to form layers of loess.*)

Apply Ask: **Which do you think would be better soil—old sand dunes or old loess deposits?** (*Loess deposits, such as those in the Midwest*) **learning modality: verbal**

Independent Practice ⬛L2

All in One Teaching Resources

• Guided Reading and Study Worksheet: *Wind*

🔘 **Student Edition on Audio CD**

FIGURE 24
Wind Erosion
Wind erosion moves sediment particles of different sizes in the three ways shown at right. *Comparing and Contrasting Compare the movement of sediment by wind with the movement of sediment by water in Figure 14 earlier in the chapter. How are the processes similar? How are they different?*

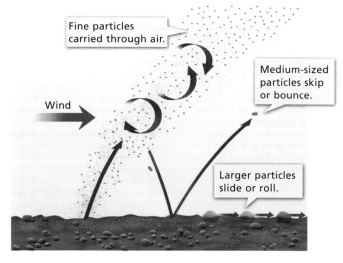

Fine particles carried through air.

Medium-sized particles skip or bounce.

Wind

Larger particles slide or roll.

FIGURE 25
Desert Pavement
Wind erosion formed this desert pavement in the Arizona desert. Wind-driven sand may polish and shape individual stones.

102 ◆

Deflation The main way that wind causes erosion is by deflation. Geologists define **deflation** as the process by which wind removes surface materials. When wind blows over the land, it picks up the smallest particles of sediment. This sediment is made of bits of clay and silt. The stronger the wind, the larger the particles that it can pick up. Slightly heavier particles, such as sand, might skip or bounce for a short distance. But sand soon falls back to the ground. Strong winds can even roll heavier sediment particles over the ground. Figure 24 shows how wind erodes by deflation.

Deflation does not usually have a great effect on land. However, in parts of the Great Plains in the 1930s, deflation caused the loss of about 1 meter of topsoil in just a few years. In deserts, deflation can sometimes create an area of rock fragments called desert pavement. You can see an area of desert pavement in Figure 25. There, wind has blown away the smaller sediment. All that remains are rocky materials that are too heavy to be moved. Where there is already a slight depression in the ground, deflation can produce a bowl-shaped hollow called a blowout.

Abrasion Abrasion by wind-carried sand can polish rock, but it causes little erosion. At one time, geologists thought that the sediment carried by wind cut the stone shapes seen in deserts. But now evidence shows that most desert landforms are the result of weathering and water erosion.

✓ **Reading Checkpoint** **Where would you be most likely to see evidence of wind erosion?**

— **Differentiated Instruction** —

English Learners/Beginning ⬛L1
Vocabulary: Word Analysis Explain that the word *deflate* means "to lower." Ask students to infer the effect of *deflation* on an area of Earth's surface. Have students look up the meaning of the word *abrade*. Ask them to infer the meaning of the key term *abrasion*. **learning modality: verbal**

English Learners/Intermediate ⬛L2
Vocabulary: Word Analysis Expand on the *Beginning* activity by having students use the words *deflation* and *abrasion* in sentences. **learning modality: verbal**

Wind Deposition

All the sediment picked up by wind eventually falls to the ground. This happens when the wind slows down or some obstacle, such as a boulder or a clump of grass, traps the windblown sand sediment. **Wind erosion and deposition may form sand dunes and loess deposits.** When the wind strikes an obstacle, the result is usually a sand dune. Sand dunes can be seen on beaches and in deserts where wind-blown sediment has built up.

Sand Dunes Sand dunes come in many shapes and sizes. Some are long, with parallel ridges, while others are U-shaped. They can also be very small or very large—some sand dunes in China have grown to heights of 500 meters. Sand dunes move over time. Little by little, the sand shifts with the wind from one side of the dune to the other. This process is shown in Figure 26. Sometimes plants begin growing on a dune. Plant roots can help to anchor the dune in one place.

Loess Deposits Sediment that is finer than sand, such as particles of clay and silt, is sometimes deposited in layers far from its source. This fine, wind-deposited sediment is **loess** (LES). Large loess deposits are found in central China and in such states as Nebraska, South Dakota, Iowa, Missouri, and Illinois. Loess helps to form fertile soil. Many areas with thick loess deposits are valuable farmlands.

Crescent-shaped dunes form where the wind usually blows in the same direction.

Star-shaped dunes form where the wind direction changes frequently.

Wind direction

FIGURE 26
Movement of Sand Dunes
Wind direction is one factor that helps determine the shape and size of sand dunes.

Section 6 Assessment

Target Reading Skill Sequencing Refer to your flowchart as you answer the questions below.

Reviewing Key Concepts

1. **a. Reviewing** What are two kinds of wind erosion?
   b. Explaining Explain how sediment particles of different sizes move during wind erosion.
   c. Predicting In a desert, soil containing a mixture of sand and small rocks is exposed to wind erosion. Over time, how would the land surface change? Explain.
2. **a. Relating Cause and Effect** What causes wind to deposit sand or other sediment?
   b. Identifying What are two types of features that result from wind deposition?
   c. Problem Solving How could sand dunes be held in place to keep them from drifting onto a parking lot?

Lab zone At-Home Activity

Desert Pavement To model desert pavement, put a few coins in a shallow pan. Sprinkle enough flour over the coins to cover them. Then blow air gently through a straw across the surface of the flour. Be careful not to draw in any flour through the straw. Be certain the blown flour will not get in your or anyone else's eyes. Ask your family to predict what would happen if the "wind" blew for a long time.

Lab zone At-Home Activity

Desert Pavement L1 Caution students to make sure that family members are far enough away to avoid getting flour in their eyes. Students should be prepared to explain what deflation is and what the coins and flour represent.

nteractive Textbook

- Complete student edition
- Section and chapter self-assessments
- Assessment reports for teachers

Help Students Read

Building Vocabulary

Vocabulary Knowledge Rating Chart
Have students construct a chart with four columns: *Term, Can Define or Use It, Have Heard or Seen It, Don't Know*. Students should copy the vocabulary words for this chapter and place a checkmark under one of the other columns for each term.

Words in Context Students select key terms checked in the *Don't Know* column of their Vocabulary Knowledge Rating Chart. Have students write a sentence for each term that places the term in a correct context.

Connecting Concepts

Concept Maps Help students develop one way to show how the information in this chapter is related. Agents of erosion and deposition provide the energy and interact in a cycle to wear down and build up landforms on Earth's surface. Have students brainstorm to identify the key concepts, key terms, details, and examples, and then write each one on a sticky note and attach it at random on chart paper or on the board.

Tell students that this concept map will be organized in hierarchical order and to begin at the top with the key concepts. Ask students these questions to guide them to categorize the information on the stickies: **What are the agents of erosion? What are the types of mass movement? What features do surface water, glaciers, groundwater, waves, and wind form?** Prompt students by using connecting words or phrases, such as "causes," "erodes by," and "forms features that include," to indicate the basis for the organization of the map. The phrases should form a sentence between or among a set of concepts.

1 Changing Earth's Surface

Key Concepts

- Weathering, erosion, and deposition act together in a cycle that wears down and builds up Earth's surface.
- Gravity causes mass movement, including landslides, mudflows, slump, and creep.

Key Terms

sediment	deposition
erosion	mass movement
gravity	

2 Water Erosion

Key Concepts

- Moving water is the major agent of the erosion that has shaped Earth's land surface.
- Through erosion, a river creates valleys, water-falls, flood plains, meanders, and oxbow lakes.
- Deposition creates alluvial fans and deltas. It can also add soil to a river's flood plain.
- Groundwater can cause erosion through a process of chemical weathering.

Key Terms

- runoff • rill • gully • stream • tributary
- flood plain • meander • oxbow lake
- alluvial fan • delta • groundwater
- stalactite • stalagmite • karst topography

3 The Force of Moving Water

Key Concepts

- As gravity pulls water down a slope, the water's potential energy changes to kinetic energy.
- Most sediment washes or falls into a river as a result of mass movement and runoff.
- A river's slope, volume of flow, and the shape of its streambed all affect how fast the river flows and how much sediment it can erode.

Key Terms

energy	load
potential energy	friction
kinetic energy	turbulence
abrasion	

4 Glaciers

Key Concepts

- There are two kinds of glaciers—continental glaciers and valley glaciers.
- Glaciers can form only in an area where more snow falls than melts. Once the depth of snow and ice reaches more than 30 to 40 meters, gravity begins to pull the glacier downhill.
- The two processes by which glaciers erode the land are plucking and abrasion.
- When a glacier melts, it deposits the sediment it eroded from the land, creating various landforms.

Key Terms

glacier	plucking
continental glacier	till
ice age	moraine
valley glacier	kettle

5 Waves

Key Concepts

- The energy in waves comes from wind that blows across the water's surface.
- Waves shape the coast through erosion by breaking down rock and transporting sand and other sediment.
- Waves shape a coast when they deposit sediment, forming coastal features such as beaches, spits, and barrier beaches.

Key Terms

headland	longshore drift
beach	spit

6 Wind

Key Concepts

- Wind causes erosion by deflation and abrasion.
- Wind erosion and deposition may form sand dunes and loess deposits.

Key Terms

sand dune	deflation	loess

Answer
Accept logical presentations by students.

All in One Teaching Resources

- Key Terms Review: *Erosion and Deposition*
- Connecting Concepts: *Erosion and Deposition*

Review and Assessment

Organizing Information

Flowcharts Copy the flowchart about stream formation onto a separate sheet of paper. Then complete it and add a title. (For more on flowcharts, see the Skills Handbook).

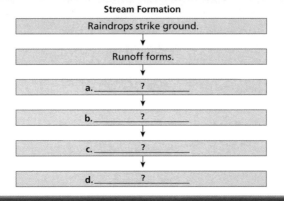

Stream Formation

Raindrops strike ground.
↓
Runoff forms.
↓
a. _____?_____
↓
b. _____?_____
↓
c. _____?_____
↓
d. _____?_____

Reviewing Key Terms

Choose the letter of the best answer.

1. The eroded materials carried by water or wind are called
   a. stalactites.
   b. desert pavement.
   c. sediment.
   d. moraines.

2. The downhill movement of eroded materials is known as
   a. mass movement.
   b. abrasion.
   c. deposition.
   d. deflation.

3. Where a streambed is rough, the stream flows more slowly because of
   a. sediment.
   b. friction.
   c. deposition.
   d. potential energy.

4. A mass of rock and soil deposited directly by a glacier is called
   a. load.   b. till.
   c. loess.   d. erosion.

5. The erosion of sediment by wind is
   a. deposition.   b. deflation.
   c. plucking.   d. glaciation.

If the statement is true, write *true*. If it is false, change the underlined word or words to make the statement true.

6. The process by which sediment in water settles in new locations is <u>mass movement</u>.

7. <u>Groundwater</u> that flows in a thin layer over the land causes sheet erosion.

8. Because it is moving, flowing water has a type of energy called <u>kinetic energy</u>.

9. A looplike bend in the river is a <u>meander</u>.

10. The sediment deposited at the edge of a glacier forms a ridge called a <u>kettle</u>.

Writing in Science

Article Suppose that you have just returned from a visit to a limestone cave, such as Mammoth Cave in Kentucky. Write an article describing your visit to the cave. Include how the cave formed, what you saw during your visit, and how features inside the cave developed.

DISCOVERY CHANNEL SCHOOL

Erosion and Deposition
Video Preview
Video Field Trip
▶ Video Assessment

Chapter 3 G ◆ 105

All in One Teaching Resources
- Transparency G32
- Chapter Test
- Performance Assessment Teacher Notes
- Performance Assessment Student Worksheet
- Performance Assessment Scoring Rubric

ExamView® Computer Test Bank CD-ROM

Review and Assessment

Organizing Information
a. Rills form.
b. Gullies form.
c. Gullies join together.
d. Stream forms.

Reviewing Key Terms
1. c 2. a 3. b 4. b 5. b
6. deposition
7. Runoff
8. true
9. true
10. moraine

Writing in Science

Writing Mode Description
Scoring Rubric
4 Exceeds criteria in some way, for example, uses vivid adjectives and gives a personalized account
3 Meets criteria but does not go beyond requirements
2 Includes only brief description of required elements
1 Is incorrect and incomplete

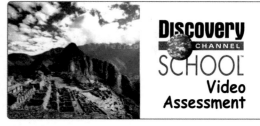

DISCOVERY CHANNEL SCHOOL
Video Assessment

Erosion and Deposition

Show the Video Assessment to review chapter content and as a prompt for the writing assignment. Discussion question: **How do weathering and erosion contribute to the formation of caves?** *(Water seeping through the soil carries carbon dioxide, which dissolves in the water, forming a mild solution of carbonic acid. Chemical weathering occurs as the carbonic acid solution flows through cracks in the limestone and breaks down the rock. Erosion occurs as the rock is carried away. This results in cavities within the once-solid rock.)*

Checking Concepts

11. The agents of erosion that are assisted by the force of gravity are moving water and glaciers. Gravity itself causes mass movement and is therefore also an agent of erosion.

12. In general, higher slope and higher volume of flow increase a river's sediment load.

13. Turbulence is rough-flowing water. It slows the speed of a river but often increases its power to erode.

14. The speed of the flowing water in a river is the slowest near the bottom, where friction is greatest.

15. Ice ages are times when glaciers cover large parts of Earth's surface.

16. Kettle lakes form when a large piece of glacial ice is left in a glacial deposit. When the ice melts, a depression forms and fills with water.

17. Loess deposits form as fine particles that are carried by wind fall to the ground and accumulate.

Checking Concepts

11. What agents of erosion are assisted by the force of gravity?

12. How do a river's slope and volume of flow affect the river's sediment load?

13. What is turbulence? How does it affect the speed of a river and the river's power to cause erosion?

14. Where is the speed of the flowing water in a river the slowest? Explain.

15. What are ice ages?

16. How does a kettle lake form?

17. How does a loess deposit form?

Thinking Critically

18. Comparing and Contrasting Compare and contrast landslides and mudflows.

19. Applying Concepts Under what conditions would you expect abrasion to cause the most erosion of a riverbed?

20. Making Judgments A salesperson offers to sell your family a new house right on a riverbank for very little money. Why might your family hesitate to buy this house?

21. Relating Cause and Effect What caused the features labeled A, B, and C in the diagram below to form? Explain.

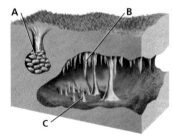

22. Problem Solving Suppose you are a geologist studying a valley glacier. What method could you use to tell if it is advancing or retreating?

23. Inferring You see a sandy beach along a coastline. Where did the sand come from?

Applying Skills

Use the table below to answer Questions 24–26.

The table shows how a river's volume of flow and sediment load change over six months.

Month	Volume of Flow (cubic meters/second)	Sediment Load (metric tons/day)
January	1.5	200
February	1.7	320
March	2.6	725
April	4.0	1,600
May	3.2	1,100
June	2.8	900

24. Graphing Make one graph with the month on the *x*-axis and the volume of flow on the *y*-axis. Make a second graph with the sediment load on the *y*-axis. Compare your two graphs. When were the river's volume of flow and load the greatest? The lowest?

25. Developing Hypotheses Use your graphs to develop a hypothesis about the relationship between volume of flow and sediment load.

26. Relating Cause and Effect What may have occurred in the river's drainage basin in April to cause the changes in volume of flow and sediment load? Explain.

Lab zone Chapter **Project**

Performance Assessment Now you are ready to present to your class. Explain which types of soil you chose and why you chose them. Discuss the design of your dam, the tests you conducted, and the results. In your journal, write about the easiest and hardest parts of this project. How would you design your dam differently if you did the project again?

Lab zone Chapter **Project**   **L3**

Performance Assessment Students can make a chart or graph showing which sediment type eroded most easily and which withstood erosion. They can do the same for the permeability of the materials. Have students describe the materials that they used to construct their dams and the reasons for their choices.

Ask students to consider the following questions: If you redesigned your dam, what did you change and why? If you did not have an opportunity to redesign your dam, what might you do differently next time? What part of the project was the most difficult?

Standardized Test Prep

Choose the letter of the best answer.

1. As a stream flows from a mountainous area to a flatter area, what happens to the size of the sediment the stream normally carries?
   A The sediment size does not change.
   B The sediment size carried by the stream increases.
   C The sediment size carried by the stream decreases.
   D The stream drops all the sediment it was carrying.

2. How does wind carry sediment particles?
   F as fine particles carried through the air
   G as particles that bounce along the ground
   H as larger particles that slide or roll along the ground
   J all of the above

Use the diagram below and your knowledge of science to answer Questions 3–4.

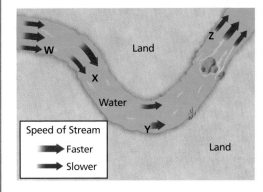

3. What is the erosional feature in the diagram?
   A a meander
   B a delta
   C a flood plain
   D karst topography

4. In the diagram, where is the speed of the stream the greatest?
   F at Y
   G at X
   H at W
   J at Z

5. What is the process by which weathered rock, sediment, and soil is moved from place to place?
   A erosion
   B delta formation
   C running water
   D runoff

Constructed Response

6. Describe how gravity is involved in the erosion of Earth's surface by mass movement, running water, and glaciers. Be sure to first explain what erosion is.

Thinking Critically

18. Both are types of mass movement that occur rapidly and can be triggered by an earthquake. Unlike landslides, which are mostly dry, mudflows have a high percentage of water.

19. Abrasion occurs when particles of sediment in flowing water bump into the stream bed again and again. A very turbulent stream or the fast-flowing water of a flooding river would cause the most abrasion.

20. A house right on a riverbank is probably within the river's flood plain. A family should hesitate because the house might be damaged or destroyed by a future flood.

21. **a.** A sinkhole forms when the roof of a cave collapses. **b.** Stalactites form as calcium carbonate precipitates from water dripping from the ceiling. **c.** Stalagmites form as calcium carbonate precipitates from drops that fall to the cave floor.

22. Answers will vary. Possible answer: You could observe the landforms in front of the glacier. If it is retreating, terminal moraines and other till deposits should exist far in front of the glacier.

23. The sand came from rivers that carried the grains to the ocean, where waves dropped them to form the beach.

Applying Skills

24. The flow and load were greatest in April. They were lowest in January.

25. A river's load varies directly with its volume of flow.

26. Rainfall or melting snow probably increased throughout the drainage basin in April, creating more runoff and eroding more sediment.

Standardized Test Prep

1. C **2.** J **3.** A **4.** F **5.** A
6. Erosion is the picking up and moving of rock, sediment, or soil. Gravity causes erosion by mass movement, running water, and glaciers. During mass movement, gravity pulls rock or sediment downhill. Running water moves downhill because of the force of gravity. As the water flows, it erodes Earth's surface. Gravity also causes glacier ice to flow. The flowing ice erodes rock and sediment from some places and deposits rock and sediment at other places.

Chapter at a Glance

 Chapter Project *A Journey Back in Time*

Technology **Local Standards**

 Teaching Resources
- Chapter Project Teacher Notes, pp. 234–235
- Chapter Project Student Overview, pp. 236–237
- Chapter Project Student Worksheets, pp. 238–239
- Chapter Project Scoring Rubric, p. 240

 Video Preview

Section 1 **Fossils**

G.4.1.1 Explain how fossils form.

G.4.1.2 Identify the different kinds of fossils.

2–3 periods
1–1 1/2 blocks **G.4.1.3** Describe what fossils tell about organisms and environments of the past.

 SCI LINKS NSTA

Section 2 **The Relative Age of Rocks**

G.4.2.1 State the law of superposition.

1–2 periods
1/2–1 block **G.4.2.2** Describe how geologists determine the relative age of rocks.

G.4.2.3 Explain how index fossils are useful to geologists.

 active art

 Video Field Trip

Section 3 **Radioactive Dating**

G.4.3.1 Explain what happens during radioactive decay.

1–2 periods
1/2–1 block **G.4.3.2** Describe what can be learned from radioactive dating.

 PHSchool.com

---

Section 4 **The Geologic Time Scale**

G.4.4.1 Explain why the geologic time scale is used to show Earth's history.

1–2 periods
1/2–1 block **G.4.4.2** Describe the different units of the geologic time scale.

 PHSchool.com

---

Section 5 **Early Earth**

G.4.5.1 State when Earth was formed.

1 period
1/2 block **G.4.5.2** Explain how Earth's physical features developed during Precambrian Time.

G.4.5.3 Describe what early Precambrian organisms were like.

 SCI LINKS NSTA

Section 6 **Eras of Earth's History**

G.4.6.1 Describe the major events in the Paleozoic Era.

3–4 periods
1 1/2–2 blocks **G.4.6.2** Describe the major events in the Mesozoic Era.

G.4.6.3 Describe the major events in the Cenozoic Era.

 active art

---

Review and Assessment

 Teaching Resources
- Key Terms Review, p. 288
- Transparency G48
- Performance Assessment Teacher Notes, p. 295

- Performance Assessment Scoring Rubric, p. 296
- Performance Assessment Student Worksheet, p. 297
- Chapter Test, pp. 298–301

 PHSchool.com

 Video Assessment

Test Preparation

Test Preparation Blackline Masters

Chapter Activities Planner

For more activities

LAB ZONE Easy Planner CD-ROM

Student Edition	Inquiry	Time	Materials	Skills	Resources
Chapter Project, p. 109	Open-Ended	Ongoing (2 to 3 weeks)	**All in One Teaching Resources** See p. 234	Interpreting data, applying concepts	**Lab zone Easy Planner** **All in One Teaching Resources** Support pp. 234–235
Section 1					
Discover Activity, p. 110	Open-Ended	10 minutes	Hand lens, rock sample containing fossils	Inferring	**Lab zone Easy Planner**
Try This Activity, p. 113	Guided	10 minutes	Modeling compound, 3 sugar cubes, bowl, water, plastic spoon	Observing	**Lab zone Easy Planner**
Section 2					
Discover Activity, p. 117	Guided	10 minutes	4 or 5 different colors of modeling compound, small bowl, cheese slicer or plastic knife	Inferring	**Lab zone Easy Planner**
Try This Activity, p. 119	Guided	10 minutes	Cylindrical pasta noodle about 1.5 cm in diameter, sandwich of different soft cheeses and meats	Making models	**Lab zone Easy Planner**
Skills Lab, p. 122	Guided	30 minutes	No special materials are required	Interpreting data, drawing conclusions	**Lab zone Easy Planner** **Lab Activity Video** **All in One Teaching Resources** Skills Lab: *Finding Clues to Rock Layers*, pp. 256–257
Section 3					
Discover Activity, p. 123	Guided	10 minutes	Modeling clay, metric ruler, plastic knife	Predicting	**Lab zone Easy Planner**
Section 4					
Discover Activity, p. 127	Guided	15 minutes	Metric ruler, adding-machine paper	Making models	**Lab zone Easy Planner**
Section 5					
Discover Activity, p. 130	Guided	10 minutes	Circular magnet, iron filings, paper, straw	Making models	**Lab zone Easy Planner**
Skills Activity, p. 132	Directed	10 minutes	Calculators	Calculating	**Lab zone Easy Planner**
Section 6					
Discover Activity, p. 134	Open-ended	15 minutes	Sheet of unlined paper	Posing questions	**Lab zone Easy Planner**
Try This Activity, p. 144	Guided	15 minutes	Adding-machine paper, metric ruler	Interpreting data	**Lab zone Easy Planner**
Skills Lab, pp. 146–147	Guided	30 minutes	Worksheet with 2,000 asterisks, one ream of paper	Measuring, calculating	**Lab zone Easy Planner** **Lab Activity Video** **All in One Teaching Resources** Skills Lab: *As Time Goes By*, pp. 285–287

Section 1 **Fossils**

 *2–3 periods, 1–1 1/2 blocks*

Objectives

G.4.1.1 Explain how fossils form.

G.4.1.2 Identify the different kinds of fossils.

G.4.1.3 Describe what fossils tell about organisms and environments of the past.

Local Standards

Key Terms

• fossil • sedimentary rock • mold • cast • petrified fossil • carbon film
• trace fossil • paleontologist • scientific theory • evolution • extinct

---

Preteach

Build Background Knowledge

Elicit definitions of the word *fossil*.

 **Discover Activity** *What's in a Rock?* **L1**

Targeted Print and Technology Resources

 Teaching Resources

L2 Reading Strategy Transparency
G33: *Using Prior Knowledge*

PresentationExpress™ CD-ROM

Instruct

How a Fossil Forms Use illustrations to explain the steps in fossil formation.

Change Over Time Describe evidence provided by fossils of past environments and evolution of organisms.

Targeted Print and Technology Resources

Teaching Resources

L2 Guided Reading, pp. 243–246
L2 Transparency G34

www.SciLinks.org Web Code: scn-0741

Student Edition on Audio CD

Assess

Section Assessment Questions

Have students use their reading strategy graphic organizers to help answer the questions.

Reteach

Make a table that compares and contrasts the different kinds of fossils.

Targeted Print and Technology Resources

Teaching Resources

• Section Summary, p. 242
L1 Review and Reinforce, p. 247
L3 Enrich, p. 248

Section 2 The Relative Age of Rocks

1–2 periods, 1/2–1 block

Objectives

G.4.2.1 State the law of superposition.
G.4.2.2 Describe how geologists determine the relative age of rocks.
G.4.2.3 Explain how index fossils are useful to geologists.

Local Standards

Key Terms

• relative age • absolute age • law of superposition • extrusion • intrusion
• fault • unconformity • index fossil

Preteach

Targeted Print and Technology Resources

Build Background Knowledge

Invite students to describe what happens to sediment carried to an ocean by a river. Explain that this hardens into rock.

 **Discover Activity** *Which Layer Is the Oldest?* **L2**

 Teaching Resources
L2 Reading Strategy Transparency
G35: *Asking Questions*

 PresentationExpress™ CD-ROM

Instruct

Targeted Print and Technology Resources

The Position of Rock Layers Apply the concepts in the Discover Activity to a definition of superposition.

Determining Relative Age Make relative age comparisons of sedimentary rock, using other rock formations.

Using Fossils to Date Rocks Explain how scientists use index fossils to date rocks.

 Skills Lab *Finding Clues to Rock Layers* **L2**

 **Teaching Resources**
L2 Guided Reading, pp. 251–253
L2 Transparencies G36, G37, G38
L2 Skills Lab: *Finding Clues to Rock Layers*, pp. 256–257

Lab Activity Video/DVD
Skills Lab: *Finding Clues to Rock Layers*

 DISCOVERY CHANNEL
SCHOOL
Video Field Trip

PHSchool.com Web Code: cfp-2042

 Student Edition on Audio CD

Assess

Targeted Print and Technology Resources

Section Assessment Questions

Have students use their completed graphic organizers to answer the questions.

Reteach

Make a drawing with features that illustrate relative dating of rock layers.

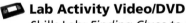 **Teaching Resources**
• Section Summary, p. 250
L1 Review and Reinforce, p. 254
L3 Enrich, p. 255

Section 3 **Radioactive Dating**

🕐 *1–2 periods, 1/2–1 block*

Objectives

G.4.3.1 Explain what happens during radioactive decay.

G.4.3.2 Describe what can be learned from radioactive dating.

Key Terms

• atom • element • radioactive decay • half-life

Local Standards

Preteach

Build Background Knowledge

Ask students to tell what an atom is and what it contains.

Lab zone **Discover Activity** *How Long Till It's Gone?*   L2

Targeted Print and Technology Resources

 **Teaching Resources**

L2   Reading Strategy Transparency G39: *Identifying Main Ideas*

⊙ **PresentationExpress™ CD-ROM**

Instruct

Radioactive Decay Ask leading questions for a discussion on what happens during radioactive decay.

Determining Absolute Ages Sequence the steps used to determine the absolute ages of rocks and fossils using radioactive dating.

Targeted Print and Technology Resources

 **Teaching Resources**

L2   Guided Reading, pp. 260–262
L2   Transparencies G40, G41

PHSchool.com Web Code: cfd-2043

⊙ **Student Edition on Audio CD**

Assess

Section Assessment Questions

🔄 Have students use their graphic organizers with main ideas and details to answer the questions.

Reteach

Use a graph and a chart to summarize how radioactive elements determine half-life.

Targeted Print and Technology Resources

 **Teaching Resources**

• Section Summary, p. 259
L1   Review and Reinforce, p. 263
L3   Enrich, p. 264

Section 4 The Geologic Time Scale

 1–2 periods, 1/2–1 block

Objectives

G.4.4.1 Explain why the geologic time scale is used to show Earth's history.

G.4.4.2 Describe the different units of the geologic time scale.

Local Standards

Key Terms

• geologic time scale • era • period

Preteach

Build Background Knowledge

Ask students to discuss how long ago dinosaurs lived and when the Earth formed.

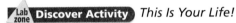 **Discover Activity** *This Is Your Life!* **L1**

Targeted Print and Technology Resources

All in One Teaching Resources

L2 Reading Strategy Transparency G42: *Sequencing*

PresentationExpress™ CD-ROM

Instruct

The Geologic Time Scale Use a diagram to demonstrate why the geologic time scale is used to show Earth's history.

Divisions of Geologic Time Use a diagram to analyze the different units into which the geologic time scale is divided.

Targeted Print and Technology Resources

All in One Teaching Resources

L2 Guided Reading, pp. 267–268
L2 Transparency G43

PHSchool.com Web Code: cfd-2044

Student Edition on Audio CD

Assess

Section Assessment Questions

Have students use their flowcharts sequencing the eras and periods of geologic time to answer the questions.

Reteach

Use a diagram to review the purpose and arrangement of the geologic time scale.

Targeted Print and Technology Resources

All in One Teaching Resources

• Section Summary, p. 266
L1 Review and Reinforce, p. 269
L3 Enrich, p. 270

Section 5 Early Earth

1 period, 1/2 block

ABILITY LEVELS
L1 Basic to Average
L2 For All Students
L3 Average to Advanced

Objectives

G.4.5.1 State when Earth was formed.

G.4.5.2 Explain how Earth's physical features developed during Precambrian Time.

G.4.5.3 Describe what early Precambrian organisms were like.

Key Terms

• comet • continental drift

Local Standards

Preteach

Build Background Knowledge

Show a photograph of Earth, and invite students to comment on its features.

 **Discover Activity** *How Could Planet Earth Form in Space?*
L1

Targeted Print and Technology Resources

All in One Teaching Resources

L2 Reading Strategy Transparency G44: *Comparing and Contrasting*

PresentationExpress™ CD-ROM

Instruct

The Planet Forms Explain when Earth formed and how scientists know.

Earth's Surface Forms Use illustrations to identify how the second atmosphere formed. Discuss the formation of oceans and continents.

Life Develops Ask questions to discuss what early life-forms looked like and how they lived.

Targeted Print and Technology Resources

All in One Teaching Resources

L2 Guided Reading, pp. 273–275
L2 Transparency G45

www.SciLinks.org Web Code: scn-0745

Student Edition on Audio CD

Assess

Section Assessment Questions

 Have students use their graphic organizers comparing and contrasting early Earth and later Precambrian Earth to answer the questions.

Reteach

Summarize how the features of early Earth formed.

Targeted Print and Technology Resources

All in One Teaching Resources

• Section Summary, p. 272
L1 Review and Reinforce, p. 276
L3 Enrich, p. 277

Section 6 Eras of Earth's History

🕐 *3–4 periods, 1 1/2–2 blocks*

ABILITY LEVELS
L1 Basic to Average
L2 For All Students
L3 Average to Advanced

Objectives

G.4.6.1 Describe the major events in the Paleozoic Era.
G.4.6.2 Describe the major events in the Mesozoic Era.
G.4.6.3 Describe the major events in the Cenozoic Era.

Local Standards

Key Terms

• invertebrate • vertebrate • amphibian • reptile • mass extinction • mammal

---

Preteach

Build Background Knowledge

Show pictures of a mammoth and a dinosaur, and invite discussion on when each lived.

 **Discover Activity** *What Do Fossils Reveal About Earth's History?* **L1**

Targeted Print and Technology Resources

All in One Teaching Resources

L2 Reading Strategy Transparency
G46: *Previewing Visuals*

⊙ **PresentationExpress™ CD-ROM**

Instruct

The Paleozoic Era Use the geologic time scale and illustrations to discuss major events of this era.

The Mesozoic Era Ask leading questions to identify major events of this era.

The Cenozoic Era Examine the events that characterize this era.

 Skills Lab *As Time Goes By* **L2**

Targeted Print and Technology Resources

All in One Teaching Resources

L2 Guided Reading, pp. 280–282
L2 Transparency G47
L2 Skills Lab: *As Time Goes By*, pp. 285–286

📼 **Lab Activity Video/DVD**
Skills Lab: *As Time Goes By*

PHSchool.com Web Code: cfp-1015

⊙ **Student Edition on Audio CD**

Assess

Section Assessment Questions

🔄 Have students use the questions and answers they developed previewing visuals to answer the questions.

Reteach

Read the boldfaced sentences, and have students supply the period or era that they describe.

Targeted Print and Technology Resources

All in One Teaching Resources

• Section Summary, p. 279
L1 Review and Reinforce, p. 283
L3 Enrich, p. 284

Chapter 4 Content Refresher

Section 1 Fossils

Burgess Shale One of the best sources of fossils from the Cambrian Explosion is the Burgess shale, an outcropping of rock in the Canadian Rockies of British Columbia. The Burgess shale contains fossils of some 120 different types of marine invertebrates. It remains the most important window on the explosion of life that marks the Cambrian Period. The fossils were discovered in 1909 by Charles Walcott, a well-respected paleontologist who at that time headed the Smithsonian Institution in Washington, D.C. Since the discovery of the Burgess shale, over 70,000 fossils have been collected from the site.

Development of the Theory of Evolution The English scientist Charles Darwin (1809–1882) explained his theory of evolution in his book *On the Origin of Species,* published in 1859. The theory has been revised since then, but it remains much as Darwin explained it. The variety and regular sequence of life forms found in the fossil record has made the theory of evolution central to an understanding of life on Earth, how life has changed over time, and how living things are related today.

Address Misconceptions

Some students understand the word theory *to mean an opinion put forward that is less than sure or proven. However, in science, a theory is a broad explanation based on many observations.* For a strategy for overcoming this misconception, see **Address Misconceptions** in the section *Fossils.*

Section 2 The Relative Age of Rocks

Nicolaus Steno Danish geologist Nicolaus Steno (1638–1686) developed the law of superposition in the 1660s. On a visit to the Mediterranean island of Malta, Steno noticed that the "tongue stones" sold there as good-luck charms were actually fossilized shark teeth from the island's rock layers. Steno hypothesized that the island had once been under water and that the rock layers had been laid down in succession. He concluded that the deepest rocks were the oldest, thus demonstrating "Steno's law," or the law of superposition.

Trilobites Scientists use certain types of trilobites, like the one shown below, as index fossils. Trilobites ("three-lobed" organisms) were a type of arthropod that was widespread in the Paleozoic Era. Arthropods now living include insects, spiders, and crustaceans. Trilobites could be as small as a few millimeters long, but some were as much as 40 cm long. They scavenged the muddy sea bottom for food, walking on slender, jointed legs. Trilobites became extinct in the Permian mass extinction.

Section 3 Radioactive Dating

Isotopes An element has a specific number of protons in its atoms, and this number never varies. Atoms of the same element, however, can have different numbers of neutrons. Atoms of an element with different numbers of neutrons are called isotopes. In some isotopes—radioactive isotopes—forces that bind protons and neutrons together are weak. The result is that these nuclei spontaneously decay.

All carbon atoms have six protons. Carbon-14, which has eight neutrons, is absorbed by living things while they are alive. After an organism dies, the carbon-14 in its body begins to decay to form nitrogen-14, which escapes into the air. Carbon-12, which has six neutrons and is the most common isotope of carbon, is not radioactive and does not decay. By comparing the amounts of carbon-14 and carbon-12 in a fossil, researchers can determine when the organism lived. The more carbon-12 there is in a sample compared with the amount of carbon-14, the older the sample is.

Unstable radioactive isotopes occur naturally in Earth's crust. For instance, granite forms when molten material hardens underground (an intrusion). Within that granite may be some potassium-40. The moment the rock hardens, the "clock" starts running, as the potassium-40 in the granite begins to decay into argon-40.

Section 4 The Geologic Time Scale

Development of the Time Scale The concept of geologic time was first developed in the late 1700s and early 1800s. Geologists in England and other parts of Europe devised the geologic time scale during the 1800s. They established these eras, periods, and epochs through relative dating methods, carefully correlating rock layers throughout the world using index fossils—a monumental achievement.

The Tertiary Period includes these five epochs (with starting date in millions of years ago): Paleocene (66.4), Eocene (57.8), Oligocene (36.6), Miocene (23.7), and Pliocene (5.3). The Quaternary Period includes these two epochs: Pleistocene (1.8) and Holocene (0.01). Today, we are in the Holocene Epoch of the Quaternary Period of the Cenozoic Era.

Section 5 Early Earth

Origin of Life on Earth There is more than one scientific hypothesis of how life began on Earth. Perhaps comets striking Earth brought organic molecules necessary for life, or perhaps conditions on Earth were right for complex chemicals to come together as a primitive organism. Many scientists now think that life originated in hot springs or deep-sea vents. Organisms that might resemble such early life have been found in hot springs at Yellowstone National Park.

Section 6 Eras of Earth's History

Movement of Earth's Plates Toward the end of the Paleozoic Era, the continents came together to form Pangaea ("all lands"). One result was the formation of the Appalachian Mountains, which dominate eastern North America. These mountains probably rose as Africa collided with North America. The mountains have since weathered and eroded from a once greater height.

Both the formation and breakup of Pangaea were the result of movements of Earth's lithospheric plates, caused in part by very slow convection currents in the pliable, or plastic, material of Earth's mantle. These plates fit closely together along cracks in the lithosphere. As they move, they collide, pull apart, or slide past one another. Near Hawaii, the Pacific plate is moving at a rate of about 8.3 cm per year.

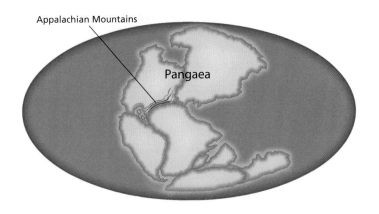

Appalachian Mountains

Pangaea

Help Students Read

Identifying Supporting Evidence
Following a Chain of Reasoning

Strategy Help students understand the structure of the text they are reading. One way is to use a graphic organizer as a device for identifying supporting evidence for hypotheses that are presented in the text.

Example
1. Have students choose a section within this chapter, for example, *Early Earth*.
2. Have students look for the hypothesis of the section. In this case, the hypothesis is that Earth and the solar system formed about 4.6 billion years ago. Write the hypothesis on the board, leaving enough room around it to add supporting evidence. This will be the center of your graphic organizer.
3. As students read, have them call out the supporting evidence for the hypothesis. For example, they may note that radiocarbon dating indicates that the oldest rocks on Earth are about 4 billion years old.
4. Write the supporting evidence on the board around the center of your graphic organizer. Draw "spokes" from each piece of evidence to the hypothesis.
5. After reading the section and completing the graphic organizer, ask students whether they think the text has provided sufficient supporting evidence for the hypothesis. Suggest to students that a graphic organizer such as this one can be used to help understand a concept.

interactive **Textbook**
- Complete student edition
- Video and audio
- Simulations and activities
- Section and chapter activities

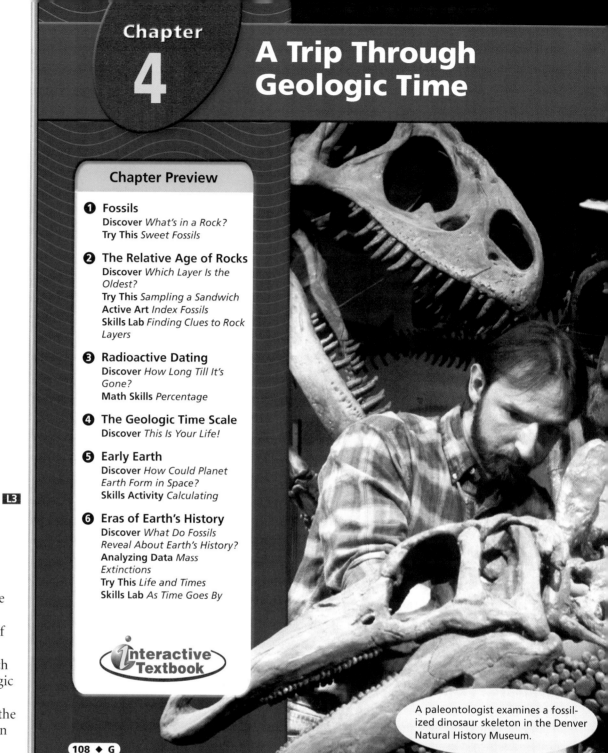

Chapter 4
A Trip Through Geologic Time

Chapter Preview

❶ Fossils
Discover *What's in a Rock?*
Try This *Sweet Fossils*

❷ The Relative Age of Rocks
Discover *Which Layer Is the Oldest?*
Try This *Sampling a Sandwich*
Active Art *Index Fossils*
Skills Lab *Finding Clues to Rock Layers*

❸ Radioactive Dating
Discover *How Long Till It's Gone?*
Math Skills *Percentage*

❹ The Geologic Time Scale
Discover *This Is Your Life!*

❺ Early Earth
Discover *How Could Planet Earth Form in Space?*
Skills Activity *Calculating*

❻ Eras of Earth's History
Discover *What Do Fossils Reveal About Earth's History?*
Analyzing Data *Mass Extinctions*
Try This *Life and Times*
Skills Lab *As Time Goes By*

interactive **Textbook**

A paleontologist examines a fossilized dinosaur skeleton in the Denver Natural History Museum.

Lab zone **Chapter Project**   L3

Objectives
This project will enhance students' understanding of the richness and complexity of the history of life on Earth. After this Chapter Project, students will be able to
- Interpret data about a selected period of geologic time in reference materials
- Apply concepts learned through research in making a travel brochure for a geologic time period
- Communicate what they learned about the period of geologic time in a presentation to the class

Skills Focus
interpreting data, applying concepts, communicating

Project Time Line 2 to 3 weeks
All in One **Teaching Resources**
- Chapter Project Teacher Notes
- Chapter Project Overview
- Chapter Project Worksheet 1
- Chapter Project Worksheet 2
- Chapter Project Scoring Rubric

Developing a Plan
First, students research their chosen time period, using reference books, magazine articles, and Internet sites. Next, students plan and write their travel brochures, including illustrations for the brochure and for the timeline. Finally, students make their presentations to the class.

Possible Materials
- Collect books and magazine articles on Earth's history. Provide a list of reliable Web sites, including those of natural history museums.
- For illustrations, students will need colored pencils, markers, water colors, tape, and glue.
- For the timeline, you will need butcher or table-covering paper and art materials.

Lab zone™ Chapter **Project**

A Journey Back in Time

This chapter will take you on a journey through geologic time. You will learn how fossils reveal the history of life on Earth. To guide you on your journey, you and your classmates will make a timeline showing the many periods of geologic time.

Your Goal To become an expert on one geologic time period and assist in constructing a timeline

To complete this project, you must

- research a geologic time period of your choice
- create a travel brochure that shows what life was like in this time period
- illustrate your time period for the timeline
- follow the safety guidelines in Appendix A

Plan It! Begin by selecting a time period you would like to investigate. Check with your teacher to be sure that all the time periods will be covered by members of your class. Then, collect information on your time period's animals, plants, and environment. Use this information to write a travel brochure about your time period. Create illustrations that depict your time period and place them on the timeline. Use the travel brochure to present your geologic time period to your classmates.

DISCOVERY CHANNEL SCHOOL Video Preview

A Trip Through Geologic Time

Show the Video Preview to introduce the Chapter Project and overview the chapter content. Discussion question: **Why is traveling through the Grand Canyon like passing through geologic time?** (*Because the canyon reveals over a billion years of geologic time through its exposed rock layers*)

Possible Shortcuts

- Divide the class into small groups with each one responsible for one time period.
- Have students make a large, illustrated time scale rather than travel brochures.

Launching the Project

Gather travel brochures (available from travel agents or state tourist boards) that focus on states, foreign countries, and national parks. Show them to students, and give them time to examine them. Discuss features of the brochures that are most informative and attractive. Tell students that they will create such a brochure to show what life was like in a specific period of Earth's history.

Performance Assessment

The Chapter Project Scoring Rubric will help you evaluate how well students complete the Chapter Project. You may want to share the scoring rubric with your students so that they know what is expected. Students will be assessed on

- How accurately and comprehensively the information in the brochure describes the geologic time period
- How appropriately and artistically they create the illustrations for the brochure and for the timeline
- How effectively they present their brochure to the class

Portfolio

Objectives

After this lesson, students will be able to
G.4.1.1 Explain how fossils form.
G.4.1.2 Identify the different kinds of fossils.
G.4.1.3 Describe what fossils tell about organisms and environments of the past.

Target Reading Skill

Using Prior Knowledge Explain that using prior knowledge helps students connect what they already know to what they are about to read.

Answers

Possible answers:

What You Know

1. Fossils come from ancient organisms.
2. Fossils are found in hardened rock.
3. Fossils show us how some present-day organisms looked different in the past.

What You Learned

1. Molds and casts are types of fossils.
2. Organisms are also preserved in amber, tar, and ice.
3. Fossils tell us about past climates, changes in Earth's surface, and how organisms have changed over time.

All in One Teaching Resources

• Transparency G33

Preteach

Build Background Knowledge   **L1**

What Are Fossils?
Ask: **How do scientists know that different kinds of plants and animals lived in Earth's past?** (*Many students will mention evidence from fossils.*) **What is a fossil?** (*A typical answer might suggest that a fossil is an organism that has turned to rock.*) Explain that in this section students will find out about different types of fossils and the processes that cause each type to form.

Section
1 Fossils

Reading Preview

Key Concepts
• How do fossils form?
• What are the different kinds of fossils?
• What does the fossil record tell about organisms and environments of the past?

Key Terms
• fossil
• sedimentary rock
• mold
• cast
• petrified fossil
• carbon film
• trace fossil
• paleontologist
• scientific theory
• evolution
• extinct

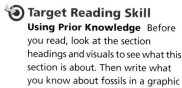

Target Reading Skill
Using Prior Knowledge Before you read, look at the section headings and visuals to see what this section is about. Then write what you know about fossils in a graphic organizer like the one below. As you read, write what you learn.

What You Know
1. Fossils come from ancient organisms. 2.

What You Learned
1. 2.

Lab zone Discover **Activity**

What's in a Rock?

1. Use a hand lens to carefully observe the rock sample provided by your teacher. You may also study the photograph of limestone below.
2. Make a drawing of any shapes you see in the rock. Include as many details as you can. Beneath your drawing, write a description of what you see.

Think It Over
Inferring What do you think the rock contains? How do you think the shapes you observed in the rock got there?

Millions of years ago, a fish died and sank to the bottom of a lake. Before the fish could decay completely, layers of sediment covered it. Minerals in the sediment seeped into the fish's bones. Slowly, pressure changed the sediment into solid rock. Inside the rock, the fish became a fossil.

Fossils are the preserved remains or traces of living things. Fossils like the ancient fish in Figure 1 provide evidence of how life has changed over time. Fossils can also help scientists infer how Earth's surface has changed. Fossils are clues to what past environments were like.

How a Fossil Forms

Most fossils form when living things die and are buried by sediments. The sediments slowly harden into rock and preserve the shapes of the organisms. Fossils are usually found in sedimentary rock. **Sedimentary rock** is the type of rock that is made of hardened sediment. Recall that sediment is the material removed by erosion. Sediment is made up of rock particles or the remains of living things. Sandstone, limestone, and coal are examples of sedimentary rocks. Most fossils form from animals or plants that once lived in or near quiet water such as swamps, lakes, or shallow seas where sediments build up. In Figure 1, you can see how a fossil might form.

Lab zone Discover **Activity**

Skills Focus Inferring

Materials hand lens, rock sample containing fossils

Time 10 minutes

Tips Organize students into small groups, and give each group a fossil-bearing rock. Ask each student to complete his or her drawings and answers before discussing the rock with other group members.

L1 **Think It Over** The rock contains one or more fossils. A typical explanation of how the fossils formed might suggest that an organism fell into sediments that later solidified.

FIGURE 1
How a Fossil Forms
A fossil may form when sediment quickly covers an animal's body. Classifying *In what type of rock would this fossil be found?*

An animal dies and sinks into shallow water.

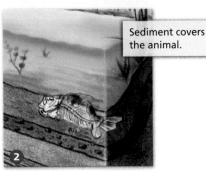

Sediment covers the animal.

The sediment becomes rock, preserving parts of the animal.

Weathering and erosion eventually expose the fossil at the surface.

When an organism dies, its soft parts often decay quickly or are eaten by animals. That is why only hard parts of an organism generally leave fossils. These hard parts include bones, shells, teeth, seeds, and woody stems. It is rare for the soft parts of an organism to become a fossil.

For a fossil to form, the remains or traces of an organism must be protected from decay. Then several processes may cause a fossil to form. **Fossils found in rock include molds and casts, petrified fossils, carbon films, and trace fossils. Other fossils form when the remains of organisms are preserved in substances such as tar, amber, or ice.**

Molds and Casts The most common fossils are molds and casts. Both copy the shape of ancient organisms. A **mold** is a hollow area in sediment in the shape of an organism or part of an organism. A mold forms when the hard part of the organism, such as a shell, is buried in sediment.

Later, water carrying dissolved minerals and sediment may seep into the empty space of a mold. If the water deposits the minerals and sediment there, the result is a cast. A **cast** is a solid copy of the shape of an organism. A cast is the opposite of its mold. Both the mold and cast preserve details of the animal's structure. Figure 1 shows a process that could form a mold and cast fossil.

How a Fossil Forms

Teach Key Concepts   L1
Differences Among Fossils

Focus Review the definition of a fossil.

Teach Point out that fossils are not only the remains of plants or animals that were once living but that they also include physical evidence, such as tracks or burrows that the organism left behind. Refer students to Figure 1, and have student volunteers read each step. Ask: **Which organisms or parts of organisms could become fossils?** (*Organisms with hard parts such as shells and bones*) Point out that the formation of a fossil is the exception rather than the rule when an organism dies.

Apply Ask: **Suppose you found a fossil of a clamshell. What can you conclude about the organism that once lived and how it became a fossil?** (*The organism may once have lived under water or near an ocean. The clamshell must have been covered with sediments, which eventually hardened.*)
learning modality: logical/mathematical

All in One Teaching Resources
• Transparency G34

Independent Practice   L2
All in One Teaching Resources
• Guided Reading and Study Worksheet: *Fossils*

Student Edition on Audio CD

Differentiated Instruction

Gifted and Talented   L3
Researching Grand Canyon Fossils
Tell students that the Grand Canyon was cut into sedimentary rocks that formed over hundreds of millions of years. Many fossils in the canyon made up the bottom of an ancient sea. Encourage students to research the types of fossils found in the canyon. **learning modality: logical/ mathematical**

Less Proficient Readers   L1
Comparing and Contrasting Types of Fossils Help students make up a chart consisting of five columns labeled *Petrified Fossils, Molds and Casts, Carbon Films, Trace Fossils,* and *Preserved Remains.* As students read through the section, help them add details and drawings to their charts. **learning modality: verbal**

Monitor Progress   L2

Skills Check Have students make a flowchart that represents how an organism becomes a fossil. Students can place their flowcharts in their portfolios.

Portfolio

Answer
Figure 1 Sedimentary rock

Modeling Petrified Fossils L1

Materials pan, paper towel, white glue, paper plate, water

Time 5 minutes twice a day for 2 days

Focus Review how a petrified fossil forms.

Teach Mix two parts water to one part white glue. Roll a paper towel in the mixture, making sure the whole towel is moistened. Then stand the towel on end on a paper plate, and allow it to dry. The result will be a rock-hard "petrified fossil" that retains the original towel's shape.

Apply Ask: **How did this model the formation of a petrified fossil?** (*The glue dissolved in water seeped into spaces in the paper towel and hardened when the water evaporated, just as minerals dissolved in water seep into cells of an organism and harden.*)
learning modality: visual

Making Models of Mold and Cast Fossils L2

Materials shell, petroleum jelly, modeling compound, plaster of Paris, water, paper cup, plastic spoon

Time 20 minutes

Focus Review how a mold fossil and a cast fossil form.

Teach Students coat a shell with petroleum jelly and then press the shell into modeling compound. From that mold, students can make a cast by pouring plaster of Paris into the mold. (Mix 2 parts plaster of Paris with 1 part water.) Allow the plaster of Paris to harden overnight. Then students can separate the plaster from the modeling compound.

Apply Have students write a description comparing and contrasting the mold and the cast they made. **learning modality: kinesthetic**

FIGURE 2
Kinds of Fossils

In addition to petrified fossils, fossils may be molds and casts, carbon films, trace fossils, or preserved remains.
Classifying *You split apart a rock and find the imprint of a seashell on one half of the rock. What type of fossil have you found?*

▲ **Petrified Fossils**
These petrified tree trunks in Arizona were formed 200 million years ago, yet look as if they were just cut down.

112 ◆ G

Molds and Casts ▼
The fossil mold (left) clearly shows the shape of the animal called *Cryptolithus*. So does the fossil cast (right). *Cryptolithus* lived in the oceans about 450 million years ago.

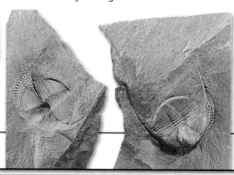

▲ **Carbon Films**
This carbon film fossil of insects is between 5 million and 23 million years old.

Petrified Fossils A fossil may form when the remains of an organism become petrified. The term *petrified* means "turned into stone." **Petrified fossils** are fossils in which minerals replace all or part of an organism. The fossil tree trunks shown in Figure 2 are examples of petrified wood. These fossils formed after sediment covered the wood. Then water rich in dissolved minerals seeped into spaces in the plant's cells. Over time, the minerals come out of solution and harden, filling in all of the spaces. Some of the original wood remains, but the minerals have hardened and preserved it.

Carbon Films Another type of fossil is a **carbon film,** an extremely thin coating of carbon on rock. How does a carbon film form? Remember that all living things contain carbon. When sediment buries an organism, some of the materials that make up the organism evaporate, or become gases. These gases escape from the sediment, leaving carbon behind. Eventually, only a thin film of carbon remains. This process can preserve the delicate parts of plant leaves and insects.

Trace Fossils Most types of fossils preserve the shapes of ancient animals and plants. In contrast, **trace fossils** provide evidence of the activities of ancient organisms. A fossilized footprint is one example of a trace fossil. A dinosaur made the fossil footprint shown in Figure 2. The mud or sand that the animal stepped in was buried by layers of sediment. Slowly the sediment became solid rock, preserving the footprint for millions of years.

Differentiated Instruction

Gifted and Talented L3
Researching the La Brea Tar Pits
Encourage students to research the preserved remains discovered in the La Brea tar pits of Los Angeles. Students can prepare a brief presentation that includes visual aids. **learning modality: verbal**

Special Needs L1
Comparing and Contrasting Fossils
Provide a hand lens and samples of each of the different kinds of fossils. Encourage students to examine the fossils with the hand lens and to handle them. Have them note differences in how they feel, for example, between a mold and a cast. Emphasize that trace fossils were made in mud or sand, not rock, that later hardened into rock. **learning modality: kinesthetic**

From fossil footprints, scientists can find answers to questions about an animal's size and behavior. Did the animal walk on two or four legs? Did it live alone or as part of a group?

Other types of trace fossils also provide clues about ancient organisms. A trail or burrow can give clues about the size and shape of an organism, where it lived, and how it obtained food.

Preserved Remains Some processes preserve the remains of organisms with little or no change. For example, some remains are preserved when organisms become trapped in tar. Tar is sticky oil that seeps from Earth's surface. Many fossils preserved in tar have been found at the Rancho La Brea tar pits in Los Angeles, California. Thousands of years ago, animals came to drink the water that covered these pits. Somehow, they became stuck in the tar and then died. The tar soaked into their bones, preserving the bones from decay.

Ancient organisms also have been preserved in amber. Amber is the hardened resin, or sap, of evergreen trees. First, an insect is trapped on sticky resin. After the insect dies, more resin covers it, sealing it from air and protecting its body from decay.

Freezing can also preserve remains. The frozen remains of woolly mammoths, huge ancient relatives of elephants, have been found in very cold regions of Siberia and Alaska. Freezing has preserved even the mammoths' hair and skin.

Reading Checkpoint) What are three ways in which the remains of an organism can be preserved with little change?

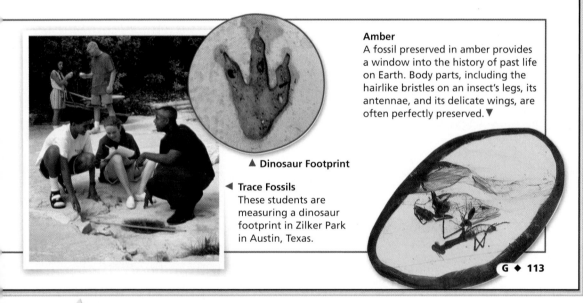

▲ **Dinosaur Footprint**

◀ **Trace Fossils**
These students are measuring a dinosaur footprint in Zilker Park in Austin, Texas.

Amber
A fossil preserved in amber provides a window into the history of past life on Earth. Body parts, including the hairlike bristles on an insect's legs, its antennae, and its delicate wings, are often perfectly preserved. ▼

G ◆ 113

Change Over Time

Teach Key Concepts L1

The Fossil Record

Focus Remind students that fossils provide us with information about organisms that lived long ago.

Teach Direct attention to Figure 3. Point out that the area depicted is a dry area today. Ask: **How do we know this region used to have many shallow lakes and swamps?** *(The fossils found there were of animals that lived in lakes and swamps.)* **How does the fossil record provide evidence for evolution?** *(Fossils provide evidence that life has changed over time.)*

Apply Remind students that in many parts of America's Midwest there are thick deposits of limestone containing fossil sea shells. Ask: **What can you conclude from this?** *(The area was covered with water long ago)* **learning modality: logical/mathematical**

Help Students Read L1

Identifying Supporting Evidence Refer to the Content Refresher for guidelines on identifying supporting evidence. As students read, have them fill out graphic organizers identifying supporting evidence for past environments, climates, and life forms.

FIGURE 3
Fossil Clues to Past Environments
Fossils of many different kinds of organisms were formed in this ancient lakeshore environment.
Inferring *How do you think the fossil of the bat was preserved?*

Cattails

Icaronycteris (bat)

Crocodilian

Bat

Gar fossil

Sunfish

Gar

Herring

114 ◆ G

Change Over Time

Scientists who study fossils are called **paleontologists** (pay lee un TAHL uh jists). Paleontologists collect fossils from sedimentary rocks all over the world. They use this information to determine what past life forms were like. They want to learn what these organisms ate, what ate them, and in what kind of environment they lived.

Paleontologists also classify organisms. They group similar organisms together. They arrange organisms in the order in which they lived, from earliest to latest. Together, all the information that paleontologists have gathered about past life is called the fossil record. **The fossil record provides evidence about the history of life and past environments on Earth. The fossil record also shows that different groups of organisms have changed over time.**

Frigate birds

Sequoia

Sycamore leaves

Sycamores

Uintatherium

Hyracotherium

Coryphodon

Phenacodus

Palms

Fossils and Past Environments Paleontologists use fossils to build up a picture of Earth's past environments. The fossils found in an area tell whether the area was a shallow bay, an ocean bottom, or a freshwater swamp.

Fossils also provide evidence about the past climate of a region. For example, coal has been found in Antarctica. But coal only forms from the remains of plants that grow in warm, swampy regions. As you probably know, thick layers of ice and snow now cover Antarctica. The presence of coal shows that the climate of Antarctica was once much warmer than it is today.

Scientists can use fossils to learn about changes in Earth's surface. For example, the fossils in Figure 3 are about 50 million years old. They were found in a region of dry plains and plateaus in the state of Wyoming. From these fossils, scientists have inferred that back then the region had many shallow lakes and swamps. Lush forests with many different kinds of plants and animals flourished in a warm, subtropical climate.

G ◆ 115

Lab zone **Build Inquiry** L2

Modeling the Fossil Record

Materials different colors of clay and paper, reference books, art materials

Time 25 minutes

Focus Remind students that the fossil record supports evolution because the younger the rock is, the more complex the organism indicated by the fossil.

Teach Have small groups design and build a model representing rock layers and how organisms have changed through time. They can make sketches (or use printouts from the Internet) of how a particular organism has changed and then label each rock layer with the sketches. Ask students to present and explain their models to the class.

Apply Ask students to infer the conditions under which scientists would not be able to tell from the order of rocks how an organism evolved. (*If the rock layers are disturbed, such as by an earthquake or mining activities, the order of the fossils could be mixed up.*)
learning modality: kinesthetic

Address Misconceptions L2

The Meaning of "Theory"

Focus Some students understand the word *theory* to mean an opinion put forward that is less than sure or proven, as in the phrase "That's just your theory about what happened."

Teach Explain that this common use of the word is not the scientific use. For a scientist, a theory is a broad explanation based on many observations, as in the "theory of gravity." Scientists know that gravity exists, just as they know that evolution takes place.

Apply Ask students to name some scientific theories they know. (*Possible answers: Cell theory, germ theory of disease, continental drift*) **learning modality: verbal**

Differentiated Instruction

English Learners/Beginning L1
Comprehension: Key Concept Write "The fossil record provides evidence that . . ." three times. Pair ELL students with English-proficient students. Have them identify key phrases from the section that complete each statement to show how the fossil record "provides evidence about the history of life on Earth," "evidence about past environments," and "evidence

that different groups of organisms have changed over time." **learning modality: verbal**

English Learners/Intermediate L2
Comprehension: Key Concept Students can do the *Beginning* activity and then write complete sentences in their own words to support each statement. **learning modality: verbal**

Monitor Progress L2

Writing Have students make a list of the kinds of information that scientists obtain through studying the fossil record.

Answer
Figure 3 The bat's body may have fallen into the mud when the bat died. Accept all reasoned responses.

Answers

Figure 4 It is an extinct animal.

✓ **Reading Checkpoint** A well-tested concept that explains a wide range of observations

Assess

Reviewing Key Concepts

1. a. The preserved remains or traces of a living thing **b.** Most fossils are formed when living things die and are buried by sediments. The sediments slowly harden into rock and preserve the shapes of the organisms. **c.** Hard parts of an organism usually form fossils because they are less likely to be lost by decay.

2. a. Petrified fossils, molds, casts, carbon films, and trace fossils **b.** When an organism is buried by sediment, some of the materials that make up the organism evaporate, leaving behind a thin film of carbon that preserves parts of the organism. **c.** They are similar because the remains of both are not destroyed by decay. They are different because preserved remains are the actual organism, whereas the soft parts of petrified organisms are replaced by minerals.

3. a. Past environments and how groups of organisms have changed over time **b.** Life on Earth has evolved, or changed over time. Simple organisms have given rise to more complex plants and animals.

Reteach   L1

With the class, make a table that compares and contrasts the different kinds of fossils.

Performance Assessment   L2

Writing Have students suppose that they are scientists on an archaeological dig. Ask them to use each key term in this section to write a short story describing their experience.

All in One Teaching Resources

- Section Summary: Fossils
- Review and Reinforce: *Fossils*
- Enrich: *Fossils*

FIGURE 4
Ancestry of the Elephant
From fossils, scientists have reconstructed the paleomastodon (left). This animal had a short trunk and short tusks on both upper and lower jaws. The paleomastodon is an ancestor of the modern elephant (right). **Inferring** *Why is the paleomastodon only known from its fossils?*

Change and the Fossil Record The fossil record reveals a surprising fact: Fossils occur in a particular order. Older rocks contain fossils of simpler organisms. Younger rocks contain fossils of more complex organisms. In other words, the fossil record shows that life on Earth has evolved, or changed over time. Simple, one-celled organisms have given rise to complex plants and animals.

The fossil record provides evidence to support the theory of evolution. A **scientific theory** is a well-tested concept that explains a wide range of observations. **Evolution** is the gradual change in living things over long periods of time.

The fossil record shows that millions of types of organisms have evolved. But many others have become extinct. A type of organism is **extinct** if it no longer exists and will never again live on Earth.

✓ **Reading Checkpoint** What is a scientific theory?

Section 1 Assessment

 Target Reading Skill **Using Prior Knowledge** Review your graphic organizer and revise it based on what you just learned in the section.

Reviewing Key Concepts

1. a. **Defining** What is a fossil?
   b. **Summarizing** In general, how does a fossil form?
   c. **Relating Cause and Effect** Which parts of an organism are most likely to be preserved as fossils? Why?
2. a. **Listing** What are the five different kinds of fossils?
   b. **Explaining** How does a carbon film fossil form?
   c. **Comparing and Contrasting** How are petrified fossils similar to preserved remains? How are they different?
3. a. **Reviewing** What are two things that scientists can learn from the fossil record?
   b. **Making Generalizations** What does the fossil record show about how life has changed over time?

Lab zone At-Home **Activity**

Family Fossils A fossil is something old that has been preserved. With your parents' permission, look around your house for the oldest object you can find. Interview family members to determine how old the object is, why it has been preserved, and how it may have changed since it was new. Make a drawing of the object and bring it to class. Tell your class the story of this "fossil."

Lab zone At-Home **Activity**

Family Fossils L1 Encourage students to ask older members of their families to find something that has been passed down from generation to generation. Suggest that they write down why the object was preserved to help them remember in telling the story to the class. Caution students not to bring these objects to school but rather to make drawings of them.

The Relative Age of Rocks

Reading Preview

Key Concepts
- What is the law of superposition?
- How do geologists determine the relative age of rocks?
- How are index fossils useful to geologists?

Key Terms
- relative age • absolute age
- law of superposition
- extrusion • intrusion • fault
- unconformity • index fossil

 **Target Reading Skill**

Asking Questions Before you read, preview the red headings. In a graphic organizer like the one below, ask a *what* or *how* question for each heading. As you read, write answers to your questions.

Relative Age

Question	Answer
What does the position of rock layers reveal?	The position of rock layers shows . . .

Lab zone Discover **Activity**

Which Layer Is the Oldest?

1. Make a stack of different-colored layers of clay. Each layer should be about the size and thickness of a pancake. If these flat layers are sediments, which layer of sediment was deposited first? (*Hint:* This is the oldest layer.)

2. Now form the stack into a dome by pressing it over a small rounded object, such as a small bowl. With a cheese-slicer or plastic knife, carefully cut off the top of the dome. Look at the layers that you have exposed. Which layer is the oldest?

Think It Over

Inferring If you press the stack into a small bowl and trim away the clay that sticks above the edge, where will you find the oldest layer?

As sedimentary rock forms, the remains of organisms in the sediment may become fossils. Millions of years later, if you split open the rock, you might see the petrified bones of an extinct reptile or insect.

Your first question about a new fossil might be, "What is it?" Your next question would probably be, "How old is it?" Geologists have two ways to express the age of a rock and any fossil it contains. The **relative age** of a rock is its age compared to the ages of other rocks. You have probably used the idea of relative age when comparing your age with someone else's age. For example, if you say that you are older than your brother but younger than your sister, you are describing your relative age.

The relative age of a rock does not provide its absolute age. The **absolute age** of a rock is the number of years since the rock formed. It may be impossible to know a rock's absolute age exactly. But sometimes geologists can determine a rock's absolute age to within a certain number of years.

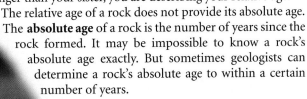

◀ The age of each family member could be given as relative age or absolute age.

Chapter 4 G ◆ 117

Objectives

After this lesson, students will be able to
G.4.2.1 State the law of superposition.
G.4.2.2 Describe how geologists determine the relative age of rocks.
G.4.2.3 Explain how index fossils are useful to geologists.

Target Reading Skill ⟳

Asking Questions Explain that changing a heading into a question helps students anticipate the ideas, facts, and events they are about to read.

Answers
Possible questions and answers:
What does the position of rock layers reveal? (*The oldest layers—and the oldest fossils—are at the bottom.*) **How do geologists determine the relative age of a rock?** (*The position of rock layers, extrusions and intrusions of igneous rock, faults, and gaps in the geologic record*) **How are fossils used to date rocks?** (*The age of an index fossil tells the age of the rock layer in which it occurs.*)

All in One Teaching Resources
- Transparency G35

Preteach

Build Background Knowledge   L1

How Sediments Are Deposited
Ask: **What happens to the sediment load carried to an ocean by a river?** (*Some is deposited on beaches and some on the ocean floor.*) Explain that this sediment can harden over time into layers of rock.

Lab zone Discover **Activity**

Skills Focus Inferring   L2

Materials 4 to 5 different colors of modeling compound, small bowl, cheese slicer or plastic knife

Time 10 minutes

Tips When students begin cutting off the top of the dome, advise them not to cut all the way to the bowl; have them leave one layer covering the bowl.

Expected Outcome The oldest layer is the bottom layer when the layers are flat. When the layers are pressed over the bowl and the top of the dome is cut off, the oldest layer is in the center of the dome, even if it rises above the other layers.

Think It Over The oldest layer is found on the outside ring, touching the bowl.

The Position of Rock Layers

Discovery CHANNEL SCHOOL™
Video Field Trip

A Trip Through Geologic Time

Show the Video Field Trip to let students experience the geology of the Grand Canyon. Discussion question: **How does the evidence found in the Grand Canyon's layers help scientists re-create the geologic history of the region?** *(The rock layers of the Grand Canyon follow the law of superposition. The oldest rock is at the bottom, and the most recent layers are near the top.)*

Teach Key Concepts   **L1**

The Law of Superposition

Focus Remind students that, as a noun, *relative* means a family member. But as an adjective, *relative* is used as a means of comparison.

Teach Have students recall the Discover Activity in which they made flat layers from modeling clay. Ask: **How was your model like the illustration of the Grand Canyon you see in Figure 5?** *(The oldest layer is on the bottom.)* **How do scientists use this concept to determine the relative ages of rocks?** *(In horizontal sedimentary rock layers, the oldest layer is at the bottom. Each higher layer is younger than the layers below it.)* **What is this principle called?** *(The law of superposition)*

Apply Have students examine the layers of rock in the illustration. Ask: **Why couldn't the Hermit Shale layer be older than the Supai Sandstone layer?** *(Because the Hermit Shale lies above the Supai Sandstone, the sedimentary rock must have been formed more recently.)* **learning modality: visual**

All in One Teaching Resources

• Transparency G36

Independent Practice   **L2**

All in One Teaching Resources

• Guided Reading and Study Worksheet: *The Relative Age of Rocks*

Student Edition on Audio CD

Discovery CHANNEL SCHOOL

A Trip Through Geologic Time
Video Preview
▶ Video Field Trip
Video Assessment

FIGURE 5
The Grand Canyon
More than a dozen rock layers make up the walls of the Grand Canyon. You can see five layers clearly in the photograph. **Applying Concepts** *In which labeled layers would you find the oldest fossils? Explain.*

The Position of Rock Layers

Have you ever seen rock layers of different colors on a cliff beside a road? What are these layers, and how did they form? The sediment that forms sedimentary rocks is deposited in flat layers one on top of the other. Over time, the sediment hardens and changes into sedimentary rock. These rock layers provide a record of Earth's geologic history.

It can be difficult to determine the absolute age of a rock. So geologists use a method to find a rock's relative age. Geologists use the **law of superposition** to determine the relative ages of sedimentary rock layers. **According to the law of superposition, in horizontal sedimentary rock layers the oldest layer is at the bottom. Each higher layer is younger than the layers below it.**

The walls of the Grand Canyon in Arizona illustrate the law of superposition. You can see some of the rock layers found in the Grand Canyon in Figure 5. The deeper down you go in the Grand Canyon, the older the rocks.

 Reading Checkpoint Why do sedimentary rocks have layers?

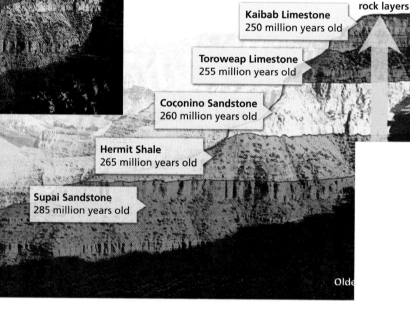

Younger rock layers

Kaibab Limestone
250 million years old

Toroweap Limestone
255 million years old

Coconino Sandstone
260 million years old

Hermit Shale
265 million years old

Supai Sandstone
285 million years old

Olde

Differentiated Instruction

Special Needs   **L1**
Relative and Absolute Ages Clarify the meaning of *relative age* and *absolute age* by writing the following statements about children in a family on the board: "Anthony is the youngest." *(Relative)* "Melony is 4 years old." *(Absolute)* "Michael is older than Shatiqua." *(Relative)* "Ashley is older than Melony but younger than Shatiqua."

(Relative) Help students place the children in order from youngest to oldest. *(Michael, Shatiqua, Ashley, Melony, Anthony)* Ask: **How does this example model how scientists determine the ages of rock layers?** *(Scientists are able to fill in gaps in the geologic record by comparing the ages of rocks.)* **learning modality: logical/ mathematical**

Fault

FIGURE 6
Intrusions and Faults
Intrusions and faults give clues to the relative ages of rocks. An intrusion (left) cuts through rock layers. Rock layers are broken and shifted along a fault (right).

Determining Relative Age

There are other clues besides the position of rock layers to the relative ages of rocks. **To determine relative age, geologists also study extrusions and intrusions of igneous rock, faults, and gaps in the geologic record.**

Clues From Igneous Rock Igneous rock forms when magma or lava hardens. Magma is molten material beneath Earth's surface. Magma that flows onto the surface is called lava.

Lava that hardens on the surface is called an **extrusion.** An extrusion is always younger than the rocks below it.

Beneath the surface, magma may push into bodies of rock. There, the magma cools and hardens into a mass of igneous rock called an **intrusion.** An intrusion is always younger than the rock layers around and beneath it. Figure 6 shows an intrusion. Geologists study where intrusions and extrusions formed in relation to other rock layers. This helps geologists understand the relative ages of the different types of rock.

Clues From Faults More clues come from the study of faults. A **fault** is a break in Earth's crust. Forces inside Earth cause movement of the rock on opposite sides of a fault.

A fault is always younger than the rock it cuts through. To determine the relative age of a fault, geologists find the relative age of the youngest layer cut by the fault.

Movements along faults can make it harder for geologists to determine the relative ages of rock layers. You can see in Figure 6 how the rock layers no longer line up because of movement along the fault.

Lab zone Try This Activity

Sampling a Sandwich
Your teacher will give you a sandwich that represents rock layers in Earth's crust.

1. Use a round, hollow, uncooked noodle as a coring tool. Push the noodle through the layers of the sandwich.
2. Pull the noodle out of the sandwich. Break the noodle gently to remove your core sample.
3. Draw a picture of what you see in each layer of the core.

Making Models Which layer of your sandwich is the "oldest"? The "youngest"? Why do you think scientists study core samples?

Lab zone Try This Activity

Skills Focus Making models L2

Materials cylindrical pasta noodle about 1.5 cm in diameter, sandwich of different soft cheeses and meats

Time 15 minutes

Tips One sandwich can be used for several samples. Explain that geologists use drills to cut through rock layers and bring core samples to the surface to study.

Expected Outcome The oldest is the bottom; the youngest is the top. Core samples provide information about layers of rock.

Extend Ask: **If these were layers of sedimentary rock, why couldn't layer 4 be younger than layer 3?** (*The sediment that formed layer 3 could not have been deposited underneath the hardened rock of layer 4.*)
learning modality: kinesthetic

Determining Relative Age

Teach Key Concepts L1
Clues to Determine Relative Age

Focus Review the definition of relative age.

Teach Ask: **How do geologists use extrusions and intrusions to determine relative age?** (*They are always younger than the rocks beneath and surrounding them.*) **Are faults younger or older than the rock they cut through?** (*Younger*) **What might cause a gap in the geologic record?** (*Erosion might wear away a layer of rock. When a new layer forms, the layer that was originally there was lost.*)

Apply Ask: **How are faults, intrusions, and extrusions similar?** (*They are all younger than the rocks they push into or disturb.*)
learning modality: verbal

Lab zone Build Inquiry L2

Comparing Rock Samples

Materials hand lens, samples of granite, basalt, sandstone, and shale

Time 15 minutes

Focus Ask students to recall the origins of sedimentary and igneous rocks.

Teach Label the samples: **Granite—forms intrusions, Basalt—forms extrusions, Sandstone—formed mainly of sandy sediment,** and **Shale—formed mainly of muddy sediment.** Have students examine the samples and write descriptions of them, including textures and grain size.

Apply Ask: **Which of the rocks would occur as a layer?** (*Basalt, sandstone, and shale*) **Which rock would cut across other rock layers?** (*Granite*) **learning modality: kinesthetic**

Monitor Progress L2

Drawing Have students draw several sedimentary rock layers; add and label an intrusion, extrusion, and a fault; then label the layers from oldest to youngest.

Answers
Figure 5 The Supai Sandstone; the oldest layer is at the bottom.

✓ Reading Checkpoint The sediment that forms sedimentary rocks is deposited in flat layers one on top of the other.

Using Fossils to Date Rocks

Teach Key Concepts   **L1**
Index Fossils

Focus Review the difference between absolute age and relative age.

Teach Ask: **Is an index fossil used to determine absolute age or relative age? Explain.** *(Relative age—the index fossil is compared to other fossils in other locations.)* **How does an index fossil help date rocks?** *(Rock layers that contain the same index fossil are about the same age.)*

Apply Pose this problem to students: **Suppose two rock layers in two different locations contain fossils of a dinosaur that lived only during the Jurassic Period. What can you conclude about the rock layers?** *(They must have been formed at about the same time during the Jurassic Period.)* **learning modality: logical/mathematical**

Modeling Index Fossils   **L3**

Materials newspapers, common classroom objects such as pencils, erasers, paper clips, and buttons

Time 20 minutes

Focus Review the definition of an index fossil.

Teach Create a model of several locations by using layers of newspapers. Place common objects between sections of a newspaper, labeling the layers A, B, C, and D. Use one object, such as a button, to represent an index fossil. Give each group of students one newspaper pile, and have them remove the layers, recording the "fossils" found. After groups have examined the layers, record their observations on the board. Have them determine which of the "fossils" can be used as an index fossil by its distribution and location.

Apply Ask: **How were you able to determine which fossil is an index fossil?** *(The fossil was found in several stacks of newspapers in the same layer, but not in any other layers.)* **learning modality: kinesthetic**

All in One Teaching Resources
• Transparencies G37, G38

FIGURE 7
Unconformity
An unconformity occurs where erosion wears away layers of sedimentary rock. Other rock layers then form on top.
Sequencing *What two processes must take place before an unconformity can form?*

1 Sedimentary rocks form in horizontal layers.

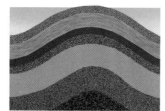

2 Folding tilts the rock layers.

3 The surface is eroded.

Unconformity

4 New sediment is deposited, forming rock layers above the unconformity.

120 ◆ G

Gaps in the Geologic Record The geologic record of sedimentary rock layers is not always complete. Deposition slowly builds layer upon layer of sedimentary rock. But some of these layers may erode away, exposing an older rock surface. Then deposition begins again, building new rock layers.

The surface where new rock layers meet a much older rock surface beneath them is called an **unconformity**. An unconformity is a gap in the geologic record. An unconformity shows where some rock layers have been lost because of erosion. Figure 7 shows how an unconformity forms.

 Reading Checkpoint What is an unconformity?

Using Fossils to Date Rocks

To date rock layers, geologists first give a relative age to a layer of rock at one location. Then they can give the same age to matching layers of rock at other locations.

Certain fossils, called index fossils, help geologists match rock layers. To be useful as an **index fossil**, a fossil must be widely distributed and represent a type of organism that existed only briefly. A fossil is considered widely distributed if it occurs in many different areas. Geologists look for index fossils in layers of rock. **Index fossils are useful because they tell the relative ages of the rock layers in which they occur.**

Geologists use particular types of organisms as index fossils—for example, certain types of ammonites. Ammonites (AM uh nyts) were a group of hard-shelled animals. Ammonites evolved in shallow seas more than 500 million years ago and became extinct about 65 million years ago.

Ammonite fossils make good index fossils for two reasons. First, they are widely distributed. Second, many different types of ammonites evolved and then became extinct after a few million years.

Geologists can identify the different types of ammonites through differences in the structure of their shells. Based on these differences, geologists can identify the rock layers in which a particular type of ammonite fossil occurs.

You can use index fossils to match rock layers. Look at Figure 8, which shows rock layers from four different locations. Notice that two of the fossils are found in only one of these rock layers. These are the index fossils.

 Reading Checkpoint What characteristics must a fossil have to be useful as an index fossil?

Differentiated Instruction

Less Proficient Readers
Understanding Causes of Unconformities Pair students with more proficient readers. Refer them to Figure 7, and write the questions that follow on the board. Ask them to draw on previous knowledge to give detailed answers. Encourage them to use the table of contents and index to locate information in other parts of the textbook. Questions:

L1 **What process could have made the sedimentary layers?** *(Deposition from water, wind, waves, or glaciers)* **What could have caused the folding of the layers?** *(Forces from inside Earth can cause movement.)* **What could have caused the wearing away of the surface?** *(Chemical or mechanical weathering, and then erosion by water, wind, waves, or glaciers)* **learning modality: visual**

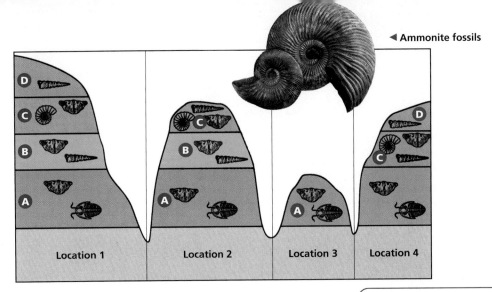

◄ Ammonite fossils

| Location 1 | Location 2 | Location 3 | Location 4 |

FIGURE 8
Using Index Fossils
Scientists use index fossils to match up rock layers at locations that may be far apart. The ammonites in layer C are index fossils. *Interpreting Diagrams Can you find another index fossil in the diagram? (Hint: Look for a fossil that occurs in only one time period, but in several different locations.)*

Go **Online**
active art

For: Index Fossils activities
Visit: PHSchool.com
Web Code: cfp-2042

Section 2 Assessment

🔄 **Target Reading Skill Asking Questions** Use the answers to the questions you wrote about the headings to help you answer the questions below.

Reviewing Key Concepts

1. **a. Defining** In your own words, define the terms *relative age* and *absolute age*.
   b. Explaining What is the law of superposition?
   c. Inferring A geologist finds a cliff where the edges of several different rock layers can be seen. Which layer is the oldest? Explain.

2. **a. Reviewing** Besides the law of superposition, what are three types of clues to the relative age of rock layers?
   b. Comparing and Contrasting Compare and contrast extrusions and intrusions.
   c. Sequencing An intrusion crosses an extrusion. Which layer is the older? Explain.

3. **a. Defining** What is an index fossil?

b. Applying Concepts The fossil record shows that horseshoe crabs have existed with very little change for about 200 million years. Would horseshoe crabs be useful as an index fossil? Explain why or why not.

Lab zone At-Home Activity

Drawer to the Past Collect ten items out of a drawer full of odds and ends such as keys, coins, receipts, photographs, and souvenirs. Have your family members put them in order from oldest to newest. What clues will you use to determine their relative ages? How can you determine the oldest object of all? List the ten items in order of their relative age. Do you know the absolute age of any of the items?

Chapter 4 G ◆ 121

Lab zone At-Home Activity

Drawer to the Past **L2** Encourage students to carry out the activity at home and then bring a list of the ten items to class. Clues used to determine relative ages might include the memories of family members and the condition of an item. Some items, such as coins, may contain dates that indicate an absolute age.

Lab zone Chapter Project

Keep Students on Track Point students toward research materials that will provide information about their chosen time periods, and encourage them to keep a bibliography of their sources. Tell students to keep in mind the pictures and facts they will need for the class timeline and travel brochure.

Monitor Progress _____ L2

Answers
Figure 7 Erosion and deposition
Figure 8 The trilobites in Layer A

✓ **Reading Checkpoint** A gap in the geological record

✓ **Reading Checkpoint** It must be widely distributed, and it must have existed for only a brief period of time.

Assess

Reviewing Key Concepts

1. a. Relative age states whether a rock is younger or older than another rock. Absolute age is a rock's age in years. **b.** In horizontal layers of sedimentary rock, the oldest layer is at the bottom, and each higher layer is younger than the layer below it. **c.** The bottom; it was the first to be formed by deposits.
2. a. Igneous rock intrusions and extrusions, faults, and unconformities
b. Both form from molten material. Lava that hardens on the surface is an extrusion. Magma that cools below the surface is an intrusion. **c.** The extrusion; intrusions are always younger than the rock layers through which they pass.
3. a. A fossil that is used to determine the relative age of rocks **b.** No. They have existed with little change for a long time.

Reteach L1
With the class, make a drawing that includes sedimentary rock layers, an unconformity, a fault, an intrusion, an extrusion, and several index fossils. Discuss the relative ages of each layer.

All in One Teaching Resources
- Section Summary: *The Relative Age of Rocks*
- Review and Reinforce: *The Relative Age of Rocks*
- Enrich: *The Relative Age of Rocks*

Finding Clues to Rock Layers L2

Prepare for Inquiry

Key Concept
Index fossils as well as intrusions and extrusions can be used to determine the relative ages of rock layers.

Skills Objectives
Students will be able to
- Interpret data about various fossils found in rock layers
- Draw conclusions about the relative ages of rock layers

 Class Time 30 minutes

All in One Teaching Resources
- LabWorksheet: *Finding Clues to Rock Layers*

Guide Inquiry

Introduce the Procedure
Allow students time to read through the entire procedure. Then ask: **Where can you find out what kinds of fossils are in the different rock layers?** *(In the key to symbols)* **What kind of fossils do geologists use to match rock layers?** *(Index fossils)*

Analyze and Conclude
1. Fossils of marine animals in layers A and B indicate a marine environment. Dinosaur tracks and a leaf suggest that a land environment created layer D.

2. According to the law of superposition, layer A is the oldest because it is below all other layers.

3. According to the law of superposition, layer G formed most recently because it is above all other layers.

4. Layers C and E are extrusions of igneous rock, in which fossils can't form.

5. Dinosaur, plant, and bird fossils

6. Layer B

7. Rock layers that are missing from the sequence at Site 2 provide clues of an unconformity. Layers E and D are missing between layers X and Y, which suggests that the boundary between Y and X is an unconformity. Layer A is also missing, which suggests that there is an unconformity below W.

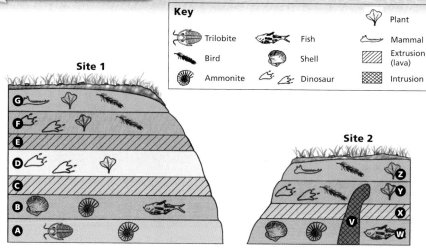

Key
- Trilobite
- Bird
- Ammonite
- Fish
- Shell
- Dinosaur
- Plant
- Mammal
- Extrusion (lava)
- Intrusion

Finding Clues to Rock Layers

Problem
How can you use fossils and geologic features to interpret the relative ages of rock layers?

Skills Focus
interpreting data, drawing conclusions

Procedure
1. Study the rock layers at Sites 1 and 2. Write down the similarities and differences between the layers at the two sites.
2. List the kinds of fossils that are found in each rock layer of Sites 1 and 2.

Analyze and Conclude

Site 1

1. **Interpreting Data** What "fossil clues" in layers A and B indicate the kind of environment that existed when these rock layers were formed? How did the environment change in layer D?
2. **Drawing Conclusions** Which layer is the oldest? How do you know?
3. **Drawing Conclusions** Which of the layers formed most recently? How do you know?

4. **Inferring** Why are there no fossils in layers C and E?
5. **Observing** What kind of fossils are found in layer F?

Site 2

6. **Inferring** Which layer at Site 1 might have formed at the same time as layer W at Site 2?
7. **Interpreting Data** What clues show an unconformity or gap in the horizontal rock layers? Which rock layers are missing? What might have happened to these rock layers?
8. **Drawing Conclusions** Which is older, intrusion V or layer Y? How do you know?
9. **Communicating** Write a journal entry describing how the environment at Site 2 changed over time. Starting with the earliest layer, describe the types of organisms, their environment, and how the environment changed.

More to Explore
Draw a sketch similar to Site 2 and include a fault that cuts across the intrusion. Have a partner then identify the relative age of the fault, the intrusion, and the layers cut by the fault.

---

8. Layer Y is older because an intrusion is always younger than the layer through which it passes.

9. The environment most likely started out as an ocean environment. Volcanic extrusions covered the environment over many years, eventually creating a swamplike environment in which dinosaurs lived.

Extend Inquiry

More to Explore Because faults can occur only after rock layers have formed, any layers the fault cuts across would be older than the fault. Encourage students to test one another with their sketches.

Radioactive Dating

Section
3
Radioactive Dating

Reading Preview

Key Concepts
- What happens during radioactive decay?
- What can be learned from radioactive dating?

Key Terms
- atom • element
- radioactive decay • half-life

Target Reading Skill
Identifying Main Ideas As you read the Determining Absolute Ages section, write the main idea in a graphic organizer like the one below. Then write three supporting details that give examples of the main idea.

Main Idea

Using radioactive dating, scientists can determine . . .

Detail	Detail	Detail

Lab zone Discover **Activity**

How Long Till It's Gone?

1. Make a small cube—about 5 cm × 5 cm × 5 cm —from modeling clay.
2. Carefully use a knife to cut the clay in half. Put one half of the clay aside.
3. Cut the clay in half two more times. Each time you cut the clay, put one half of it aside.

Think It Over

Predicting How big will the remaining piece of clay be if you repeat the process several more times?

In Australia, scientists have found sedimentary rocks that contain some of the world's oldest fossils. These are fossils of stromatolites (stroh MAT uh lyts). Stromatolites are the remains of reefs built by organisms similar to present-day bacteria. Sediment eventually covered these reefs. As the sediment changed to rock, so did the reefs. Using absolute dating, scientists have determined that some stromatolites are more than 3 billion years old. To understand absolute dating, you need to learn more about the chemistry of rocks.

FIGURE 9
Stromatolites
Scientists think that ancient stromatolites were formed by organisms similar to blue-green bacteria (above). Modern stromatolites (right) still form reefs along the western coast of Australia.

G ◆ 123

Lab zone Discover **Activity**

Skills Focus Predicting

Materials modeling clay, metric ruler, plastic knife

Time 10 minutes

Tips Advise students that exact measurements are unnecessary and to estimate what a half is.

L1 **Expected Outcome** By cutting the clay in half three times, students will reduce the size of the cube to one-eighth the original size.

Think It Over The remaining piece will be very small, possibly too small to cut in half again with the knife.

Objectives

After this lesson, students will be able to
G.4.3.1 Explain what happens during radioactive decay.
G.4.3.2 Describe what can be learned from radioactive dating.

Target Reading Skill

Identifying Main Ideas Explain that identifying main ideas and details helps students sort the facts from the information into groups. Each group can have a main topic, subtopics, and details.

Answers

Possible answers:
Main Idea: Using radioactive dating, scientists can determine . . .
Detail: the absolute ages of the most ancient rocks using potassium-40.
Detail: the absolute ages of fossils using carbon-14 up to about 50,000 years ago.
Detail: the ages of sedimentary rocks by dating the igneous intrusions and extrusions near the sedimentary rock.

All in One Teaching Resources

- Transparency G39

Preteach

Build Background Knowledge L1

Atoms

Ask: **What is an atom?** (*Students may know that an atom is the smallest part of an element that has all the properties of that element.*)
What does an atom contain? (*A typical answer might mention electrons, protons, neutrons, and energy.*) Use these responses to judge how much review individual students need to understand this section.

Radioactive Decay

Teach Key Concepts L2

What Happens During Radioactive Decay

Focus Remind students that the absolute ages of some rocks can be determined.

Teach Ask: **In which type of rock can scientists determine absolute age?** *(Igneous; radioactive elements occur naturally in it)* **What happens during radioactive decay?** *(Atoms in an element break down so that another element is formed.)*

Apply Ask: **Why does the slope of the graph in Figure 11 begin to level out after several half-lives?** *(Less and less of an element is left after each half-life.)* **learning modality: logical/mathematical**

 **Teaching Resources**

- Transparency G40

Independent Practice L2

 **Teaching Resources**

- Guided Reading and Study Worksheet: *Radioactive Dating*

Student Edition on Audio CD

Lab zone Build **Inquiry** L2

Modeling Radioactive Dating

Materials 100 pennies, paper cup

Time 20 minutes

Focus Review the definition of half-life.

Teach Have students place the pennies in a cup, dump them out, and remove the pennies that come up heads. Then have students take the remaining pennies and repeat the procedure three more times. Ask: **How does this model half-life?** *(Coins have a 50% chance of turning up heads or tails. Half-life is the time it takes for 50% of radioactive atoms to decay.)*

Apply Have students graph their results and explain why the slope looks the same as the slope in Figure 11. **learning modality: kinesthetic**

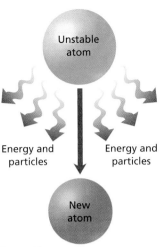

FIGURE 10
Radioactive Decay
In the process of radioactive decay, an atom releases energy and particles as it changes to a new kind of atom.

Radioactive Decay

Rocks are a form of matter. All the matter you see, including rocks, is made of tiny particles called **atoms.** When all the atoms in a particular type of matter are the same, the matter is an **element.** Carbon, oxygen, iron, lead, and potassium are just some of the more than 110 currently known elements.

Most elements are stable. They do not change under normal conditions. But some elements exist in forms that are unstable. Over time, these elements break down, or decay, by releasing particles and energy in a process called **radioactive decay.** These unstable elements are said to be radioactive. **During radioactive decay, the atoms of one element break down to form atoms of another element.**

Radioactive elements occur naturally in igneous rocks. Scientists use the rate at which these elements decay to calculate the rock's age. You calculate your age based on a specific day—your birthday. What's the "birthday" of a rock? For an igneous rock, that "birthday" is when it first hardens to become rock. As a radioactive element within the igneous rock decays, it changes into another element. So the composition of the rock changes slowly over time. The amount of the radioactive element goes down. But the amount of the new element goes up.

The rate of decay of each radioactive element is constant—it never changes. This rate of decay is the element's half-life. The **half-life** of a radioactive element is the time it takes for half of the radioactive atoms to decay. You can see in Figure 11 how a radioactive element decays over time.

Reading Checkpoint What is the meaning of the term "half-life"?

FIGURE 11
The half-life of a radioactive element is the amount of time it takes for half of the radioactive atoms to decay.
Calculating *After three half-lives, how much of the radioactive element remains?*

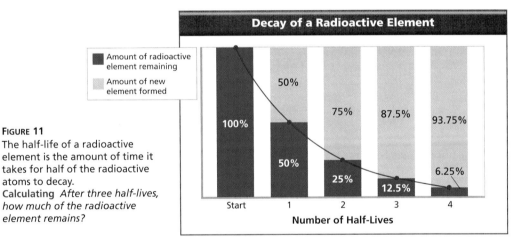

Decay of a Radioactive Element

- Amount of radioactive element remaining
- Amount of new element formed

100% | 50% | 25% | 12.5% | 6.25%
50% | 75% | 87.5% | 93.75%

Start | 1 | 2 | 3 | 4
Number of Half-Lives

Elements Used in Radioactive Dating		
Radioactive Element	Half-life (years)	Dating Range (years)
Carbon-14	5,730	500–50,000
Potassium-40	1.3 billion	50,000–4.6 billion
Rubidium-87	48.8 billion	10 million–4.6 billion
Thorium-232	14 billion	10 million–4.6 billion
Uranium-235	713 million	10 million–4.6 billion
Uranium-238	4.5 billion	10 million–4.6 billion

FIGURE 12
The half-lives of different radioactive elements vary greatly.

Determining Absolute Ages

Geologists use radioactive dating to determine the absolute ages of rocks. In radioactive dating, scientists first determine the amount of a radioactive element in a rock. Then they compare that amount with the amount of the stable element into which the radioactive element decays. Figure 12 lists several common radioactive elements and their half-lives.

Potassium–Argon Dating Scientists often date rocks using potassium-40. This form of potassium decays to stable argon-40 and has a half-life of 1.3 billion years. Potassium-40 is useful in dating the most ancient rocks because of its long half-life.

Carbon-14 Dating A radioactive form of carbon is carbon-14. All plants and animals contain carbon, including some carbon-14. As plants and animals grow, carbon atoms are added to their tissues. After an organism dies, no more carbon is added. But the carbon-14 in the organism's body decays. It changes to stable nitrogen-14. To determine the age of a sample, scientists measure the amount of carbon-14 that is left in the organism's remains. From this amount, they can determine its absolute age. Carbon-14 has been used to date fossils such as frozen mammoths, as well as pieces of wood and bone. Carbon-14 even has been used to date the skeletons of prehistoric humans.

Carbon-14 is very useful in dating materials from plants and animals that lived up to about 50,000 years ago. Carbon-14 has a half-life of only 5,730 years. For this reason, it can't be used to date very ancient fossils or rocks. The amount of carbon-14 left would be too small to measure accurately.

Math Skills

Percentage What percentage of a radioactive element will be left after 3 half-lives? First, multiply $\frac{1}{2}$ three times to determine what fraction of the element will remain.

$$\frac{1}{2} \times \frac{1}{2} \times \frac{1}{2} = \frac{1}{8}$$

You can convert this fraction to a percentage by setting up a proportion:

$$\frac{1}{8} = \frac{d\%}{100\%}$$

To find the value of d, begin by cross multiplying, as for any proportion:

$$1 \times 100 = 8 \times d$$
$$d = \frac{100}{8}$$
$$d = 12.5\%$$

Practice Problems What percentage of a radioactive element will remain after 5 half-lives?

Differentiated Instruction

Less Proficient Readers L1
Writing Questions Have students rewrite the section heads and subheads as questions such as: **What is radioactive decay? How does the rate of radioactive decay allow scientists to date an element? What is a half-life? How do geologists use** radioactive decay to determine the absolute ages of rocks? and **What is potassium-argon dating?** Suggest that students write the answers to each question and use their questions and answers as a study guide. **learning modality: verbal**

Determining Absolute Ages

Teach Key Concepts L1
Absolute Ages of Rocks

Focus Remind students that the absolute age of a rock is the number of years since it formed.

Teach Explain that different radioactive elements are used in the absolute dating of rocks and fossils. Ask: **What must scientists do first to date a rock radioactively?** *(Determine the amount of a radioactive element in a rock)* **Second?** *(Compare that amount with the amount of the stable element into which the radioactive element decays)* Refer students to Figure 12. Ask: **Would you use carbon-14 to date a rock that you suspect is several million years old?** *(No. Carbon-14 has a relatively short half-life of 5,730 years. After several million years, the amount left would be undetectable.)*

Apply Tell students that scientists estimated that the moon is about 4.5 billion years old using the rocks brought back by the Apollo astronauts. Ask: **Which elements could be used to date the moon rocks?** *(Any except carbon-14)* **learning modality: logical/mathematical**

All in One Teaching Resources
• Transparency G41

Math Skill Percentage

Focus Remind students that fractions, percents, and decimals are all different ways of expressing the same part-to-whole relationships.

Teach Tell students to think of 1/2 × 1/2 as "one-half of one-half." Use the graph in Figure 11 to show how the amount gets smaller as they multiply.

Answer
3.125%

Monitor Progress L2

Oral Presentation Call on students to make sentences with *radioactive decay, half-life, radioactive dating, potassium-argon dating,* and *carbon-14 dating.*

Answers
Figure 11 12.5% or 1/8

Reading Checkpoint The time it takes for half of the radioactive atoms in an element to decay

G ● 125

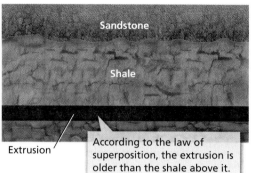
Sandstone

Shale

Extrusion

According to the law of superposition, the extrusion is older than the shale above it.

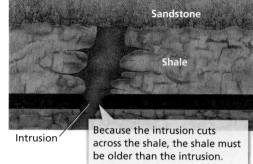
Sandstone

Shale

Intrusion

Because the intrusion cuts across the shale, the shale must be older than the intrusion.

FIGURE 13
Inferring the Age of Rocks
A layer of shale forms above an extrusion (left). Later (right), an intrusion crosses the shale. *Inferring What can you infer about the age of the shale?*

Go Online
PHSchool.com

For: More on radioactive dating
Visit: www.SciLinks.org
Web Code: cfd-2043

Students can review radioactive dating in an online activity.

Monitor Progress _____ L2

Answers
Figure 13 The shale is younger than the extrusion but older than the intrusion.

 Potassium-argon dating and carbon-14 dating

Assess

Reviewing Key Concepts

1. a. Possible answer: The process in which an element changes to another element because the atoms break down **b.** The amount of the radioactive element decreases. The amount of the new element increases. **c.** The rate of decay is constant—it never changes.
2. a. Radioactive dating **b.** The particles in sedimentary rocks are made up of different substances of different ages. **c.** The scientist could use radioactive dating to find the ages of the two igneous extrusions. The age of the sedimentary rock would be somewhere in between the two ages.

3.  0.78125%

Reteach L1

Use Figures 11 and 12 to summarize how radioactive elements are used to determine the half-life of an element.

Performance Assessment L2
Writing Have students explain which of the following types of fossils can be dated using carbon-14 and why: molds, casts, trace fossils, frozen remains, remains preserved in tar. *(Frozen remains and remains preserved in tar because they still contain organic material)*

All in One Teaching Resources
• Section Summary: *Radioactive Dating*
• Review and Reinforce: *Radioactive Dating*
• Enrich: *Radioactive Dating*

Radioactive Dating of Rock Layers Radioactive dating works well for igneous rocks, but not for sedimentary rocks. The rock particles in sedimentary rocks are from other rocks, all of different ages. Radioactive dating would provide the age of the particles. It would not provide the age of the sedimentary rock.

How, then, do scientists date sedimentary rock layers? They date the igneous intrusions and extrusions near the sedimentary rock layers. Look at Figure 13. As you can see, sedimentary rock (sandstone) above an igneous intrusion must be younger than that intrusion.

Reading Checkpoint What are two types of radioactive dating?

Section 3 Assessment

Target Reading Skill Identifying Main Ideas Use your graphic organizer to help you answer Question 2 below.

Reviewing Key Concepts
1. a. Defining In your own words, define the term *radioactive decay*.
 b. Describing How does the composition of a rock containing a radioactive element change over time?
 c. Applying Concepts How is a radioactive element's rate of decay like the ticking of a clock? Explain.
2. a. Identifying What method do geologists use to determine the absolute age of a rock?
 b. Explaining Why is it difficult to determine the absolute age of a sedimentary rock?

c. Problem Solving A geologist finds a fossil in a layer of sedimentary rock that lies in between two igneous extrusions. How could the geologist determine the age of the fossil?

 Practice

3. Percentage What percentage of a radioactive element will remain after 7 half-lives?

4 The Geologic Time Scale

Reading Preview

Key Concepts
- Why is the geologic time scale used to show Earth's history?
- What are the different units of the geologic time scale?

Key Terms
- geologic time scale
- era
- period

Target Reading Skill
Sequencing As you read, make a flowchart like the one below that shows the eras and periods of geologic time. Write the name of each era and period in the flowchart in the order in which it occurs.

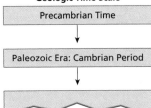

Geologic Time Scale

Precambrian Time

↓

Paleozoic Era: Cambrian Period

↓

Lab zone — Discover **Activity**

This Is Your Life!

1. Make a list of about 10 to 15 important events that you remember in your life.
2. On a sheet of paper, draw a timeline to represent your life. Use a scale of 3.0 cm to 1 year.
3. Write each event in the correct year along the timeline.
4. Now divide the timeline into parts that describe major periods in your life, such as preschool years, elementary school years, and middle school years.

Think It Over
Making Models Along which part of your timeline are most of the events located? Which period of your life does this part of the timeline represent? Why do you think this is so?

Imagine squeezing Earth's 4.6-billion-year history into a 24-hour day. Earth forms at midnight. About seven hours later, the earliest one-celled organisms appear. Over the next 14 hours, simple, soft-bodied organisms such as jellyfish and worms develop. A little after 9:00 P.M.—21 hours later—larger, more complex organisms evolve in the oceans. Reptiles and insects first appear about an hour after that. Dinosaurs arrive just before 11:00 P.M., but are extinct by 11:30 P.M. Modern humans don't appear until less than a second before midnight!

The Geologic Time Scale

Months, years, or even centuries aren't very helpful for thinking about Earth's long history. **Because the time span of Earth's past is so great, geologists use the geologic time scale to show Earth's history.** The **geologic time scale** is a record of the life forms and geologic events in Earth's history. You can see this time scale in Figure 14.

Scientists first developed the geologic time scale by studying rock layers and index fossils worldwide. With this information, scientists placed Earth's rocks in order by relative age. Later, radioactive dating helped determine the absolute age of the divisions in the geologic time scale.

Chapter 4 G ◆ 127

Objectives
After this lesson, students will be able to
G.4.4.1 Explain why the geologic time scale is used to show Earth's history.
G.4.4.2 Describe the different units of the geologic time scale.

Target Reading Skill 🎯

Sequencing Explain that organizing information from beginning to end helps students understand a step-by-step process.

Answers
The flowchart will be filled in as follows:
Geologic Time Scale
Precambrian Time
Paleozoic Era: Cambrian Period
Paleozoic Era: Ordovician Period
Paleozoic Era: Silurian
Paleozoic Era: Devonian
Paleozoic Era: Carboniferous
Paleozoic Era: Permian
Mesozoic Era: Triassic
Mesozoic Era: Jurassic
Mesozoic Era: Cretaceous
Cenozoic Era: Tertiary
Cenozoic Era: Quaternary

All in One Teaching Resources
- Transparency G42

Preteach

Build Background Knowledge L1
The History of Earth
Ask: **How long ago did the dinosaurs live?** *(A typical answer may mention millions of years.)* **How long before that did Earth form?** *(Again, students will likely mention millions of years.)* Explain that dinosaurs lived much longer ago than most people think and that Earth formed so long ago that it is almost unimaginable. In this section, students will learn how scientists organize the history of Earth.

Lab zone — Discover **Activity**

Skills Focus Making models

Materials metric ruler, paper

Time 15 minutes

Tips Students need not list very personal events. Suggest that they list birth date, graduations, important birthdays, and so on.

L1 **Expected Outcome** Students will place ten or more events along the timeline.

Think It Over If students follow the suggested divisions, the most important events of their lives will probably fall within the middle school years because students can more easily remember recent events than events earlier in life.

The Geologic Time Scale

Teach Key Concepts   L1

Dating Events in Earth's History

Focus Refer students to Figure 14.

Teach Ask: **Why is a time scale used to represent Earth's history instead of a calendar?** (*A calendar would be hard to use because Earth's history is so long.*) **When did geologic time begin?** (*About 4.6 billion years ago*) **When does geologic time end?** (*It doesn't—we are now in the Quaternary Period of the Cenozoic Era.*)

Apply Ask: **If this chart were drawn to scale, which era would take up the most space?** (*Precambrian Time*) **learning modality: logical/mathematical**

Divisions of Geologic Time

Teach Key Concepts   L1

Eras and Periods

Focus Remind students that major changes in the fossil record mark the beginning and end of each time unit.

Teach Ask: **How long is a geologic period?** (*A period doesn't have an exact length; they vary from the 30 million years of the Silurian to the 78 million years of the Cretaceous.*) **Which is the largest division of geologic time?** (*Era*)

Apply Have small groups place the 4.6 billion years of Earth history on a football field. Precambrian Time should take up about 88 yards, the Paleozoic Era should be from about the 12-yard line to the 5-yard line, and so on. **learning modality: logical/ mathematical**

All in One Teaching Resources

• Transparency G43

Independent Practice   L2

All in One Teaching Resources

• Guided Reading and Study Worksheet: *The Geologic Time Scale*

🔘 **Student Edition on Audio CD**

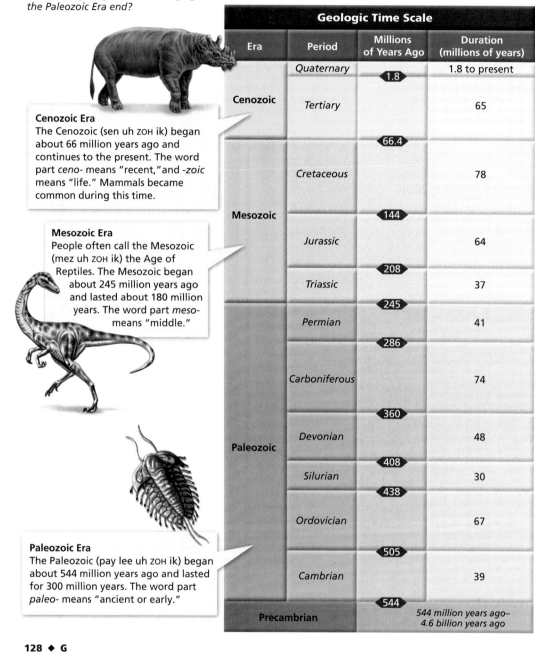

FIGURE 14

The Geologic Time Scale

The eras and periods of the geologic time scale are used to date the events in Earth's long history. *Interpreting Diagrams* How long ago did the Paleozoic Era end?

Cenozoic Era
The Cenozoic (sen uh ZOH ik) began about 66 million years ago and continues to the present. The word part *ceno-* means "recent," and *-zoic* means "life." Mammals became common during this time.

Mesozoic Era
People often call the Mesozoic (mez uh ZOH ik) the Age of Reptiles. The Mesozoic began about 245 million years ago and lasted about 180 million years. The word part *meso-* means "middle."

Paleozoic Era
The Paleozoic (pay lee uh ZOH ik) began about 544 million years ago and lasted for 300 million years. The word part *paleo-* means "ancient or early."

Era	Period	Millions of Years Ago	Duration (millions of years)
Cenozoic	Quaternary	1.8	1.8 to present
Cenozoic	Tertiary		65
		66.4	
Mesozoic	Cretaceous		78
		144	
Mesozoic	Jurassic		64
		208	
Mesozoic	Triassic		37
		245	
Paleozoic	Permian		41
		286	
Paleozoic	Carboniferous		74
		360	
Paleozoic	Devonian		48
		408	
Paleozoic	Silurian		30
		438	
Paleozoic	Ordovician		67
		505	
Paleozoic	Cambrian		39
		544	
Precambrian			544 million years ago–4.6 billion years ago

128 ◆ G

Differentiated Instruction

Less Proficient Readers   L1
Understanding Tables Make sure that students understand the table by asking questions such as **What is the name of the earliest era in geologic time? What are the Periods of the Paleozoic Era, from oldest to most recent? How long did the Jurassic Period last?** You may wish to redraw the table horizontally for students who have difficulty interpreting a vertical timeline. **learning modality: visual**

Gifted and Talented   L3
Creating a Timeline Invite students to research Earth's ice ages and create a timeline, noting the length of each ice age and some of the animal life that characterized each. **learning modality: logical/mathematical**

Divisions of Geologic Time

As geologists studied the fossil record, they found major changes in life forms at certain times. They used these changes to mark where one unit of geologic time ends and the next begins. Therefore the divisions of the geologic time scale depend on events in the history of life on Earth.

When speaking of the past, what names do you use for different spans of time? You probably use names such as century, decade, year, month, week, and day. Scientists use similar divisions for the geologic time scale.

Geologic time begins with a long span of time called Precambrian Time (pree KAM bree un). Precambrian Time, which covers about 88 percent of Earth's history, ended 544 million years ago. **After Precambrian Time, the basic units of the geologic time scale are eras and periods.** Geologists divide the time between Precambrian Time and the present into three long units of time called **eras.** They are the Paleozoic Era, the Mesozoic Era, and the Cenozoic Era.

Eras are subdivided into units of geologic time called **periods.** You can see in Figure 14 that the Mesozoic Era includes three periods: the Triassic Period, the Jurassic Period, and the Cretaceous Period.

The names of many of the geologic periods come from places around the world where geologists first described the rocks and fossils of that period. For example, the name Cambrian refers to Cambria, the old Roman name for Wales.

 Reading Checkpoint To what era does the Jurassic Period belong?

FIGURE 15
Fossil of the Quaternary Period
This saber-toothed cat lived during the Quaternary Period.

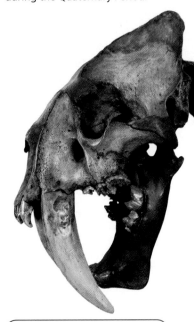

For: More on the geologic time scale
Visit: PHSchool.com
Web Code: cfd-2044

For: More on the geologic time scale
Visit: PHSchool.com
Web Code: cfd-2044

Students can review the geologic time scale in an online activity.

Assess

Reviewing Key Concepts
1. a. A record of the life forms and geological events in Earth's history
b. Scientists studied rock layers and fossils worldwide and placed Earth's rock layers in order by relative age. Later, radioactive dating helped them determine the absolute ages of the divisions.
2. a. Eras and periods **b.** Precambrian Time; 4.6 billion years ago; 544 million years ago **c.** Triassic, Jurassic, Cretaceous, Tertiary, Quaternary

Reteach L1
Use Figure 14 to review the purpose of the geologic time scale and how it is divided.

Performance Assessment L2
Skills Check Have students make a circle graph showing the percentage of Earth's history that each era represents. Have students use a different color for each era.

Section 4 Assessment

⊙ **Target Reading Skill** Sequencing Refer to your flowchart about the geologic time scale as you answer Question 2.

Reviewing Key Concepts
1. a. Defining What is the geologic time scale?
   b. Explaining What information did geologists use in developing the geologic time scale?
2. a. Listing What are the basic units into which the geologic time scale is divided?
   b. Interpreting Diagrams Study Figure 14. Which major division of geologic time was the longest? When did it begin? When did it end?

c. Sequencing Place the following in the correct order from earliest to latest: Tertiary, Jurassic, Quaternary, Triassic, Cretaceous.

Writing in Science

An Address in Time Pick one of the periods in the geologic time scale. Write a paragraph that describes, as completely as you can, that period's place in geologic time relative to the other periods and eras.

Chapter 4 G ◆ 129

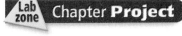 **Chapter Project**

Keep Students on Track Discuss with each student plans for illustrating the brochure and the timeline. Provide materials whenever possible, or direct students to where they can acquire art materials. Review each student's basic design for the brochure, making suggestions about content and presentation. Art can be drawn by hand or on a computer or can be constructed as a model.

Writing in Science

Writing Skill Description
Scoring Rubric
4 Exceeds criteria, includes its length, the era to which it belongs, the names of the periods before and after it, and its position relative to the present
3 Meets criteria except position relative to the present
2 Includes two of the three criteria
1 Includes only one criterion or inaccurate information

Objectives
After this lesson, students will be able to
G.4.5.1 State when Earth was formed.
G.4.5.2 Explain how Earth's physical features developed during Precambrian Time.
G.4.5.3 Describe what early Precambrian organisms were like.

Target Reading Skill ⟳
Comparing and Contrasting Explain that comparing and contrasting information shows how ideas, facts, and events are similar and different. The results of comparison can have importance.

Answers
Possible answers:
Early Earth:
Atmosphere—Hydrogen and helium
Oceans—Earth's surface is too hot. All water evaporates into water vapor.
Continents—Less dense rock at surface forms continents.
Later Precambrian Earth:
Atmosphere—Carbon dioxide, nitrogen, and water vapor
Oceans—Earth cools, water vapor condenses, and rain falls. Rain forms oceans.
Continents—Old continents break apart and new continents form as a result of continental drift.

All in One Teaching Resources
• Transparency G44

Preteach

Build Background Knowledge   L1

Characteristics of Earth
Show students a photo of Earth taken from outer space by astronauts. Ask: **What are some of the features that you see on Earth?** *(A typical answer will include cloud formations, oceans, landmasses, or continents.)* **Do you think that Earth had any of these features when it first formed? What were they?** *(Accept all reasonable responses. Record them on the board to refer to as students read through the section.)*

Reading Preview

Key Concepts
• When did Earth form?
• How did Earth's physical features develop during Precambrian Time?
• What were early Precambrian organisms like?

Key Terms
• comet • continental drift

⟳ Target Reading Skill
Comparing and Contrasting As you read, compare and contrast early Earth with Earth later in Precambrian Time by completing a table like the one below.

Precambrian Earth

Feature	Early Earth	Later Precambrian Earth
Atmosphere		
Oceans		
Continents		

Lab zone Discover **Activity**

How Could Planet Earth Form in Space?

1. Place a sheet of paper on top of a small magnet. The paper represents outer space and the magnet models gravity.
2. Sprinkle a half teaspoon of iron filings along one end of the paper to model the materials that formed Earth.
3. Gently blow through a straw for about 10 seconds from the end of the paper with the iron filings toward the magnet. **CAUTION:** *Be sure the straw is pointed away from other students.*
4. Observe what happens to the iron filings.

Think It Over
Making Models If you repeated Steps 2 and 3, what would happen to the size of your "planet"? How is this model like the early Earth? How is it different?

Your science class is going on a field trip, but this trip is a little out of the ordinary. You're going to travel back billions of years to the earliest days on Earth. Then you will move forward through time to the present. Enter the time machine and strap yourself in. Take a deep breath—you're off!

A dial on the dashboard shows the number of years before the present. You stare at the dial—it reads 4.6 billion years. You peer out the window as the time machine flies above the planet. Earth looks a little strange. Where are the oceans? Where are the continents? How will Earth change over the next billions of years? You'll answer these and other questions about Earth's history as you take this extraordinary trip.

The Planet Forms

Your journey starts at the beginning of Precambrian Time with the formation of planet Earth. **Scientists hypothesize that Earth formed at the same time as the other planets and the sun, roughly 4.6 billion years ago.**

The Age of Earth How do scientists know the age of Earth? Using radioactive dating, scientists have determined that the oldest rocks ever found on Earth are about 4 billion years old. But scientists think Earth formed even earlier than that.

Lab zone Discover **Activity**

Skills Focus Making models
Materials circular magnet, iron filings, paper, straw
Time 10 minutes
Tips Caution students to blow gently through the straw so as not to spread iron filings all over. Be sure students do not blow the iron filings in the direction of other students.

L1 **Expected Outcome** The iron filings will gather around the poles of the magnet.
Think It Over The iron filings would continue to gather in clumps around the magnet. The model shows how early materials in space were gathered in a ball by the force of gravity to form Earth. In the magnet model, the force is the attraction of iron to the poles of the magnet.

According to this hypothesis, Earth and the moon are about the same age. When Earth was very young, it collided with a large object. The collision threw a large amount of material from both bodies into orbit around Earth. This material combined to form the moon. Scientists have dated moon rocks that were brought to Earth by astronauts during the 1970s. Radioactive dating shows that the oldest moon rocks are about 4.6 billion years old. Scientists infer that Earth is also roughly 4.6 billion years old—only a little older than those moon rocks.

Earth Takes Shape Scientists think that Earth began as a ball of dust, rock, and ice in space. Gravity pulled this mass together. As Earth grew larger, its gravity increased, pulling in dust, rock, and ice nearby. As objects made of these materials struck Earth at high speed, their kinetic energy was changed into thermal energy.

The energy from these collisions caused Earth's temperature to rise until the planet was very hot. Scientists think that Earth may have become so hot that it melted. Denser materials sank toward the center, forming Earth's dense, iron core. At the same time, Earth continuously lost heat to the cold of space. Less dense, molten material hardened to form Earth's outer layers—the solid crust and mantle.

As the growing Earth traveled around the sun, its gravity also captured gases such as hydrogen and helium. But this first atmosphere was lost when the sun released a strong burst of particles. These particles blew away Earth's first atmosphere.

 Reading Checkpoint What force caused the materials that formed Earth to come together?

FIGURE 16
Early Earth
This artist's illustration shows Earth shortly after the moon formed. Notice the rocky objects from space striking Earth, and the molten rock flowing over the surface.

For: Links on Precambrian Earth
Visit: www.SciLinks.org
Web Code: scn-0745

Chapter 4 G ◆ 131

Earth's Surface Forms

Teach Key Concepts L2
Development of Physical Features

Focus Ask volunteers to read the captions in Figure 17 that describe the atmosphere.

Teach Ask: **What factors contributed to Earth's second atmosphere?** *(Volcanic eruptions and comets)* **How did oceans form?** *(Water vapor condensed to form rain and began to accumulate.)* **How were the continents formed?** *(Earth's rock cooled and hardened to form large landmasses.)*

Apply Ask: **Could humans or other animals have survived on early Earth after oceans and continents formed?** *(No. They could not have breathed the atmosphere because it did not contain the oxygen they need.)*
learning modality: visual

Life Develops

Teach Key Concepts L2
Early Precambrian Organisms

Focus Remind students that oxygen is a product of photosynthesis.

Teach Ask: **What did the first life forms look like?** *(Single-celled; resembled present-day bacteria)* **How did they get energy?** *(They used energy from the sun to make their own food.)* **What was the effect of the release of oxygen in the atmosphere?** *(The amount of oxygen in the atmosphere slowly increased.)*

Apply Ask: **If photosynthetic organisms had not appeared during Precambrian Time, what do you think Earth would be like today?** *(Possible answers: The atmosphere would contain little or no oxygen; life that depends on oxygen as we know it would probably not exist.)* **learning modality: visual**

All in One **Teaching Resources**
• Transparency G45

FIGURE 17
Development of the Atmosphere
Earth soon lost its first atmosphere (left) of hydrogen and helium. Earth's second atmosphere (right) slowly developed the mixture of gases—nitrogen, oxygen, carbon dioxide, water vapor, and argon—of the atmosphere today. As oxygen levels increased, the ozone layer also developed. *Comparing and Contrasting Compare and contrast Earth's first and second atmospheres.*

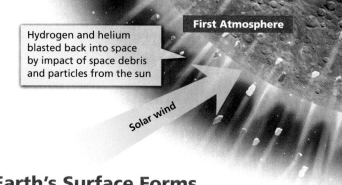

Hydrogen and helium blasted back into space by impact of space debris and particles from the sun

First Atmosphere

Solar wind

Lab zone Skills Activity

Calculating
Precambrian Time lasted about 4 billion years. What percentage is this of Earth's entire history of 4.6 billion years? If the first continents formed about 500 million years after Earth itself formed, what percentage of Precambrian Time had elapsed? (*Hint:* To review percentages, see the Math Review section in the Skills Handbook.)

Earth's Surface Forms

Watching early Earth from your time machine, you can see the planet change as the years speed by. **During the first several hundred million years of Precambrian Time, an atmosphere, oceans, and continents began to form.**

The Atmosphere After Earth lost its first atmosphere, a second atmosphere formed. This new atmosphere was made up mostly of carbon dioxide, water vapor, and nitrogen. Volcanic eruptions released carbon dioxide, water vapor, and other gases from Earth's interior. Collisions with comets added other gases to the atmosphere. A **comet** is a ball of dust and ice that orbits the sun. The ice in a comet consists of water and frozen gases, including carbon dioxide.

The Oceans At first, Earth's surface was too hot for water to remain as a liquid. All water evaporated into water vapor. However, as Earth's surface cooled, the water vapor began to condense to form rain. Gradually, rainwater began to accumulate to form an ocean. Rain also began to erode Earth's rocky surface. Over time, the oceans affected the composition of the atmosphere by absorbing much of the carbon dioxide.

The Continents During early Precambrian Time, more and more of Earth's rock cooled and hardened. Less than 500 million years after Earth's formation, the less dense rock at the surface formed large landmasses called continents.

Scientists have found that the continents move very slowly over Earth's surface because of forces inside Earth. This process is called **continental drift.** The movement is very slow—only a few centimeters per year. Over billions of years, Earth's landmasses have repeatedly formed, broken apart, and then crashed together again, forming new continents.

 Reading Checkpoint What is continental drift?

Lab zone Skills Activity

Skills Focus Calculating

Materials calculators

Time 10 minutes

Tips Tell students to write out the zeroes in the large numbers and then cancel them before entering the numbers in their calculators.

L2 **Expected Outcome** Precambrian Time lasted for 86% of Earth's history. About 11% of Precambrian Time elapsed before the development of the continents.

Extend Have students refer to the geologic time scale and calculate the percentage of Earth's history for which each era lasted. **learning modality: logical/mathematical**

Second Atmosphere

Carbon dioxide, water vapor, and nitrogen from volcanic eruptions and comet impacts

Oxygen from bacteria in the oceans

Ozone layer gradually forms as amount of oxygen increases

Ozone layer

Ultraviolet light

Life Develops

Scientists cannot pinpoint when or where life began on Earth. **But scientists have found fossils of single-celled organisms in rocks that formed about 3.5 billion years ago. These earliest life forms were probably similar to present-day bacteria.** Scientists hypothesize that all other forms of life on Earth arose from these simple organisms.

About 2.5 billion years ago, many organisms began using energy from the sun to make their own food. This process is called photosynthesis. One waste product of photosynthesis is oxygen. As organisms released oxygen into the air, the amount of oxygen in the atmosphere slowly increased. Processes in the atmosphere changed some of this oxygen into a form called ozone. The atmosphere developed a layer rich in ozone that blocked out the deadly ultraviolet rays of the sun. Shielded from the sun's ultraviolet rays, organisms could live on land.

Section 5 Assessment

Target Reading Skill Comparing and Contrasting Use the information in your table about early Earth to answer the questions below.

Reviewing Key Concepts

1. a. Reviewing How long ago did Earth form?
 b. Summarizing Summarize the process by which scientists determined the age of Earth.
2. a. Listing What physical features formed during Earth's first several hundred million years?
 b. Explaining How did volcanic eruptions and comets change early Earth?
 c. Relating Cause and Effect What caused water erosion to begin on Earth's surface?

3. a. Identifying What do scientists think were the first organisms to evolve on Earth?
 b. Predicting How would Earth's atmosphere be different if organisms capable of photosynthesis had not evolved? Explain.

Writing in Science

Web Site Plan a Web site for early Earth. To plan your Web site, make a list of the topics you will include. Make sketches of the screens that visitors to the Web site will see. Then write short descriptions for each topic.

Writing in Science

Writing Mode Description
Scoring Rubric
4 Exceeds criteria; plan includes information about early Earth's atmosphere, oceans, continents, and life forms; sketches and descriptions are accurate and informative
3 Meets criteria but sketches and descriptions are not imaginative
2 Includes only some criteria
1 Is inaccurate and incomplete

Comparing and Contrasting Atmospheric Gases

Materials paper, colored pencils
Time 15 minutes
Focus Review early Earth's atmosphere.
Teach Tell students that Earth's early atmosphere was about 92% carbon dioxide, 5% nitrogen, 0% oxygen, and 3% other gases. Today's atmosphere is about 78% nitrogen, 21% oxygen, and 1% other gases, including carbon dioxide. Have students make circle graphs of each atmosphere and discuss the differences.
Apply Ask: **Why did the percentage of oxygen change?** *(Early life forms gave off oxygen as a waste product.)* **learning modality: logical/mathematical**

Monitor Progress

Answers
Figure 17 The first atmosphere contained hydrogen and helium. The second atmosphere contained nitrogen, oxygen, carbon dioxide, water vapor, and argon.

Reading Checkpoint The process by which the continents move very slowly over Earth's surface because of forces inside Earth

Assess

Reviewing Key Concepts

1. a. About 4.6 billion years ago
b. Radioactive dating of rocks from Earth and the moon
2. a. Oceans, the atmosphere, and continents **b.** They released carbon dioxide and water vapor into the atmosphere.
c. Rain
3. a. Bacteria-like organisms **b.** It would have little or no oxygen.

Reteach

Summarize how oceans, the atmosphere, and continents were formed.

 Teaching Resources
• Section Summary: *Early Earth*
• Review and Reinforce: *Early Earth*
• Enrich: *Early Earth*

Objectives

After this lesson, students will be able to
G.4.6.1 Describe the major events in the Paleozoic Era.
G.4.6.2 Describe the major events in the Mesozoic Era.
G.4.6.3 Describe the major events in the Cenozoic Era.

Target Reading Skill ⟳

Previewing Visuals Explain that looking at the visuals before they read helps students activate prior knowledge and predict what they are about to read.

Answers

Possible questions and answers:
What geologic events happened during Precambrian Time? (*Earth, the oceans, and the first sedimentary rocks formed.*)
When did dinosaurs appear on Earth? (*About 225 million years ago*) **What caused the mass extinction at the end of the Cretaceous Period?** (*An object from space struck Earth and blocked the sunlight.*)

All in One Teaching Resources

• Transparency G46

Preteach

Build Background Knowledge
L1

Evolution of Life on Earth
Show students a picture of a woolly mammoth and a familiar dinosaur, both of which students will probably recognize. Then ask: **Did these organisms live at the same time?** (*Many students will say no.*) **Which lived first?** (*Most students will say that the dinosaur lived before the mammoth.*) Explain that the students have begun the task of organizing the evolution of life on Earth. This section will focus on the same task.

Reading Preview

Key Concepts
• What were the major events in the Paleozoic Era?
• What were the major events in the Mesozoic Era?
• What were the major events in the Cenozoic Era?

Key Terms
• invertebrate • vertebrate
• amphibian • reptile
• mass extinction • mammal

⟳ Target Reading Skill
Previewing Visuals Before you read, preview Figure 22. Then write three questions that you have about Earth's history in a graphic organizer like the one below. As you read, answer your questions.

Earth's History

Q.	What geologic events happened during Precambrian Time?
A.	
Q.	

FIGURE 18
Paleontologist at Work
This paleontologist in Australia is uncovering fossil animals from late Precambrian Time.

134 ◆ G

Lab zone Discover **Activity**

What Do Fossils Reveal About Earth's History?

1. Compare the two fossils in photos A and B. How did these organisms become fossils?
2. Work with one or two other students to study the organisms in the two photos. Think about how these organisms may have lived. Then make sketches showing what each of these organisms may have looked like.

Think It Over
Posing Questions If you were a paleontologist, what questions would you want to ask about these organisms?

As your time machine nears the end of Precambrian Time, you notice that Earth's organisms have begun to change. Along with organisms made up of single cells, living things resembling jellyfish now float in Earth's oceans. You also notice the fronds of feathery, plantlike organisms anchored to the seafloor. Scientists have found fossils of such organisms in Australia, Russia, China, and southern Africa. Fossils like the ones in Figure 18 are more than 600 million years old! But a much greater variety of living things evolved during the next phase of geologic time—the Paleozoic Era.

Lab zone Discover **Activity**

Skills Focus Posing questions

Materials sheet of unlined paper

Time 15 minutes

Tips Organize the class into small groups. Before talking to other group members, have each student write a description of how each fossil formed and make a sketch of each organism. Then have them work together to make a list of questions.

L1 **Expected Outcome** Each fossil is an impression or carbon film. Fossil A is a leaf. Fossil B is a eurypterid, which students will probably not be able to identify.

Think It Over Students' questions will vary. Typical questions: *When did each of these organisms live? In what type of environment did these organisms live? What organisms ate these organisms?*

FIGURE 19
The Cambrian Explosion
During the early Cambrian period, Earth's oceans were home to many strange organisms unlike any animals that are alive today.

The Paleozoic Era

Your time machine slows. You observe the "explosion" of life that began the Paleozoic Era.

The Cambrian Explosion During the Cambrian Period life took a big leap forward. **At the beginning of the Paleozoic Era, a great number of different kinds of organisms evolved.** Paleontologists call this event the Cambrian Explosion because so many new life forms appeared within a relatively short time. For the first time, many organisms had hard parts, including shells and outer skeletons.

At this time, all animals lived in the sea. Many were animals without backbones, or **invertebrates.** Invertebrates such as jellyfish, worms, and sponges drifted through the water, crawled along the sandy bottom, or attached themselves to the ocean floors.

Brachiopods and trilobites were common in the Cambrian seas. Brachiopods were small ocean animals with two shells. They resembled modern clams, but are only distantly related.

Vertebrates Arise During the Ordovician (awr duh VISH ee un) and Silurian (sih LOOR ee un) periods, the ancestors of the modern octopus and squid appeared. But these invertebrates soon shared the seas with a new type of organism. **During this time, jawless fishes evolved. Jawless fishes were the first vertebrates.** A **vertebrate** is an animal with a backbone. These fishes had suckerlike mouths, and they soon became common.

Differentiated Instruction

Less Proficient Readers **L1**
Understanding Major Events Provide several pages of paper with columns drawn in, similar to Figure 22 but with wider columns to provide more writing space. As students read through the chapter, they can identify the major events in each era and period and then write those events in their own words in the columns. You may wish to pair students with more proficient readers for this activity. Advise students to use different colors to indicate the different divisions. Encourage them to use the chart as a study guide. **learning modality: visual**

The Paleozoic Era

Teach Key Concepts **L2**
Events During the Paleozoic Era

Focus Remind students that the different geologic eras are based on the major events that occurred in each.

Teach Have students refer to the Geologic Time Scale. Point out that the Paleozoic Era lasted from about 544 million years ago to about 245 million years ago and consisted of six periods. Ask: **What major event marked the beginning of the Paleozoic era?** (*Many different kinds of organisms evolved.*) **What major events occurred after the end of the Cambrian Period?** (*The first vertebrates evolved, animals and plants began to live on land, reptiles evolved, and giant forests developed.*) Direct attention to Figure 19, and ask: **How was this organism and others of the early Cambrian Period different from most organisms of the Precambrian Time?** (*These organisms were more complex, and many had hard parts such as shells and outer skeletons.*)

Apply Ask: **Why do you think that scientists have found many more fossils from the Cambrian Period than from Precambrian Time?** (*Organisms from the Cambrian Period had hard body parts, such as shells and outer skeletons, and were more likely to form fossils than organisms with only soft body parts.*) **learning modality: verbal**

Independent Practice **L2**

All in One Teaching Resources

• Guided Reading and Study Worksheet: *Eras of Earth's History*

⊙ Student Edition on Audio CD

Monitor Progress ———— **L2**

Writing Have students write a brief description of the environment in which *Anomalocaris* lived.

Use Visuals: Figure 21
L2

The Coal Forest

Focus Ask students to describe the life forms they see in the picture.

Teach Ask: **How do you know by looking at the picture that this illustration does not depict life in the Cambrian or Ordovician Periods?** (*The figure shows plants on land. However, plants did not reach land until the Silurian Period.*) **Because this is a scene from the Carboniferous Period, about how long ago was this?** (*360 to 286 million years*)

Apply Ask: **To represent evolution in sequence, in what order would you place amphibians, fishes, and reptiles?** (*Fishes, amphibians, reptiles*) Emphasize that reptiles evolved from amphibians, which evolved from fishes. **learning modality: visual**

Comparing and Contrasting Amphibians and Reptiles

Materials frog, lizard, separate containers for each

Time 20 minutes

Focus Remind students that amphibians appeared on Earth before reptiles.

Teach Bring a frog and a reptile to class in separate containers. Have students write a description of each, noting similarities and differences. Ask: **How are these organisms alike and different?** (*A typical answer might suggest that their body shapes are similar. An amphibian has thinner, moist skin and webbed feet, and a reptile has thick skin and clawed feet.*)

Apply Ask: **Which is more adapted for water, and which is more adapted for land? Explain.** (*An amphibian is more adapted for water because of its webbed feet and moist skin. A reptile is more adapted for land because its rough, scaly covering helps keep in water and its claws help it hold on to land surfaces.*) **learning modality: visual**

FIGURE 20
Devonian Armored Fish
Paleontologists have found fossils of huge armored fish, like this *Dunkleosteus,* that lived during the Devonian Period.

FIGURE 21
The Coal Forest
Forests of the Carboniferous Period later formed coal deposits. **Predicting** *What types of fossils would you expect to find from the Carboniferous Period?*

Life Reaches Land Until the Silurian Period, only one-celled organisms lived on the land. But during the Silurian Period, plants became abundant. These first, simple plants grew low to the ground in damp areas. By the Devonian Period (dih VOH nee un), plants that could grow in drier areas had evolved. Among these plants were the earliest ferns. The first insects also appeared during the Silurian Period.

Both invertebrates and vertebrates lived in the Devonian seas. Even though the invertebrates were more numerous, the Devonian Period is often called the Age of Fishes. Every main group of fishes was present in the oceans at this time. Most fishes now had jaws, bony skeletons, and scales on their bodies. Some fishes, like the one in Figure 20, were huge. Sharks appeared in the late Devonian Period.

During the Devonian Period, animals began to invade the land. The first vertebrates to crawl onto land were lungfish with strong, muscular fins. The first amphibians evolved from these lung fish. An **amphibian** (am FIB ee un) is an animal that lives part of its life on land and part of its life in water.

The Carboniferous Period Throughout the rest of the Paleozoic, life expanded over Earth's continents. Other vertebrates evolved from the amphibians. For example, small reptiles developed during the Carboniferous Period. **Reptiles** have scaly skin and lay eggs with tough, leathery shells. Some types of reptiles became very large during the later Paleozoic.

136 ♦ G

Math — Analyzing Data

Mass Extinctions

The graph shows how the number of families of animals in Earth's oceans has changed.

1. **Reading Graphs** What variable is shown on the *x*-axis? On the *y*-axis of the graph?

2. **Interpreting Data** How long ago did the most recent mass extinction occur?

3. **Interpreting Data** Which mass extinction produced the greatest drop in the number of families of ocean animals?

4. **Relating Cause and Effect** In general, how did the number of families change between mass extinctions?

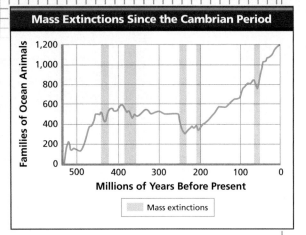

Mass Extinctions Since the Cambrian Period

Families of Ocean Animals (y-axis): 0, 200, 400, 600, 800, 1,000, 1,200

Millions of Years Before Present (x-axis): 500, 400, 300, 200, 100, 0

Mass extinctions

During the Carboniferous Period, winged insects evolved into many forms, including huge dragonflies and cockroaches. Giant ferns and cone-bearing plants and trees formed vast swampy forests called "coal forests." The remains of the coal forest plants formed thick deposits of sediment that changed into coal over millions of years.

Mass Extinction Ends the Paleozoic At the end of the Paleozoic Era, many kinds of organisms died out. This was a **mass extinction,** in which many types of living things became extinct at the same time. **The mass extinction at the end of the Paleozoic affected both plants and animals, on land and in the seas.** Scientists do not know what caused the mass extinction, but many kinds of organisms, such as trilobites, suddenly became extinct.

The Supercontinent Pangaea Scientists hypothesize that climate change resulting from continental drift may have caused the mass extinction at the end of the Paleozoic. **During the Permian Period, about 260 million years ago, Earth's continents moved together to form a great landmass, or supercontinent, called Pangaea** (pan JEE uh). The formation of Pangaea caused deserts to expand in the tropics. At the same time, sheets of ice covered land closer to the South Pole. Many organisms could not survive the new climate. After Pangaea formed, it broke apart again, as shown in Figure 22.

 Reading Checkpoint What was Pangaea?

Go **Online**
active art

For: Continental Drift activity
Visit: PHSchool.com
Web Code: cfp-1015

Chapter 4 G ◆ 137

Differentiated Instruction

Special Needs   L1
Drawing Pictures Show students examples or photos of ferns, horsetails, and club mosses. Point out that the vast swamp forests of the Carboniferous Period contained giant ancestors of these modern plants. Allow students to examine and feel the plants and then make drawings of what a swamp forest might have looked like.
learning modality: visual

Gifted and Talented   L3
Locating Coal Deposits Provide students with a map of the United States. Challenge them to use reference materials to locate the general area of coal deposits in North America that formed during the Carboniferous Period and to list what the coal deposits are used for today. **learning modality: visual**

Go Online
active art

For: Continental Drift activity
Visit: PHSchool.com
Web Code: cfp-1015

Students can interact with the art of continental drift online.

Math — Analyzing Data

Math Skill Making and interpreting graphs

Focus Remind students that line graphs are used to show how quantities change over a period of time.

Teach Make sure that students understand that the numbers on the *x*-axis are decreasing, not increasing, as they appear from left to right.

Answers
1. The *x*-axis shows time in millions of years before the present; the *y*-axis shows the number of families of ocean animals
2. Slightly more than 50 million years ago
3. The one that occurred about 230 million years ago
4. The number of families of ocean animals immediately dropped but then increased.

Help Students Read   L1
Visualizing Instruct students to close their eyes and form mental pictures as you slowly read aloud selected passages describing the life forms and environment that evolved during the Paleozoic Era. Then tell students to reread the passages again by themselves, recreating those images as they read. Explain that visualizing the text as they read will be useful throughout this section, which details life forms that evolved throughout Earth's history.

All in One Teaching Resources
• Transparency G47

Monitor Progress   L2

Oral Presentation Call on students to explain the major events of the Paleozoic Era.

Answers
Figure 21 Amphibians, reptiles, insects, ferns, and cone-bearing plants.

 Reading Checkpoint A supercontinent formed when Earth's continents moved together about 260 million years ago

G ● 137

Use Visuals: Figure 22
Geologic History

Focus Point out that Figure 22 represents the same timeline as the one in The Geologic Time Scale section.

Teach Invite volunteers to read the items in each column. Have students ask questions about the landmark events and life forms of that time. Write any questions that you might not be able to answer on the chalkboard, and assign a student volunteer to find the answer or explanation in reference books. Ask: **What major event happened near the end of Precambrian Time?** *(A mass extinction occurred.)* Point out that the supercontinent Pangaea formed in the Permian Period and that this had a great effect on global climate. Ask: **In general, how is the climate of a region near an ocean different from the climate of a region far inland?** *(A typical answer might suggest that temperatures are more extreme inland compared to the climate near an ocean, where ocean winds produce moderate temperatures.)* Point out that when the continents came together to form Pangaea, much coastal area was lost as smaller land masses moved into one another. At some point, there were no longer oceans between continents, and as a consequence the climate changed throughout the world.

Apply Ask: **How might a change of climate affect an animal that was well adapted to a previous climate?** *(The animal might not do as well in the new climate. For example, plants that it depended on for food might not grow in the new climate.)* **learning modality: visual**

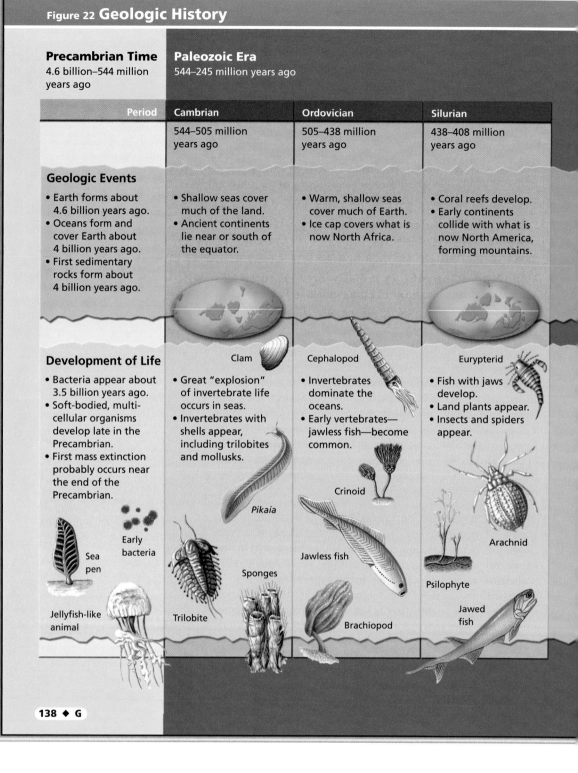

Figure 22 **Geologic History**

Precambrian Time
4.6 billion–544 million years ago

Paleozoic Era
544–245 million years ago

Period	Cambrian	Ordovician	Silurian
	544–505 million years ago	505–438 million years ago	438–408 million years ago

Geologic Events
- Earth forms about 4.6 billion years ago.
- Oceans form and cover Earth about 4 billion years ago.
- First sedimentary rocks form about 4 billion years ago.

- Shallow seas cover much of the land.
- Ancient continents lie near or south of the equator.

- Warm, shallow seas cover much of Earth.
- Ice cap covers what is now North Africa.

- Coral reefs develop.
- Early continents collide with what is now North America, forming mountains.

Development of Life
- Bacteria appear about 3.5 billion years ago.
- Soft-bodied, multi-cellular organisms develop late in the Precambrian.
- First mass extinction probably occurs near the end of the Precambrian.

Clam

- Great "explosion" of invertebrate life occurs in seas.
- Invertebrates with shells appear, including trilobites and mollusks.

Cephalopod

- Invertebrates dominate the oceans.
- Early vertebrates—jawless fish—become common.

Crinoid

Eurypterid

- Fish with jaws develop.
- Land plants appear.
- Insects and spiders appear.

Pikaia

Sea pen

Early bacteria

Jawless fish

Arachnid

Jellyfish-like animal

Trilobite

Sponges

Brachiopod

Psilophyte

Jawed fish

Paleozoic Era
544–245 million years ago

Devonian	Carboniferous 360–286 million years ago		Permian
408–360 million years ago	**Mississippian** 360–320 million years ago	**Pennsylvanian** 320–286 million years ago	286–245 million years ago

Geologic Events

Devonian:
- Seas rise and fall over what is now North America.

Carboniferous:
- Appalachian Mountains begin to form.
- North America and Northern Europe lie in warm, tropical region.

Permian:
- Deserts become larger in tropical regions.
- The supercontinent Pangaea forms as all continents join together.

Development of Life

Devonian:
- Age of Fishes begins as sharks and fish with scales and bony skeletons become common.
- Trilobites and corals flourish in the oceans.
- Lungfish develop.
- First amphibians reach land.

Carboniferous:
- Great swamp forests of huge, woody trees cover eastern North America and parts of Europe.
- First true reptiles appear.
- Winged insects appear.

Permian:
- Reptiles become dominant on land.
- Warm-blooded reptiles appear.
- Mass extinction of many marine invertebrates, including trilobites.

Dragonfly

Shark

Bony fish

Devonian forest

Cockroach

Amphibian

Coal forest

Conifer

Dimetrodon

Dicynodon

G ◆ 139

Graphing the Fossil Record

Materials graph paper, metric ruler

Time 20 minutes

Focus Challenge students to make a bar graph that shows when different groups of organisms first appear in the fossil record and, if appropriate, when they disappear.

Teach Students could begin the vertical axis at the start of the Paleozoic Era and then mark 50-million-year intervals to the present. A bar for each group of organisms would be displayed along the horizontal axis. One difference between this graph and most bar graphs is that many bars will begin above the horizontal axis. For example, the bar for dinosaurs will begin at about 245 million years and end at 65 million years.

Apply Ask students questions that pertain to the timelines on their graphs, such as **Which vertebrate group has existed for the longest period of time?** (Bony fishes) **Which group appeared more recently, birds or mammals?** (Birds) **learning modality: logical/mathematical**

Help Students Read L1
Relating Text to Visuals As students study the life forms in Figure 22, encourage them to go back and read the text describing life forms in each of the periods shown for the Paleozoic Era. Ask students whether the life forms they visualized as they read the text are similar to the visuals they see in the timeline of geologic history.

Differentiated Instruction

English Learners/Beginning L1
Vocabulary: Link to Visual Pair students with students who are proficient in English. Have them locate sentences with key terms that appear in Figure 22 and then tell in their own words what the sentences mean. **learning modality: verbal**

English Learners/Intermediate L2
Vocabulary: Science Glossary After students have defined the key terms in their science glossaries, ask them to identify the sentences in Figure 22 in which key terms appear. Have them use the sentences to write a paragraph in their own words describing the evolution of one group of organisms that is a key term, for example, *mammal* or *reptile*. **learning modality: verbal**

Monitor Progress L2

Skills Check Have students make a table that includes each instance noted on these two pages when a new group of organisms appears and then match each group with the correct geologic period.

Communicating Information on Prehistoric Life Forms

Materials reference books, poster board, art materials, printouts and pictures from the Internet (optional)

Time 1 class period for research (could be assigned as homework); 1 class period for presentations

Focus Remind students that during each of the three geologic eras, major life forms evolved and disappeared. Tell students that they will research a major life form during one era.

Teach Ask students to work in pairs or small groups to choose one group of animals or plants, research its evolution, and prepare a poster showing the changes. Choices might be related to the period that the students are focusing on in the Chapter Project. Guide students in choosing a variety of organisms so that most students are not researching dinosaurs. Students might choose to focus on a large group, such as fishes or insects, or the evolution of a specific organism, such as trilobites or horses. Encourage students to make a "tree" that shows evolution through time. Allow students class time to present their posters as you go through each of the geologic periods in Earth's history.

Apply As students make their presentations, ask them to explain how the evolution of their organism or group was made possible by other developments. (*Example: Animals were able to move from the oceans to land because plant life developed on land.*)
learning modality: visual

Figure 22 Geologic History

Mesozoic Era
245–66 million years ago

Triassic	Jurassic
245–208 million years ago	208–144 million years ago

Geologic Events

- Pangaea holds together for much of the Triassic.
- Hot, dry conditions dominate the center of Pangaea.

- Pangaea breaks apart as North America separates from Africa and South America.

Development of Life

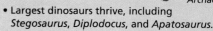

- Age of Reptiles begins.
- First dinosaurs appear.
- First mammals, which evolve from warm-blooded reptiles, appear.
- First turtles and crocodiles appear.
- Conifers, palmlike trees, and ginkgo trees dominate forests.

Morganucodon

- Largest dinosaurs thrive, including *Stegosaurus*, *Diplodocus*, and *Apatosaurus*.
- First birds appear.
- First flying reptiles, pterosaurs, appear.

Archaeopteryx

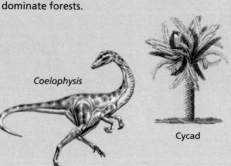

Coelophysis

Cycad

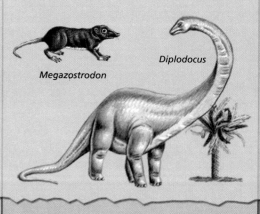

Megazostrodon

Diplodocus

| Mesozoic Era | Cenozoic Era | |
| 245–66 million years ago | 66 million years ago to present | |

Cretaceous	Tertiary	Quaternary
144–66 million years ago	66–1.8 million years ago	1.8 million years ago to the present

Geologic Events

Cretaceous:
- Continents move toward their present-day positions, as South America splits from Africa.
- Widespread volcanic activity occurs.

Tertiary:
- The Rocky Mountains and Himalayas form.
- Continents continue to move into present-day positions.
- Continental glacier covers Antarctica.

Quaternary:
- Thick glaciers advance and retreat over much of North America and Europe, parts of South America and Asia, and all of Antarctica.

Development of Life

Magnolia

Cretaceous:
- First flowering plants appear.
- Dinosaurs, including *Tyrannosaurus rex*, dominate.
- First snakes appear.
- Mass extinction at end of period causes disappearance of many land and marine life forms, including dinosaurs.

Tertiary:
- Flowering plants thrive.
- First grasses appear.
- Age of Mammals begins.
- Modern groups such as horses, elephants, bears, rodents, and primates appear.
- Ancestors of humans evolve.

Quaternary:
- Mammals, flowering plants, and insects dominate land.
- Modern humans evolve in Africa about 100,000 years ago.
- Giant mammals of North America and Eurasia become extinct when the Ice Age ends about 10,000 years ago.

Tyrannosaurus rex

Creodonts

Uintatherium

Plesiadapis

Hyracotherium

Megatherium

Homo sapiens

▲ **Address Misconceptions** L1
Geologic Time Spans

Focus Students may have a difficult time grasping the enormous spans of time represented by each geologic period. As a consequence, they might think that all the organisms listed and shown in each period lived at the same time.

Teach Tell students that the organisms shown in Figure 22 did not necessarily appear and live for the same number of years within a particular period. Provide the following familiar analogy: **Modern time periods are often viewed in terms of a century, such as the twentieth century. However, the people in the twentieth century did not all live at the same time.** Ask students to recall two presidents, one who lived early in the century and one who lived later in the century, but not at the same time. *(Possible answer: Theodore Roosevelt and Jimmy Carter)*

Apply Refer students to Figure 22. Tell them that *Megazostrodon* first appeared at the beginning of the Jurassic Period. *Archaeopteryx* and *Diplodocus* did not appear until about 50 million years later (150 million years ago and 155 to 145 million years ago, respectively). In the Cretaceous Period, flowering plants first appeared 125 million years ago, but *Tyrannosaurus rex* did not appear until 85 million years ago and then died out about 65 million years ago. However, the flowering plants continued to thrive. **learning modality: logical/mathematical**

Monitor Progress L2

Skills Check Have students make a table that includes each instance noted on these two pages when a new group of organisms appears and then match each group with the correct geologic period.

The Mesozoic Era

Teach Key Concepts L2
Events During the Mesozoic Era

Focus Tell students that the most familiar examples of life forms in the Mesozoic Era are the dinosaurs.

Teach Ask: **What major event marked the end of the Paleozoic Era?** (*A mass extinction occurred.*) **What major life forms evolved during the first part of the Mesozoic Era?** (*Reptiles became the dominant life form on Earth. Mammals also evolved.*) Ask: **Why is the Mesozoic Era called the Age of Reptiles?** (*Reptiles, including dinosaurs, were very successful.*) Stress that familiar dinosaurs did not necessarily live at the same time. For example, *Apatosaurus* lived during the Jurassic Period, and *Tyrannosaurus* lived during the Cretaceous Period. Ask: **What other life form that is dominant today first appeared during this era?** (*Mammals*) **What event ended the Mesozoic Era?** (*A mass extinction in which over half of all plant and animal groups were wiped out, including the dinosaurs*)

Apply Organize students into small groups, and have each group brainstorm a list of questions about dinosaurs. Questions might include: *How large was the largest dinosaur? Were all dinosaurs giants? Did dinosaurs live in herds, or were they solitary? What did dinosaurs eat? Did they care for their young?* When groups have finished, have them read their questions to the class. Write the most interesting questions on the board, and invite volunteers to find the answers and report back to the class. **learning modality: logical/mathematical**

FIGURE 23
Flying Reptile
Dimorphodon was a flying reptile that lived during the Jurassic Period. Like dinosaurs, flying reptiles became extinct at the end of the Cretaceous period.
Comparing and Contrasting *How is* Dimorphodon *similar to the bird in Figure 24?*

The Mesozoic Era

Millions of years flash by as your time machine travels. Watch out—there's a dinosaur! You're observing an era that you've read about in books and seen in movies.

The Triassic Period Some living things survived the Permian mass extinction. These organisms became the main forms of life early in the Triassic Period (try AS ik). Plants and animals that survived included fish, insects, reptiles, and cone-bearing plants called conifers. **Reptiles were so successful during the Mesozoic Era that this time is often called the Age of Reptiles.** About 225 million years ago, the first dinosaurs appeared. Mammals also first appeared during the Triassic Period. A **mammal** is a warm-blooded vertebrate that feeds its young milk. Mammals probably evolved from warm-blooded reptiles. The mammals of the Triassic Period were very small, about the size of a mouse or shrew. From these first small mammals, all mammals that live today evolved.

The Jurassic Period During the Jurassic Period (joo RAS ik), dinosaurs became the dominant animals on land. Scientists have identified several hundred different kinds of dinosaurs. Some were plant eaters, while others were meat eaters. Dinosaurs "ruled" Earth for about 150 million years, but different types lived at different times.

One of the first birds, called *Archaeopteryx*, appeared during the Jurassic Period. The name *Archaeopteryx* means "ancient wing thing." Many paleontologists now think that birds evolved from dinosaurs.

FIGURE 24
Early Bird
The artist of the illustration (left) has given *Archaeopteryx* colorful feathers. From a fossil (right), paleontologists can tell that *Archaeopteryx* was about 30 centimeters long, had feathers and teeth, and also had claws on its wings.

The Cretaceous Period Reptiles, including dinosaurs, were still the dominant vertebrates throughout the Cretaceous Period (krih TAY shus). Flying reptiles and birds competed for places in the sky. The hollow bones and feathers of birds made them better adapted to their environment than the flying reptiles, which became extinct during the Cretaceous Period. The Cretaceous Period also brought new forms of life. Flowering plants like the ones you see today evolved. Unlike the conifers, flowering plants produce seeds that are inside a fruit. The fruit helps the seeds survive.

Another Mass Extinction At the close of the Cretaceous Period, about 65 million years ago, another mass extinction occurred. Scientists hypothesize that this mass extinction occurred when an object from space struck Earth. This object was probably an asteroid. Asteroids are rocky masses that orbit the sun between Mars and Jupiter. Once in many millions of years, an asteroid may collide with Earth.

When the asteroid hit Earth, the impact threw huge amounts of dust and water vapor into the atmosphere. Many organisms on land and in the oceans died immediately. Dust and heavy clouds blocked sunlight around the world for years. Without sunlight, plants died, and plant-eating animals starved. This mass extinction wiped out over half of all plant and animal groups. No dinosaurs survived.

Not all scientists agree that an asteroid impact alone caused the mass extinction. Some scientists think that climate changes caused by increased volcanic activity were partly responsible.

 Reading Checkpoint What major groups of organisms developed during the Mesozoic Era?

FIGURE 25
The End of the Dinosaurs
Many scientists hypothesize that during the Cretaceous an asteroid hit Earth near the present-day Yucatán Peninsula, in southeastern Mexico.

G ◆ 143

Differentiated Instruction

Gifted and Talented L3
Comparing *Archaeopteryx* to Present-Day Birds Challenge students to find a library book or magazine article that compares a bird skeleton with a dinosaur skeleton. Have volunteers research why many paleontologists think birds evolved from dinosaurs and prepare a presentation for the class. **learning modality: logical/mathematical**

Special Needs L1
Reptiles of the Mesozoic Era Provide students with discarded science magazines or Internet sources, and have them prepare a poster showing the different types of reptiles that lived during this era. Encourage students to find examples of present-day organisms that resemble reptiles in this era. **learning modality: visual**

 **Build Inquiry** L3

Developing Hypotheses

Materials small potted evergreen plant, small flowering plant

Time 10 minutes

Focus Point out that flowering plants, which first appeared in the Cretaceous Period, include all the leafy trees and grasses that dominate Earth today.

Teach Have students compare and contrast characteristics of gymnosperms (seed plants with exposed seed, usually in a cone) and angiosperms (flowering plants with seeds in a fruit). Have students observe, make sketches, and write a description of each kind of plant.

Apply Ask students to hypothesize why flowering plants became the dominant plant after the end of the Mesozoic Era. *(Seeds in flowering plants are protected by fruits and are better able to survive than the seeds of cone-bearing plants.)* **learning modality: logical/mathematical**

Monitor Progress _____ L2

Writing Have students write a story about a small mammal group at the end of the Cretaceous Period and the beginning of the Tertiary Period. Advise students to focus on scientific aspects and not to portray the mammals as having human intelligence or emotions. Students can save their stories in their portfolios.

Portfolio

Answer
Figure 23 It has claws on its wings.
Reading Checkpoint Dinosaurs, mammals, birds, and flowering plants

The Cenozoic Era

Teach Key Concepts L2

Events of the Cenozoic Era

Focus Remind students that the Cenozoic Era is also called the Age of Mammals.

Teach Have students refer to the Geologic Time Scale. Point out that the Cenozoic Era consists of two periods. Ask: **What major event marked the end of the Mesozoic Era?** *(Mass extinction of many plant and animal groups)* **How did the mass extinction of dinosaurs allow mammals to become larger and more diverse?** *(It gave mammals an opportunity to fill the niches left by the dinosaurs.)* **How did the climate in the Tertiary Period affect the types of life that evolved?** *(The climate was warm and mild. Whales, dolphins, and many grass-eating mammals evolved.)* **What event happened later in the Quaternary Period that allowed ocean life to flourish?** *(Continental glaciers melted, causing sea levels to rise.)*

Apply Ask: **How might the ice ages have affected the kinds of animals that lived during this era?** *(Some animals may not have been able to survive because of the cold climate or lack of food and became extinct.)* **learning modality: verbal**

Lab zone Try This Activity

Life and Times

1. Place these events in their correct order: continental glaciers retreat; first fish appear; oldest fossils form; human ancestors appear; "explosion" of invertebrates occurs; dinosaurs become extinct; Pangaea forms.

2. Draw a timeline and graph these dates:

   3.5 billion years ago
   544 million years ago
   400 million years ago
   260 million years ago
   65 million years ago
   3.5 million years ago
   20,000 years ago

   Choose a scale so the oldest date fits on the paper.

Interpreting Data Match each event with the correct date on your timeline. How does the time since the dinosaurs became extinct compare with the time since the oldest fossil formed?

The Cenozoic Era

Your voyage through time continues on through the Cenozoic Era—often called the Age of Mammals. During the Mesozoic Era, mammals had a hard time competing with dinosaurs for food and places to live. **The extinction of dinosaurs created an opportunity for mammals. During the Cenozoic Era, mammals evolved to live in many different environments—on land, in water, and even in the air.**

The Tertiary Period During the Tertiary Period, Earth's climates were generally warm and mild. In the oceans, marine mammals such as whales and dolphins evolved. On land, flowering plants, insects, and mammals flourished. When grasses evolved, they provided a food source for grazing mammals. These were the ancestors of today's cattle, deer, sheep, and other grass-eating mammals. Some mammals became very large, as did some birds.

The Quaternary Period The mammals that had evolved during the Tertiary Period eventually faced a changing environment. **Earth's climate cooled, causing a series of ice ages during the Quaternary Period.** Thick continental glaciers advanced and retreated over parts of Europe and North America. Then, about 20,000 years ago, Earth's climate began to warm. Over thousands of years, the continental glaciers melted, except in Greenland and Antarctica.

FIGURE 26
Ice-Age Environment
Large mammals roamed the ice-free parts of North America and Eurasia during the Ice Ages of the Quaternary Period.

144 ◆ G

Lab zone Try This Activity

Skills Focus Interpreting data L2

Materials adding-machine paper, metric ruler

Time 15 minutes

Tips Suggest that students use a scale of 1 cm = 100 million years. The timeline will be 35 cm long.

Expected Outcome Order of events: oldest fossils form, 3.5 billion years ago; "explosion" of invertebrates occurs, 544 million years ago; first fish appear, 400 million years ago; Pangaea forms, 260 million years ago; dinosaurs become extinct, 65 million years ago; human ancestors appear, 3.5 million years ago; continental glaciers retreat, 20,000 years ago. The time since the dinosaurs' extinction is relatively recent.

Extend Have students place as many other events on their timelines as they can.
learning modality: logical/mathematical

In the oceans, algae, coral, mollusks, fish, and mammals thrived. Insects and birds shared the skies. On land, flowering plants and mammals such as bats, cats, dogs, cattle, and humans—just to name a few—became common.

The fossil record suggests that modern humans, or *Homo sapiens,* may have evolved as early as 100,000 years ago. By about 12,000 to 15,000 years ago, humans had migrated around the world to every continent except Antarctica.

Your time machine has now arrived back in the present. You and all organisms on Earth are living in the Quaternary Period of the Cenozoic Era. Is this the end of evolution and the changing of Earth's surface? No, these processes will continue as long as Earth exists. But you'll have to take your time machine into the future to see just what happens!

FIGURE 27
Ice Age Art
An early ancestor of modern humans painted these beautiful images of animals in a cave in France more than 15,000 years ago.

 Reading Checkpoint How did Earth's climate change during the Quaternary Period?

Section 6 Assessment

Target Reading Skill Previewing Visuals Compare your questions and answers about Figure 22 with those of a partner.

Reviewing Key Concepts

1. **a. Listing** What are the periods of the Paleozoic Era?
   b. Describing How did Earth's organisms change during the first period of the Paleozoic?
   c. Relating Cause and Effect What event do scientists think may have caused the mass extinction at the end of the Paleozoic?
2. **a. Reviewing** Which group of animals was dominant during the Mesozoic Era?
   b. Inferring How was their small size helpful to the mammals of the Mesozoic?
   c. Developing Hypotheses Many scientists think that the asteroid impact at the end of the Cretaceous prevented plant growth for many years. Although many dinosaurs were plant eaters, some were meat eaters. Develop a hypothesis to explain why no dinosaurs survived.

3. **a. Identifying** What term do scientists apply to the Cenozoic Era?
   b. Inferring What conditions allowed so many different kinds of mammals to evolve during the Cenozoic Era?

Writing in Science

Description Suppose that you are going on a tour of Earth during one era of geologic time. Write a paragraph describing the organisms and environments that you see on the tour. Your tour should include at least one stop in each geologic period of the era you chose.

Chapter 4 G ◆ 145

Lab zone Chapter Project

Keep Students on Track Review students' rough drafts, and make suggestions about what to include and what to delete. At this point, have volunteers make the basic timeline for the geologic time scale. Make sure that groups are creating the illustrations for their portion of the timeline. The timeline should cover at least one wall of the classroom.

Writing in Science

Writing Mode Description
Scoring Rubric
4 Exceeds criteria, includes a complete description of organisms and events for all periods of the era; description is accurate and detailed
3 Meets all criteria, but description is not detailed
2 Includes only one or two of the periods
1 Includes inaccurate information

Monitor Progress ⟶ L2

Answer

Reading Checkpoint The climate cooled, causing continental glaciers to advance and retreat over Earth's surface. Eventually, the climate warmed and glaciers melted.

Assess

Reviewing Key Concepts

1. **a.** Cambrian, Ordovician, Silurian, Devonian, Carboniferous, Permian **b.** There was an invertebrate "explosion" as many new life forms appeared. **c.** Climate change resulting from continental drift
2. **a.** Reptiles **b.** Possible answers: Mammals ate smaller organisms than themselves, such as insects, so they were not competing with dinosaurs for food. Mammals were small enough to hide from dinosaurs. **c.** Plant-eating dinosaurs were food for the meat-eating dinosaurs. When the plant-eaters died out, there was no source of food for the meat-eaters, so they also died out.
3. **a.** The Age of Mammals **b.** Dinosaurs had become extinct, so it made way for the evolution of mammals. Grasses evolved, which provided food sources for larger, grazing animals.

Reteach L1

Read each boldface statement in this section, leaving out the name of the era or period if present. Have the class tell the era or period that belongs with the statement.

Performance Assessment L2

Writing Ask students to write a paragraph summarizing the major events that marked the beginning and end of each era.

All in One Teaching Resources

- Section Summary: *Eras of Earth's History*
- Review and Reinforce: *Eras of Earth's History*
- Enrich: *Eras of Earth's History*

As Time Goes By L2

Prepare for Inquiry

Key Concept
Earth's history encompasses an immense amount of time.

Skills Objectives
Students will be able to
- Measure the size of a ream of paper
- Calculate how many reams would be necessary to represent various time spans in a model timeline
- Make a model of Earth's geologic time

 **Class Time** 30 minutes

All in One Teaching Resources
- Lab Worksheet: *As Time Goes By*

Advance Planning
One way to make a page that contains 2,000 asterisks is to have 40 lines of 50 asterisks each. An alternative would be to have 30 lines of 60 asterisks each plus an additional 4 lines of 50 asterisks each. Then print out one of these pages per student.

A 500-sheet ream of copy or multiple-use paper has a thickness of about 4.5 cm, although this thickness varies. The exact measurement is not significant, but all reams used in the activity should be the same.

A meter stick will be necessary to measure the height of the classroom's ceiling.

Alternative Materials
A textbook about the same size as a ream of paper can be used as an alternative.

Procedure
Table A: Answers may vary.
Table B: 5 sheets, 0.01 cm; 50 reams, 225 cm; 225 reams, 10.125 m; 520 reams, 23.4 m; 1,000 reams, 45 m; 3,500 reams, 157.5 m; 4,000 reams, 180 m; 4,600 reams, 207 m

As Time Goes By

Problem
How can you make a model of geologic time?

Skills
measuring, calculating, making models

Materials
- worksheet with 2,000 asterisks
- one ream of paper

Procedure

PART 1 Table A

1. Copy Table A into your lab notebook. Figure how long ago these historic events happened and write the answers on your chart.

2. Obtain a worksheet with 2,000 asterisks printed on it. Each asterisk represents one year. The first asterisk at the top represents one year ago.

3. Starting from this asterisk, circle the asterisk that represents how many years ago each event in Table A occurred.

4. Label each circled asterisk to indicate the event.

5. Obtain a ream of copy paper. There are 500 sheets in a ream. If each sheet had 2,000 asterisks on it, there would be a total of 1 million asterisks. Therefore, each ream would represent 1 million years.

Table A: Historic Events		
Event	Date	Number of Years Ago
You are born.		
One of your parents is born.		
First space shuttle sent into space.	1981	
Neil Armstrong first walks on the moon.	1969	
World War I ends.	1918	
Civil War ends.	1865	
Declaration of Independence is signed.	1776	
Columbus crosses Atlantic Ocean.	1492	
Leif Ericson visits North America.	1000	

146 ◆ G

Guide Inquiry

Invitation
Ask: **When you tell a friend that something happened a long time ago, what do you mean by "a long time?"** (*A typical answer will be within the last few years.*) Explain that the difficulty with grasping the concept of geologic time is that no time span in a human life prepares a person for understanding geologic time. This activity will help students grasp that concept.

Troubleshooting the Experiment
- Review this metric equivalent:
  1 m = 100 cm.
- Pair students who have difficulty using a calculator with students who have no trouble.

Table B: Geologic Events

Event	Number of Years Ago	Reams or Sheets of Paper	Thickness of Paper
Last ice age ends.	10,000		
Whales evolve.	50 million		
Pangaea begins to break up.	225 million		
First vertebrates develop.	530 million		
Multicellular organisms (algae) develop.	1 billion		
Single-celled organisms develop.	3.5 billion		
Oldest known rocks form.	4.0 billion		
Earth forms.	4.6 billion		

PART 2 Table B

6. Copy Table B into your lab notebook. Determine how much paper in reams or sheets would be needed to represent the events in geologic time found in Table B. (*Hint:* Recall that each ream represents 1 million years.)

7. Measure the thickness of a ream of paper. Use this thickness to calculate how thick a stack of paper would need to be to represent how long ago each geologic event occurred. (*Hint:* Use a calculator to multiply the thickness of the ream of paper by the number of reams.) Enter your results in Table B.

Analyze and Conclude

1. **Measuring** Measure the height of your classroom. How many reams of paper would you need to reach the ceiling? How many years would the height of the ceiling represent? Which geologic events listed in Table B would fall on a ream of paper inside your classroom?

2. **Calculating** At this scale, how many classrooms would have to be stacked on top of each other to represent the age of Earth? The time when vertebrates appeared?

3. **Calculating** How many times higher would the thickness of the stack be for the age of Earth than for the breakup of Pangaea?

4. **Making Models** On your model, how could you distinguish one era or period from another? How could you show when particular organisms evolved and when they became extinct?

5. **Communicating** Is the scale of your model practical? What would be the advantages and disadvantages of a model that fit geologic time on a timeline 1 meter long?

More to Explore

This model represents geologic time as a straight line. Can you think of other ways of representing geologic time graphically? Using colored pencils, draw your own version of the geologic time scale so that it fits on a single sheet of typing paper. (*Hint:* You could represent geologic time as a wheel, a ribbon, or a spiral.)

Expected Outcome

Students will become aware of the immensity of geologic time, especially when compared with the span of their own lives and the length of human history.

Analyze and Conclude

1. Answers will vary depending on the height of the classroom. The height of a classroom is typically about 2.5 m, or 250 cm. About 55 reams of paper with a width of 4.5 cm each would be needed to reach the ceiling. That would represent 55 million years. Only two events, the end of the last ice age and the evolution of whales, would fall on a ream inside the classroom.

2. Answers will vary depending on the figure obtained in Question 1. At 55 reams per classroom, about 84 classrooms (4,600 ÷ 55) would be needed to represent the age of Earth. About 9.5 (530 ÷ 55) classrooms would be needed to represent the time when vertebrates appeared.

3. The thickness of the stack would need to be about 20 times higher (4,600 ÷ 225).

4. A typical answer might suggest using different colors of paper for each of the eras and then marking the divisions between periods with cardboard dividers. Major events can be shown with flags on sticks stuck in the stack.

5. Most students will think that the scale is not practical. Advantages of a 1-m model include that it could easily fit on a wall and that it could be used for quick reference. Disadvantages include that the time from the beginning of the Paleozoic Era to the present would be such a short length that it would be difficult to include many relatively recent major events.

Extend Inquiry

More to Explore Students' versions will vary depending on the shape they choose. Have them use the geologic time scale in the section The Geologic Time Scale to mark the divisions between eras and each of their periods. Students might draw the outline of a ribbon or spiral with a black pencil and then use the colored pencils to color in the era and period lengths.

Interactive Textbook

- Complete student edition
- Section and chapter self-assessments
- Assessment reports for teachers

Help Students Read

Building Vocabulary

Word-Part Analysis Explain that many words in science consist of roots to which prefixes and/or suffixes are added. Explain that the root word is key to its meaning. For example, *extrude* means "to push out." *Intrude* means "to push in." Ask students to relate these root words to the scientific meanings of *extrusion* and *intrusion*.

Paraphrase To help students understand the vocabulary terms, paraphrase their definitions using words that students are familiar with. Example: *Radioactive decay happens when a substance breaks down, resulting in some of its particles changing into another substance.*

Connecting Concepts

Concept Maps Help students develop one way to show how the information in this chapter is related. Determining how organisms have changed through time by dating fossils has enabled scientists to develop the geologic time scale to show major events in Earth's history. Have students brainstorm to identify the key concepts, key terms, details, and examples, and then write each one on a sticky note and attach it at random on chart paper or on the board.

Tell students that this concept map will be organized in hierarchical order and begin at the top with key concepts. Ask students these questions to guide them to categorize the information on the sticky notes: **What can scientists learn from the fossil record? How do scientists determine the relative and absolute ages of rocks? What are the major events that happened during the eras and periods of the geologic time scale?**

① Fossils

Key Concepts

- Most fossils form when living things die and are buried by sediments. The sediments slowly harden into rock and preserve the shapes of the organisms.
- Fossils found in rock include molds and casts, petrified fossils, carbon films, and trace fossils. Other fossils form when the remains of organisms are preserved in substances such as tar, amber, or ice.
- The fossil record provides evidence about the history of life and past environments on Earth. The fossil record also shows that different groups of organisms have changed over time.

Key Terms

fossil	trace fossil
sedimentary rock	paleontologist
mold	scientific theory
cast	evolution
petrified fossil	extinct
carbon film	

② The Relative Age of Rocks

Key Concepts

- According to the law of superposition, in horizontal sedimentary rock layers the oldest layer is at the bottom. Each higher layer is younger than the layers below it.
- To determine relative age, geologists also study extrusions and intrusions of igneous rock, faults, and gaps in the geologic record.
- Index fossils are useful because they tell the relative ages of the rock layers in which they occur.

Key Terms

relative age	intrusion
absolute age	fault
law of superposition	unconformity
extrusion	index fossil

③ Radioactive Dating

Key Concepts

- During radioactive decay, the atoms of one element break down to form atoms of another.
- Geologists use radioactive dating to determine the absolute ages of rocks.

Key Terms

atom	radioactive decay
element	half-life

④ The Geologic Time Scale

Key Concepts

- Geologists use the geologic time scale to show the time span of Earth's history.
- After Precambrian Time, the basic units of the geologic time scale are eras and periods.

Key Terms

geologic time scale	era	period

⑤ Early Earth

Key Concepts

- Scientists hypothesize that Earth formed at the same time as the other planets and the sun, roughly 4.6 billion years ago.
- During early Precambrian Time, an atmosphere, oceans, and continents formed.
- Scientists have found fossils of single-celled organisms in rocks that formed about 3.5 billion years ago.

Key Terms

comet	continental drift

⑥ Eras of Earth's History

Key Concepts

- At the beginning of the Paleozoic Era, many different kinds of organisms evolved.
- During the Permian Period, about 260 million years ago, the supercontinent Pangaea formed.

Key Terms

invertebrate	amphibian	mass extinction
vertebrate	reptile	mammal

Prompt students by using connecting words or phrases, such as "divided into," "evolved into," and "includes," to indicate the basis for the organization of the map. The phrases should form a sentence between or among a set of concepts.

Answer

Accept logical presentations by students.

[All in One] Teaching Resources

- Key Terms Review: *A Trip Through Geologic Time*
- Connecting Concepts: *A Trip Through Geologic Time*

Review and Assessment

Go Online
PHSchool.com
For: Self-Assessment
Visit: PHSchool.com
Web Code: cfa-2040

Organizing Information

Concept Mapping Copy the concept map about fossils onto a piece of paper. Then complete it and add a title. (For more on concept maps, see the Skills Handbook.)

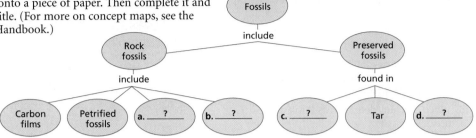

Reviewing Key Terms

Choose the letter of the best answer.

1. A hollow area in sediment in the shape of all or part of an organism is called a
   a. mold.　　　　**b.** cast.
   c. trace fossil.　　**d.** carbon film.

2. A gap in the geologic record formed when sedimentary rocks cover an eroded surface is called a(n)
   a. intrusion.　　　**b.** unconformity.
   c. fault.　　　　　**d.** extrusion.

3. The time it takes for half of a radioactive element's atoms to decay is a(n)
   a. era.　　　　　**b.** half-life.
   c. relative age.　　**d.** absolute age.

4. The geologic time scale is subdivided into
   a. relative ages.
   b. absolute ages.
   c. unconformities.
   d. eras and periods.

5. An animal that doesn't have a backbone is called a(n)
   a. vertebrate.
   b. mammal.
   c. invertebrate.
   d. amphibian.

If the statement is true, write *true*. If it is false, change the underlined word or words to make the statement true.

6. A dinosaur footprint in rock is an example of a <u>trace fossil</u>.

7. A <u>carbon film</u> is a fossil in which minerals have replaced all or part of an organism.

8. The <u>relative age</u> of something is the exact number of years since an event has occurred.

9. Earth's landmasses move slowly in a process called <u>continental drift</u>.

10. Scientists think dinosaurs became extinct as part of a(n) <u>intrusion</u> at the end of the Cretaceous Period.

Writing in Science

Field Guide Write a field guide for visitors to the Grand Canyon. In your guide, explain how geologists have learned about Earth's past by studying the canyon walls and the fossils they contain.

A Trip Through Geologic Time
Video Preview
Video Field Trip
▶ Video Assessment

Go Online
PHSchool.com
For: Self-Assessment
Visit: PHSchool.com
Web Code: cfa-2040

Students can take a practice test online that is automatically scored.

All in One Teaching Resources
- Transparency G48
- Chapter Test
- Performance Assessment Teacher Notes
- Performance Assessment Student Worksheet
- Performance Assessment Scoring Rubric

ExamView® **Computer Test Bank CD-ROM**

Review and Assessment

Organizing Information
a. Molds and casts
b. Trace fossils
c. Amber
d. Ice

Reviewing Key Terms
1. a　**2.** b　**3.** b　**4.** d　**5.** c
6. true
7. petrified fossil
8. absolute age
9. true
10. mass extinction

Writing in Science

Writing Mode Description
Scoring Rubric
4 Exceeds criteria, includes the different layers as shown in Figure 5 and the life forms that existed at those times
3 Meets all criteria but is not as detailed
2 Includes only brief description
1 Includes inaccurate information

Video Assessment

A Trip Through Geologic Time

Show the Video Assessment to review chapter content and as a prompt for the writing assignment. Discussion questions: **Explain the law of superposition. How is this law important in explaining the history of Earth?** *(The law of superposition says that the oldest rock is at the bottom and the most recent layers are near the top. The farther down into the layers of rock one goes, the farther back in time one is going. Therefore, looking at rocks and the fossils that may be in them can tell what Earth was like at certain times in the past.)* **What do fossil remains tell us about the land surrounding the Grand Canyon?** *(It tells us that half a billion years ago, this area was an ocean.)*

Checking Concepts

11. Sediment covers the remains of an organism. Then water rich in minerals seeps into the spaces of the organism's cells. Over time, the water evaporates, leaving the hardened minerals behind. Petrified fossils also form by replacement, in which minerals in water make a copy of the organism.

12. A bony fish has a better chance of leaving a fossil because it has hard parts that do not decay quickly, but a jellyfish does not have hard parts.

13. Sometimes, deeply buried layers of rock are lifted up to Earth's surface. At the surface, the exposed rock erodes away. Then sediments are deposited on top of the eroded surface of the older rocks and harden into rock layers. The place where an old eroded surface is in contact with a newer rock layer is called an unconformity.

14. A scientist would use radioactive dating to determine the absolute ages of intrusions and extrusions near the sedimentary rock in which the fossil was found.

15. Scientists think that the oceans formed during the first several hundred million years of Precambrian Time. As Earth cooled, water vapor condensed, forming rain. The rainwater eventually accumulated to form the oceans.

16. During the Tertiary Period, Earth's climates were generally warm and mild. During the Quaternary Period, Earth's climate cooled, causing a series of ice ages.

Review and Assessment

Checking Concepts

11. How does a petrified fossil form?

12. Which organism has a better chance of leaving a fossil: a jellyfish or a bony fish? Explain.

13. Describe a process that could cause an unconformity.

14. What evidence would a scientist use to determine the absolute age of a fossil found in a sedimentary rock?

15. When and how do scientists think that Earth's oceans formed?

16. How did Earth's environments change from the Tertiary Period to the Quarternary Period? Explain.

Thinking Critically

17. Applying Concepts Paleontologists find a trilobite fossil in a rock layer at the top of a hill in South America. Then they find the same kind of fossil in a rock layer at the bottom of a cliff in Africa. What could the paleontologists conclude about the two rock layers?

18. Problem Solving Which of the elements in the table below would be better to use in dating a fossil from Precambrian time? Explain.

Radioactive Elements

Element	Half-life (years)
Carbon-14	5,730
Uranium-235	713 million

19. Relating Cause and Effect When Pangaea formed, the climate changed and the land on Earth became drier. How was this climate change more favorable to reptiles than amphibians?

20. Making Judgments If you see a movie in which early humans fight giant dinosaurs, how would you judge the scientific accuracy of that movie? Give reasons for your judgment.

Math Practice

21. Percentage What percentage of a radioactive element will remain after 9 half-lives?

Applying Skills

Use the diagram of rock layers below to answer Questions 22–25.

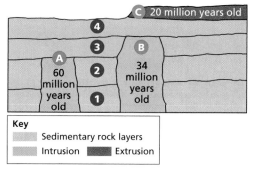

22. Inferring According to the Law of Superposition, which is the oldest layer of sedimentary rock? Which is the youngest? How do you know?

23. Measuring What method did a scientist use to determine the age of the intrusion and extrusion?

24. Interpreting Data What is the relative age of layer 3? (*Hint:* With what absolute ages can you compare it?)

25. Interpreting Data What is the relative age of layer 4?

Lab zone Chapter **Project**

Performance Assessment You have completed your illustrations for the timeline and travel brochure. Now you are ready to present the story of the geologic time period you researched. Be sure to include the awesome sights people will see when they travel to this time period. Don't forget to warn them of any dangers that await them. In your journal, reflect on what you have learned about Earth's history.

Lab zone Chapter **Project**   **L3**

Project Wrap Up As students present their brochures, assess the amount and quality of the information, as well as whether the brochures accurately cover the geological period. Also evaluate the quality and effectiveness of the illustrations. Question students about the sources used. Make sure they can support any fact with a good source.

Reflect and Record Advise students to write accurate descriptions of the most interesting thing they learned and provide good reasons for the period they would like to travel back to. Also have students reflect on how they could have made their brochures better.

Standardized Test Prep

Choose the letter of the best answer.

1. A geologist finds identical index fossils in a rock layer in the Grand Canyon in Arizona and in a rock layer in northern Utah, more than 675 kilometers away. What inference can she make about the ages of the two rock layers?
A the rock layer in the Grand Canyon is older
B the rock layer in Utah is older
C the two rock layers are about the same age
D no inferences

2. What should you use so that the geologic time scale covering Earth's 4.6 billion year history can be drawn as a straight line on a poster board one meter high?
F 1 cm = 1 million years
G 1 cm = 10,000 years
H 1 cm = 100,000 years
J 1 cm = 50,000,000 years

Use the diagram below and your knowledge of science to answer Question 3.

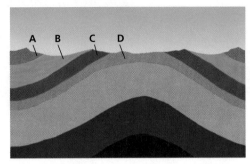

3. According to the law of superposition, the youngest layer of rock in this diagram is
A Layer A
B Layer B
C Layer C
D Layer D

4. What was used by geologists to define the beginnings and ends of the divisions of the geologic time scale?
F radioactive dating
G major changes in life forms
H types of rocks present
J volcanic events

5. A leaf falls into a shallow lake and is rapidly buried in the sediment that changes to rock over millions of years. Which type of fossil would be formed?
A mold and cast
B carbon film
C trace fossil
D amber

Constructed Response

6. Describe two methods geologists use to determine the age of a rock. In your answer, be sure to mention igneous rock, sedimentary rock, the law of superposition, index fossils, radioactive decay, and half-life.

Thinking Critically

17. The paleontologists could conclude that both rock layers formed at about the same time.

18. Precambrian Time begins with the formation of Earth 4.6 billion years ago and ends 544 million years ago. Carbon-14 would be of no use in dating the fossil because its half-life is much too short. Therefore, the uranium-235 would be better to use.

19. Amphibians live part of their lives in water, and reptiles are land animals. When the climate became drier, the amphibians had less water. A drier climate, then, would favor reptiles.

20. The movie would not be scientifically accurate because dinosaurs became extinct at the end of the Mesozoic Era and humans did not evolve until well into the Cenozoic Era, over 60 million years later.

Math Practice

21. After 9 half-lives, 0.1953125 percent of a radioactive element will remain.

Applying Skills

22. According to the law of superposition, layer 1 is the oldest layer and layer 4 is the youngest.

23. A scientist must have used radioactive dating to determine the ages of the intrusion and extrusion.

24. Layer 3 is younger than the 60-million-year-old intrusion but older than the 34-million-year-old intrusion.

25. Layer 4 is younger than the 34-million-year-old intrusion but older than the 20-million-year-old intrusion.

Standardized Test Prep

1. C **2.** J **3.** A **4.** G **5.** B
6. Possible answer: Scientists study the position of sedimentary rock layers to determine the relative ages of rocks by comparing where the rocks lie in relation to each other. According to the law of superposition, rocks on the bottom layers are generally younger than rocks on the top layers. Index fossils are also used to date rock layers. Scientists make use of the process of radioactive decay to find the absolute ages of igneous rock. They identify and measure the amount of a radioactive element in a rock and determine its half-life.

The Gift of the Nile

This interdisciplinary feature presents the central theme of the importance of the Nile River to the rise of ancient Egyptian civilization by connecting four different disciplines: language arts, science, social studies, and mathematics. The four explorations are designed to capture students' interest and help them understand how the content they are studying in science relates to other school subjects and to real-world events. The unit is particularly suited for team teaching.

All in One Teaching Resources

- Interdisciplinary Exploration: *Science*
- Interdisciplinary Exploration: *Language Arts*
- Interdisciplinary Exploration: *Mathematics*
- Interdisciplinary Exploration: *Social Studies*

Build Background Knowledge
Recalling Science Concepts

Help students recall what they learned in the chapter Erosion and Deposition. Ask: **How does water change Earth's surface?** (*Water erodes rock and sediment at some places and deposits it at other places.*) **How does the deposition of sediment change Earth's surface?** (*Deposition of sediment forms features such as alluvial fans and deltas.*) **What do you know about Egypt and the Nile River?** (*Accept all responses without comment.*)

Introduce the Exploration

Display a large map of Africa, and invite a volunteer to find the Nile River. Ask: **In which direction does the Nile flow?** (*Generally from south to north*) **Through which countries does the Nile flow?** (*Uganda, Sudan, Ethiopia, and Egypt*) Tell students that the Nile River is the longest river in the world and that it flows through a large desert. Draw students' attention to the photograph at the top of this page. Ask: **How does the Nile River change the land along its banks?** (*It makes the land lush and fertile.*) **How do you think the Nile River affects the lives of the people living near it?** (*Accept all answers without comment at this time.*)

Nile River
The Nile River gives life to the Egyptian desert.

The Gift of the Nile

What water . . .

- flows from south to north?
- travels through a scorching desert for much of its length?
- nourished a remarkable ancient culture?
- is the longest river in the world?

Water Lily
Blue water lilies grow in the Nile.

152 ◆ G

It's the Nile River. More than 5,000 years ago, people first began planting seeds and harvesting crops in the valley of the Nile. The great civilization of Egypt rose in these fertile lands. The Nile supplied water for drinking, growing crops, raising animals, and fishing. When the river flooded every year, it brought a new layer of rich soil to the flood plain.

This productive strip of land was the envy of many nations. Fortunately, the deserts west and east of the Nile helped protect ancient Egypt from invaders. The river provided a trade route from central Africa downstream to the Mediterranean Sea. Around 600 B.C., Egypt expanded its trade by digging a canal to the Red Sea.

During the months when the Nile flooded, peasants worked as builders for the Pharaoh, or king. They constructed magnificent pyramids and temples, some of which still stand today.

Lifeline of Egypt

The wealth of ancient Egypt and the lives of its people depended on the fertile flood plains that bordered the Nile River. Egyptian society was organized in classes to support agriculture. The Pharaoh was the supreme ruler to whom all Egyptians paid taxes. Below the Pharaoh was a small upper class of priests, scribes, and nobles. Traders and skilled workers, who made tools, pottery, and clothing, formed a small middle class. But the largest group in Egyptian society consisted of the peasants. Peasants used the Nile waters to raise crops that fed all of Egypt.

Priests and nobles recorded the history and literature of ancient Egypt on the walls of monuments and temples. They also wrote on papyrus, a paper made from reeds that grew in marshes along the Nile. Many writings were about the Nile.

When scholars finally found the key to hieroglyphics (hy ur oh GLIF iks), Egyptian writing, they discovered hymns, poems, legends, adventure stories, and lessons for young people. The poem at the right is from a hymn to Hapy, the god of the Nile. "Darkness by day" is the Nile filled with silt.

▼ Egyptian Hieroglyphics

Adoration of Hapy

Hail to you, Hapy,
Sprung from earth,
Come to nourish Egypt!
Of secret ways,
A darkness by day,
To whom his followers sing!
Who floods the fields that Re* has made,
To nourish all who thirst;
Lets drink the waterless desert,
His dew descending from the sky.

Food provider, bounty maker,
Who creates all that is good!
Lord of awe, sweetly fragrant,
Gracious when he comes.
Who makes herbage for the herds,
Gives sacrifice for every god.
He fills the stores,
Makes bulge the barns,
Gives bounty to the poor.

Oh joy when you come!
O joy when you come, O Hapy,
Oh joy when you come!

Amon-Re, god of the sun

Language Arts Activity

In this poem, Hapy is a personification of the Nile River. When writers and poets use personification, they give an object or animal human qualities. Write your own story or poem using personification. Choose a subject found in nature, such as a mountain, stream, river, or glacier. Jot down human behaviors and actions for your subject—"the stream gurgles, murmurs, and sighs." Before writing, think about the time, place, characters, and sequence of events in your story.

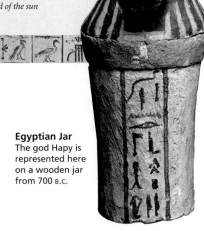

Egyptian Jar
The god Hapy is represented here on a wooden jar from 700 B.C.

G ◆ 153

Background

Cultural Diversity The ancient Egyptian civilization depended on the yearly flood of the Nile River. The Egyptians kept written records of the level at which the Nile flooded each year and records of other natural events. Pharaohs, or kings, often would refer to these records to find out whether a similar event had occurred before and how the people had reacted to it.

The Nile also provided the inspiration for stories. People wrote about the river and how it affected their lives. The Nile was a route to distant lands, and those who traveled along it told stories about their experiences.

Explore Language Arts Concepts

Choose from among the following teaching strategies for a language arts experience.

Creative Thought After students read the poem, encourage them to give their impressions of the person who might have written it. Ask: **Is it surprising to you that a poem like this was written thousands of years ago?** (*Accept all responses without comment, but encourage students to explain their reactions.*)

Organize Information As students read *Lifeline of Egypt,* have them make a graphic organizer that illustrates the class structure of ancient Egyptian society.

Use Visuals Direct students' attention to the Egyptian jar shown on this page. Ask: **What are the symbols on the side of the jar?** (*The symbols are hieroglyphics.*) **Why was learning to read hieroglyphics so important to scholars?** (*Knowing how to read hieroglyphics helped them learn about the thoughts, feelings, historical events, and daily events that were important in the ancient Egyptian civilization.*)

Language Arts Activity

Focus As a class, apply personification to objects in your classroom, such as the clock, a heating or cooling vent, or a bell.

Teach Show students how to plan the time, place, characters, and sequence of events of a story. You may want to use a concept map for this purpose.

Scoring Rubric
4 Exceeds criteria by creatively using personification in a story that includes time, place, characters, and sequence of events
3 Meets criteria by using personification in a story that includes all of the important details
2 Includes personification in a story but not all of the important details
1 Includes only one detail or does not use personification

Explore Science Concepts

Choose from among the following teaching strategies for a science experience.

Discuss Explain the effect of water and silt from the Nile River on the development of the ancient Egyptian civilization. Ask: **How was it possible for the Nile River to support a large and prosperous civilization?** (*The Nile provided water and fertile soil. This allowed the Egyptians to grow food to eat and to trade.*) **Could the Egyptian civilization have developed on land farther away from the Nile River?** (*Probably not, because the region is mostly desert*)

Use Visuals Have students use their fingers to trace the course of the Nile River on the map as they read about it. Call on students to identify the river's head, tributaries, and delta.

Review Remind students that a flood plain is the region of land along a river that is covered by water during a flood. Ask: **Why does silt settle on a flood plain during a flood?** (*As the water enters the flood plain, it flows more slowly. This causes fine sediment to be deposited.*) **Why would new sediment be fertile?** (*The silt contains a new supply of nutrients that plants can use.*)

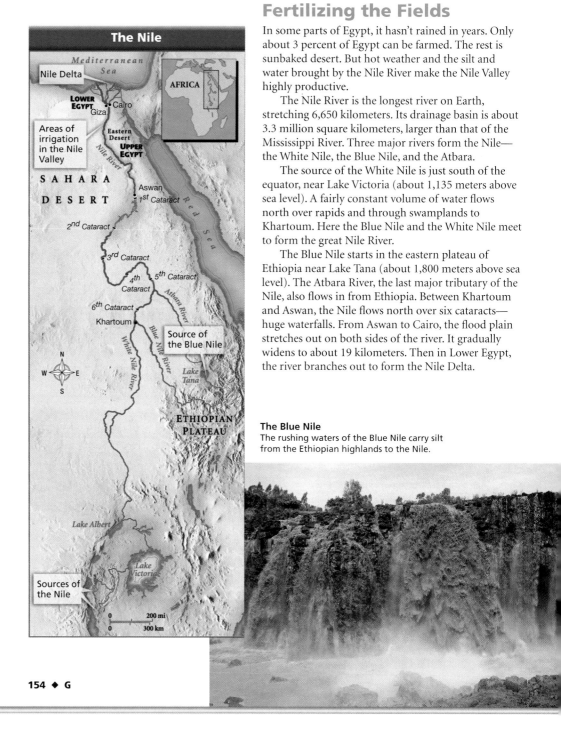

The Nile

Mediterranean Sea
Nile Delta
AFRICA
LOWER EGYPT • Cairo
Giza
Areas of irrigation in the Nile Valley
Eastern Desert
UPPER EGYPT
SAHARA DESERT
Aswan
1st Cataract
2nd Cataract
3rd Cataract
4th Cataract
5th Cataract
6th Cataract
Khartoum
Atbara River
Source of the Blue Nile
White Nile River
Blue Nile River
Lake Tana
ETHIOPIAN PLATEAU
Lake Albert
Lake Victoria
Sources of the Nile
Red Sea
N W E S
0   200 mi
0   300 km

Fertilizing the Fields

In some parts of Egypt, it hasn't rained in years. Only about 3 percent of Egypt can be farmed. The rest is sunbaked desert. But hot weather and the silt and water brought by the Nile River make the Nile Valley highly productive.

The Nile River is the longest river on Earth, stretching 6,650 kilometers. Its drainage basin is about 3.3 million square kilometers, larger than that of the Mississippi River. Three major rivers form the Nile—the White Nile, the Blue Nile, and the Atbara.

The source of the White Nile is just south of the equator, near Lake Victoria (about 1,135 meters above sea level). A fairly constant volume of water flows north over rapids and through swamplands to Khartoum. Here the Blue Nile and the White Nile meet to form the great Nile River.

The Blue Nile starts in the eastern plateau of Ethiopia near Lake Tana (about 1,800 meters above sea level). The Atbara River, the last major tributary of the Nile, also flows in from Ethiopia. Between Khartoum and Aswan, the Nile flows north over six cataracts—huge waterfalls. From Aswan to Cairo, the flood plain stretches out on both sides of the river. It gradually widens to about 19 kilometers. Then in Lower Egypt, the river branches out to form the Nile Delta.

The Blue Nile
The rushing waters of the Blue Nile carry silt from the Ethiopian highlands to the Nile.

Background

Facts and Figures As the Aswan High Dam was being built in the 1960s, the rising water behind the dam threatened many of the ancient monuments in the Nile Valley. Some monuments were moved to safety. Lake Nasser, the reservoir formed by the dam, is about 480 km long and stretches into Sudan. Water is released from Lake Nasser when it is needed for irrigation downriver. As the water pours through the dam, it is used to produce electricity.

The Aswan High Dam has changed life in modern Egypt by enabling Egyptian farmers to grow several crops per year. However, now farmers must add fertilizer to the soil to compensate for the rich silt that the Nile floods used to deposit.

Between May and August, heavy rains soak the eastern plateau of Ethiopia and wash rock and silt from the highlands into the Blue Nile. The dark water rushes over rapids and through deep gorges into the Nile River. For thousands of years, this rush of water from the Blue Nile and the Atbara caused the seasonal flooding on the Nile. In mid July, the Nile would begin to rise north of Aswan. When the flood waters went down, the silt remained on the land.

Then in the 1800s and 1900s, the government of Egypt built dams on the Nile to try to control the flood waters. The Aswan High Dam, the largest of these dams, was completed in 1970. The dam enabled Egyptians to gain control over annual flooding. The Aswan High Dam holds back water for use during dry periods.

In recent years, the population of Egypt and other nations in the Nile basin has grown rapidly. Feeding more people means increasing the area of irrigated cropland. To avoid conflicts, nations must agree to share water. Most of the water in the Blue Nile, for example, comes from Ethiopia. Yet Egypt and Sudan, the nations farther downstream, use about 90 percent of that water. Today, Ethiopia's growing population needs more Nile water. Using water efficiently and sharing it fairly are essential in the Nile basin.

Aswan High Dam
Today, the Aswan High Dam provides irrigation and electricity throughout Egypt.

Science Activity

Use the stream table (pages 82–83) to observe how the Nile builds its delta and how the Aswan High Dam affects the river. Pour water into the lower end of the stream table to model the sea.

- Make a dam. Cut off the top 2 centimeters from a plastic foam cup. Cut the cup into a semicircle to make your dam. Cut a small notch in the top of the dam for a spillway.

- Start the dripper to create the Nile. Allow it to flow for 5 minutes. What do you observe where the river flows into the sea?

- Now place the dam halfway down the river. Scoop out a small, shallow reservoir behind the dam. Start the dripper. Observe for 5 minutes.

What effect would you say the Aswan High Dam has on the movement of sediment down the Nile?

Discuss Remind students about the human need to control the Nile River by building dams. Ask: **What are some benefits of building dams?** (*Ensuring a constant water supply; preventing damage from floods; providing electricity*) **What are some costs of dams?** (*Changes in the environment and wildlife habitats; increased use of fertilizers in flood plains; accumulation of silt behind the dams and not at the river's mouth*)

Demonstrate Collect a jar of silty water from a nearby stream. Seal the jar with a lid, and bring it to class. Allow the jar to remain undisturbed for several hours. Show students the silt that settled to the bottom of the jar. Point out that the same process allows silt to settle on flood plains.

Science Activity

Materials stream table setup from the Skills Lab in "Water Erosion," plastic foam cup, scissors

Focus Remind students that when a river flows into a lake or an ocean, sediment is deposited. Ask: **What forms behind a dam in a river?** (*A lake*)

Teach Point out the reservoir on the stream table. Ask: **How does the reservoir affect the movement of sediment?** (*The reservoir catches sediment that otherwise would move downstream.*) **Why might this cause a flood plain to be less fertile?** (*Silt that normally would be deposited during floods isn't reaching the flood plain.*)

Explore Social Studies Concepts

Choose from among the following teaching strategies for a social studies experience.

Include Community Resources Have students write to your local water management resource to ask how water is used for irrigation in your region. Students should ask for any literature about the subject that might be available.

Discuss Ask: **What was the advantage of basin irrigation?** *(It held river water and allowed all of the sediment that the water contained to be deposited on the flood plain.)* **How was the shaduf used by ancient Egyptians?** *(It was used to take water directly from the river for irrigation.)* **Do people take water from rivers for irrigation today?** *(Yes.)* **How is it done?** *(Water is held by dams and removed from the reservoir; in some cases, water is piped or channeled directly from the river.)*

Use Maps Show students a map of Egypt. Have them identify the Nile River and its flood plain. Also have them identify the Nile Delta. Using the map's scale, have students estimate the size of these areas.

Basin Irrigation

The ancient Egyptians may have been the first people to irrigate their lands. The slope of the flood plain in Egypt is good for irrigation. From south to north, the land slopes down slightly. The land also slopes slightly down to the desert from the river banks on either side of the Nile.

Egyptians used basin irrigation. They divided the flood plain into a series of basins by building low banks of dirt. When the Nile flooded from July to October, it filled the basins. Then, the water level in the Nile and in the basins gradually dropped. This left a rich sediment layer ready for planting.

In November, peasants plowed the fields and scattered seeds. To push the seeds into the ground, they drove sheep over the fields.

Egyptians grew crops of wheat, barley, lentils, onions, beans, garlic, vegetables, and fruits in the Nile Valley. The crops usually could feed all of Egypt. The Egyptians traded any surplus crops for lumber, copper, and beautiful minerals that they used for decorations.

When the fields became dry, peasants brought water from irrigation channels, or deep ditches. They also used a tool called a shaduf to take water directly from the Nile. A shaduf works like a plank on a seesaw: A wooden beam balances on a pivot. Hanging from one end of the beam is a bucket. Weighing down the other end is a large stone. A farmer tips the beam to scoop water from the Nile, swivels the beam, and empties the bucket into an irrigation channel.

Farming Around 1200 B.C.
This painting from the Tomb of Sennedjem in Thebes shows Sennedjem and his wife farming in the afterworld. They plant and harvest grain and cultivate fruit-bearing trees, such as the date palm.

Background

Facts and Figures Farming provided the basis for ancient Egyptian civilization. Most Egyptian settlements were villages near the Nile River or in its delta. The farmers contributed some of the wheat and barley they grew to support the elite landowners and the central government. Egypt did not develop large cities until rather late in its history.

Originally, the months of the Egyptian calendar were numbered. Later, the months were named for festivals, and the years were named for major events, and recorded in a register. Later, kings would consult these registers to make predictions about the extent of flooding and the success of crops.

▲ Modern market in Cairo, Egypt

Shaduf
Egyptians still use the shaduf today. It dates back to about 1500 B.C.

After the harvest in April, farm animals grazed on the lands until the Nile rose again in mid July. Then a new cycle began.

The flooding of the Nile determined the lives of early Egyptians. Their year began on the day the Nile began to rise, about July 19 on our calendar. The Egyptians were the first people to have a calendar of 365 days. Their year was divided into three seasons based on the Nile's flood cycle. Each season had four months of 30 days. At the end of the 12 months, the Egyptians had five festival days to complete the year.

Social Studies Activity

Divide into groups of three to make a timeline of an Egyptian calendar year. Each member of the group should choose a four-month season—flooding, planting, or harvesting—to label and illustrate.

- Draw the timeline to begin on July 19 and end on July 18.
- Divide the timeline into 12 months and 5 days.
- Label the months and seasons.
- Illustrate the seasonal work of the farmers.

G ◆ 157

Explore Mathematics Concepts

Choose from among the following teaching strategies for a mathematics experience.

Use Math Skills Invite students to measure their own cubit and cut a piece of black construction paper of appropriate length. Have students use their cubits to measure the dimensions of the classroom. After students have finished, encourage them to compare answers.

Review Take some time to review angles with students. Remind students that a complete circle includes 360°. Draw a circle on the board, and divide it into segments of various sizes. Challenge students to approximate the angle that each segment represents.

Show Examples Obtain some photographs of ancient Egyptian structures. Point out to students that the structures were designed and built with high mathematical accuracy. Encourage students to speculate about how the ancient Egyptians measured lengths and angles so accurately.

Demonstrate Draw a 3-4-5 triangle on the board in which the sides are exactly 3 and 4 units and the hypotenuse is exactly 5 units. Tell students that a triangle with these lengths will have a 90° angle. Now multiply each side by 2 to obtain a 6-8-10 triangle. Multiply each side by 3 to obtain a 9-12-15 triangle. Draw both of these triangles on the board. Show students that these also are right triangles.

Pyramids at Giza
These pyramids were built around 2500 B.C. Egyptians used geometry to measure triangles, squares, and circles as they built pyramids.

Measuring the Land

Have you ever measured the length of a room using your feet as the unit of measurement? Around 3000 B.C., ancient Egyptians developed the cubit system of measurement. It was based on the lengths of parts of the arm and hand, rather than the foot. The Egyptian cubit was the length of a forearm from the tip of the elbow to the end of the middle finger. The cubit was subdivided into smaller units of spans, palms, digits, and parts of digits.

Of course, the length of a cubit varied from person to person. So Egypt established a standard cubit, called the Royal Cubit. It was based on the length of the Pharaoh's forearm. The Royal Cubit was a piece of black granite about 52.3 centimeters long. Although the royal architect kept the Royal Cubit, wooden copies were distributed throughout the land.

Measurement was important to Egyptian life. Every year when the Nile flooded, it wiped out the boundaries for the fields. So after the annual floods, farmers had to measure off new areas. Drawings on the walls of early tombs show that the Egyptians probably had a system for measuring distances and angles on land.

Standard measurement was also necessary for building the massive temples and pyramids that lined the Nile Valley. The cubit sticks must have been very accurate, because the lengths of the sides of the Great Pyramid at Giza vary by only a few centimeters.

158 ◆ G

Background

Facts and Figures The Egyptians developed a branch of mathematics that is now known by its Greek name, *geometry,* meaning "Earth measuring." Egyptians used geometry to survey their land and record boundaries, and to measure the squares, triangles, circles, and cubes used for building pyramids and other monuments. About 2000 B.C., they learned how to make a square or rectangle by using a 90° angle.

The ancient Greeks adopted the Egyptian method of making rectangles with a 90° angle. During the sixth century B.C., a Greek philosopher and mathematician, Pythagoras, expanded on the Egyptian method by developing the Pythagorean Theorem, which states that the square of the hypotenuse of a right triangle is equal to the sum of the square of its sides ($a^2 + b^2 = c^2$).

Math Activity

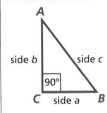

To measure fields and build pyramids, the Egyptians needed to understand geometry. They laid out their fields in squares by first making a right triangle. Look at the diagram. The two shorter sides are the legs of the triangle. The side opposite the right angle is the hypotenuse. The Egyptians might have known that the sum of the squares of the lengths of the legs is equal to the square of the hypotenuse. The equation is $a^2 + b^2 = c^2$. So if side a is 3, side b is 4, and side c is 5, then $3^2 + 4^2 = 5^2$, or $9 + 16 = 25$. Now work in groups of three to make your own right triangle.

- Measure one student's arm to make a cubit stick.
- Use the cubit stick to cut one rope 12 cubits long; mark off each of the 12 cubits.
- Have three students hold the rope at points A, B, and C so that side a is 3 cubits, side b is 4 cubits, and side c is 5 cubits.

Have you made a right triangle? How do you know? How could you make a square?

Tie It Together

Egyptian Exhibition

Plan a brochure to promote a special exhibition on Egypt at a museum. Half the class can focus on ancient Egypt. The other half can find out about the changes that have occurred on the Nile in the last 100 years. Work in small groups to research and assemble the information and illustrations. You might want to include the following:

- the Rosetta Stone and hieroglyphics
- directions for making a mummy
- the Great Pyramid at Giza
- history and treasures of King Tutankhamen

King Tutankhamen
This is a section of the King's gold mummy case.

- religion in ancient Egypt
- model of an irrigation system for fields on the Nile
- maps of ancient and modern Egypt
- construction of the Aswan Dam, 1959–1970
- water control on the Nile in Egypt today
- Nile Delta today

G ◆ 159

Math Activity

Materials metric ruler, rope, marker, scissors

Focus Make certain that students can identify a 90° angle and the hypotenuse of a right triangle.

Teach As students make their triangles, tell them not to try to layout a triangle. All that students should do is extend line segments of 3 cubits of rope, then 4 cubits of rope, then 5 cubits of rope, and connect the ends. After students have made their triangles, have them identify the hypotenuse.

Answers Students have made a right triangle; it is consistent with the Pythagorean Theorem, $3^2 + 4^2 = 5^2$. Students can make a square using the equation for a right triangle by making a and b equal to the same number. Two of these triangles joined together at the hypotenuse will form a square with four equal sides.

Tie It Together

Egyptian Exhibition

Time 1 week (2 days for research, 2 days for assembling the information and illustrations, 1 day for assembling the brochure as a class)

Tips Have students work in groups of two or three. Encourage groups to choose one of the subjects listed in the text or one of their own, according to their interests and their knowledge of Egypt. If necessary, help each group distribute the tasks and work out a plan for researching and gathering information. If possible, have students use desktop publishing software to assemble their information into a class brochure.
- After the brochure is complete, invite students to reflect on their process. Ask: **What would you do differently to make the task of publishing the brochure more efficient?** *(Accept students answers without comment.)*

Extend Visit a nearby museum so that students can observe how the museum displays information about ancient civilizations.

Think Like a Scientist

The Skills Handbook is designed as a reference for students to use whenever they need to review inquiry, reading, or math skills. You can use the activities in this part of the Skills Handbook to teach or reinforce inquiry skills.

Observing

Focus Remind students that an observation is what they can see, hear, smell, taste, or feel.

Teach Invite students to make observations of the classroom. List these observations on the board. Challenge students to identify the senses they used to make each observation. Then, ask: **Which senses will you use to make observations from the photograph on this page?** *(Sight is the only sense that can be used to make observations from the photograph.)*

Activity

Some observations that students might make include that the boy is skateboarding, wearing a white helmet, and flying in the air. Make sure that students' observations are confined to only things that they can actually see in the photograph.

Inferring

Focus Choose one or two of the classroom observations listed on the board, and challenge students to interpret them. Guide students by asking why something appears as it does.

Teach Encourage students to describe their thought processes in making their inferences. Point out where they used their knowledge and experience to interpret the observations. Then invite students to suggest other possible interpretations for the observations. Ask: **How can you find out whether an inference is correct?** *(By further investigation)*

Activity

One possible inference is that the boy just skated off a ramp at a skate park. Invite students to share their experiences that helped them make the inference.

Predicting

Focus Discuss the weather forecast for the next day. Point out that this prediction is an inference about what will happen in the

Think Like a Scientist

Scientists have a particular way of looking at the world, or scientific habits of mind. Whenever you ask a question and explore possible answers, you use many of the same skills that scientists do. Some of these skills are described on this page.

Observing

When you use one or more of your five senses to gather information about the world, you are **observing.** Hearing a dog bark, counting twelve green seeds, and smelling smoke are all observations. To increase the power of their senses, scientists sometimes use microscopes, telescopes, or other instruments that help them make more detailed observations.

An observation must be an accurate report of what your senses detect. It is important to keep careful records of your observations in science class by writing or drawing in a notebook. The information collected through observations is called evidence, or data.

Inferring

When you interpret an observation, you are **inferring,** or making an inference. For example, if you hear your dog barking, you may infer that someone is at your front door. To make this inference, you combine the evidence— the barking dog—and your experience or knowledge—you know that your dog barks when strangers approach—to reach a logical conclusion.

Notice that an inference is not a fact; it is only one of many possible interpretations for an observation. For example, your dog may be barking because it wants to go for a walk. An inference may turn out to be incorrect even if it is based on accurate observations and logical reasoning. The only way to find out if an inference is correct is to investigate further.

Predicting

When you listen to the weather forecast, you hear many predictions about the next day's weather—what the temperature will be, whether it will rain, and how windy it will be. Weather forecasters use observations and knowledge of weather patterns to predict the weather. The skill of **predicting** involves making an inference about a future event based on current evidence or past experience.

Because a prediction is an inference, it may prove to be false. In science class, you can test some of your predictions by doing experiments. For example, suppose you predict that larger paper airplanes can fly farther than smaller airplanes. How could you test your prediction?

Activity

Use the photograph to answer the questions below.

Observing Look closely at the photograph. List at least three observations.

Inferring Use your observations to make an inference about what has happened. What experience or knowledge did you use to make the inference?

Predicting Predict what will happen next. On what evidence or experience do you base your prediction?

future based on observations and experience.

Teach Help students differentiate between a prediction and an inference. You might organize the similarities and differences in a Venn diagram on the board. Both are interpretations of observations using experience and knowledge, and both can be incorrect. Inferences describe current or past events. Predictions describe future events.

Activity

Students might predict that the boy will land and skate to the other side. Others might predict that the boy will fall. Students should also describe the evidence or experience on which they based their predictions.

Classifying

Could you imagine searching for a book in the library if the books were shelved in no particular order? Your trip to the library would be an all-day event! Luckily, librarians group together books on similar topics or by the same author. Grouping together items that are alike in some way is called **classifying.** You can classify items in many ways: by size, by shape, by use, and by other important characteristics.

Like librarians, scientists use the skill of classifying to organize information and objects. When things are sorted into groups, the relationships among them become easier to understand.

Activity

Classify the objects in the photograph into two groups based on any characteristic you choose. Then use another characteristic to classify the objects into three groups.

Making Models

Have you ever drawn a picture to help someone understand what you were saying? Such a drawing is one type of model. A model is a picture, diagram, computer image, or other representation of a complex object or process. **Making models** helps people understand things that they cannot observe directly.

Scientists often use models to represent things that are either very large or very small, such as the planets in the solar system, or the parts of a cell. Such models are physical models—drawings or three-dimensional structures that look like the real thing. Other models are mental models—mathematical equations or words that describe how something works.

Activity

This student is using a model to demonstrate what causes day and night on Earth. What do the flashlight and the tennis ball in the model represent?

Communicating

Whenever you talk on the phone, write a report, or listen to your teacher at school, you are communicating. **Communicating** is the process of sharing ideas and information with other people. Communicating effectively requires many skills, including writing, reading, speaking, listening, and making models.

Scientists communicate to share results, information, and opinions. Scientists often communicate about their work in journals, over the telephone, in letters, and on the Internet.

They also attend scientific meetings where they share their ideas with one another in person.

Activity

On a sheet of paper, write out clear, detailed directions for tying your shoe. Then exchange directions with a partner. Follow your partner's directions exactly. How successful were you at tying your shoe? How could your partner have communicated more clearly?

Classifying

Focus Encourage students to think of common things that are classified.

Teach Ask: **What things at home are classified?** *(Clothing might be classified in order to place it in the appropriate dresser drawer; glasses, plates, and silverware are grouped in different parts of the kitchen; screws, nuts, bolts, washers, and nails might be separated into small containers.)* **What are some things that scientists classify?** *(Scientists classify many things they study, including organisms, geological features and processes, and kinds of machines.)*

Activity

Some characteristics students might use include color, pattern of color, use of balls, and size. Students' criteria for classification should clearly divide the balls into two, and then three, distinct groups.

Making Models

Focus Ask: **What are some models you have used to study science?** *(Students might have used human anatomical models, solar system models, maps, or stream tables.)* **How have these models helped you?** *(Models can help you learn about things that are difficult to study because they are very large, very small, or highly complex.)*

Teach Be sure students understand that a model does not have to be three-dimensional. For example, a map is a model, as is a mathematical equation. Have students look at the photograph of the student modeling the causes of day and night on Earth. Ask: **What quality of each item makes this a good model?** *(The flashlight gives off light, and the ball is round and can be rotated by the student.)*

Activity

The flashlight represents the sun and the ball represents Earth.

Communicating

Focus Have students identify the methods of communication they have used today.

Teach Ask: **How is the way you communicate with a friend similar to and different from the way scientists communicate about their work to other scientists?** *(Both may communicate using various methods, but scientists must be very detailed and precise, whereas communication between friends may be less detailed and*

precise.) Encourage students to communicate like a scientist as they carry out the activity.

Activity

Students' answers will vary but should identify a step-by-step process for tying a shoe. Help students identify communication errors such as leaving out a step, putting steps in the wrong order, or disregarding the person's handedness.

Making Measurements

Students can refer to this part of the Skills Handbook whenever they need to review how to make measurements with SI units. You can use the activities here to teach or reinforce SI units.

Measuring in SI

Focus Review SI units with students. Begin by providing metric rulers, graduated cylinders, balances, and Celsius thermometers. Use these tools to reinforce that the meter is the unit of length, the liter is the unit of volume, the gram is the unit of mass, and the degree Celsius is the unit of temperature.

Teach Ask: **If you want to measure the length and the width of the classroom, which SI unit would you use?** *(Meter)* **Which unit would you use to measure the amount of mass in your textbook?** *(Gram)* **Which would you use to measure how much water a drinking glass holds?** *(Liter)* **When would you use the Celsius scale?** *(To measure the temperature of something)* Then use the measuring equipment to review SI prefixes. For example, ask: **What are the smallest units on the metric ruler?** *(Millimeters)* **How many millimeters are there in one centimeter?** *(10 millimeters)* **How many in 10 centimeters?** *(100 millimeters)* **How many centimeters are there in one meter?** *(100 centimeters)* **What does 1,000 meters equal?** *(One kilometer)*

Activity

Length The length of the shell is 7.8 centimeters, or 78 millimeters. If students need more practice measuring length, have them use meter sticks and metric rulers to measure various objects in the classroom.

Activity

Liquid Volume The volume of water in the graduated cylinder is 62 milliliters. If students need more practice, have them use a graduated cylinder to measure different volumes of water.

Making Measurements

By measuring, scientists can express their observations more precisely and communicate more information about what they observe.

Measuring in SI

The standard system of measurement used by scientists around the world is known as the International System of Units, which is abbreviated as SI (**Système International d'Unités**, in French). SI units are easy to use because they are based on multiples of 10. Each unit is ten times larger than the next smallest unit and one tenth the size of the next largest unit. The table lists the prefixes used to name the most common SI units.

Common SI Prefixes		
Prefix	**Symbol**	**Meaning**
kilo-	k	1,000
hecto-	h	100
deka-	da	10
deci-	d	0.1 (one tenth)
centi-	c	0.01 (one hundredth)
milli-	m	0.001 (one thousandth)

Length To measure length, or the distance between two points, the unit of measure is the **meter (m)**. The distance from the floor to a doorknob is approximately one meter. Long distances, such as the distance between two cities, are measured in kilometers (km). Small lengths are measured in centimeters (cm) or millimeters (mm). Scientists use metric rulers and meter sticks to measure length.

Common Conversions	
1 km	= 1,000 m
1 m	= 100 cm
1 m	= 1,000 mm
1 cm	= 10 mm

Activity

The larger lines on the metric ruler in the picture show centimeter divisions, while the smaller, unnumbered lines show millimeter divisions. How many centimeters long is the shell? How many millimeters long is it?

Liquid Volume To measure the volume of a liquid, or the amount of space it takes up, you will use a unit of measure known as the **liter (L).** One liter is the approximate volume of a medium-size carton of milk. Smaller volumes are measured in milliliters (mL). Scientists use graduated cylinders to measure liquid volume.

Activity

The graduated cylinder in the picture is marked in milliliter divisions. Notice that the water in the cylinder has a curved surface. This curved surface is called the *meniscus.* To measure the volume, you must read the level at the lowest point of the meniscus. What is the volume of water in this graduated cylinder?

Common Conversion
1 L = 1,000 mL

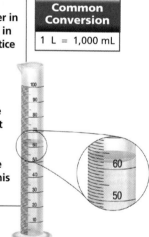

Mass To measure mass, or the amount of matter in an object, you will use a unit of measure known as the **gram (g).** One gram is approximately the mass of a paper clip. Larger masses are measured in kilograms (kg). Scientists use a balance to find the mass of an object.

Common Conversion

1 kg = 1,000 g

Activity

The mass of the potato in the picture is measured in kilograms. What is the mass of the potato? Suppose a recipe for potato salad called for one kilogram of potatoes. About how many potatoes would you need?

0.25 KG

Temperature To measure the temperature of a substance, you will use the **Celsius scale.** Temperature is measured in degrees Celsius (°C) using a Celsius thermometer. Water freezes at 0°C and boils at 100°C.

Time The unit scientists use to measure time is the **second (s).**

Activity

What is the temperature of the liquid in degrees Celsius?

Converting SI Units

To use the SI system, you must know how to convert between units. Converting from one unit to another involves the skill of **calculating,** or using mathematical operations. Converting between SI units is similar to converting between dollars and dimes because both systems are based on multiples of ten.

Suppose you want to convert a length of 80 centimeters to meters. Follow these steps to convert between units.

1. Begin by writing down the measurement you want to convert—in this example, 80 centimeters.

2. Write a conversion factor that represents the relationship between the two units you are converting. In this example, the relationship is 1 meter = 100 centimeters. Write this conversion factor as a fraction, making sure to place the units you are converting from (centimeters, in this example) in the denominator.

3. Multiply the measurement you want to convert by the fraction. When you do this, the units in the first measurement will cancel out with the units in the denominator. Your answer will be in the units you are converting to (meters, in this example).

Example

80 centimeters = ▦ meters

$$80 \text{ centimeters} \times \frac{1 \text{ meter}}{100 \text{ centimeters}} = \frac{80 \text{ meters}}{100}$$
$$= 0.8 \text{ meters}$$

Activity

Convert between the following units.
1. 600 millimeters = ▦ meters
2. 0.35 liters = ▦ milliliters
3. 1,050 grams = ▦ kilograms

Skills Handbook ◆ 163

Activity

Mass The mass of the potato is 0.25 kilograms. You would need 4 potatoes to make one kilogram. If students need more practice, give them various objects, such as coins, paper clips, and books, to measure mass.

Activity

Temperature The temperature of the liquid is 35°C. Students who need more practice can measure the temperatures of various water samples.

Converting SI Units

Focus Review the steps for converting SI units, and work through the example with students.

Teach Ask: **How many millimeters are in 80 centimeters?** (*With the relationship 10 millimeters = 1 centimeter, students should follow the steps to calculate that 80 centimeters is equal to 800 millimeters.*) Have students do the conversion problems in the activity.

Activity

1. 600 millimeters = 0.6 meters
2. 0.35 liters = 350 milliliters
3. 1,050 grams = 1.05 kilograms
If students need more practice converting SI units, have them make up conversion problems to trade with partners.

Conducting a Scientific Investigation

Students can refer to this part of the Skills Handbook whenever they need to review the steps of a scientific investigation. You can use the activities here to teach or reinforce these steps.

Posing Questions

Focus Ask: **What do you do when you want to learn about something?** (*Answers might include asking questions about it or looking for information in books or on the Internet.*) Explain that scientists go through the same process to learn about something.

Teach Tell students that the questions scientists ask may have no answers or many different answers. To answer their questions, scientists often conduct experiments. Ask: **Why is a scientific question important to a scientific investigation?** (*It helps the scientist decide if an experiment is necessary; the answer might already be known. It also helps focus the idea so that the scientist can form a hypothesis.*) **What is the scientific question in the activity on the next page?** (*Is a ball's bounce affected by the height from which it is dropped?*)

Developing a Hypothesis

Focus Emphasize that a hypothesis is one possible explanation for a set of observations. It is *not* a guess. It is often based on an inference.

Teach Ask: **On what information do scientists base their hypotheses?** (*Their observations and previous knowledge or experience*) Point out that a hypothesis does not always turn out to be correct. Ask: **When a hypothesis turns out to be incorrect, do you think the scientist wasted his or her time? Explain.** (*No. The scientist learned from the investigation and will develop another hypothesis that could prove to be correct.*)

Designing an Experiment

Focus Have a volunteer read the Experimental Procedure in the box. Invite students to identify the manipulated variable (*amount of salt*), the variables kept constant (*amount and temperature of water, location of containers*), the control (*Container 3*), and the responding variable (*time required for the water to freeze*).

Conducting a Scientific Investigation

In some ways, scientists are like detectives, piecing together clues to learn about a process or event. One way that scientists gather clues is by carrying out experiments. An experiment tests an idea in a careful, orderly manner. Although experiments do not all follow the same steps in the same order, many follow a pattern similar to the one described here.

Posing Questions

Experiments begin by asking a scientific question. A scientific question is one that can be answered by gathering evidence. For example, the question "Which freezes faster—fresh water or salt water?" is a scientific question because you can carry out an investigation and gather information to answer the question.

Developing a Hypothesis

The next step is to form a hypothesis. A **hypothesis** is a possible explanation for a set of observations or answer to a scientific question. In science, a hypothesis must be something that can be tested. A hypothesis can be worded as an *If . . . then . . .* statement. For example, a hypothesis might be *"If I add salt to fresh water, then the water will take longer to freeze."* A hypothesis worded this way serves as a rough outline of the experiment you should perform.

Teach Ask: **How might the experiment be affected if Container 1 had only 100 milliliters of water?** (*It wouldn't be an accurate comparison with the containers that have more water.*) Also make sure that students understand the importance of the control. Then, ask: **What operational definition is used in this experiment?** (*"Frozen" means the time at which a wooden stick can no longer move in a container.*)

Designing an Experiment

Next you need to plan a way to test your hypothesis. Your plan should be written out as a step-by-step procedure and should describe the observations or measurements you will make.

Two important steps involved in designing an experiment are controlling variables and forming operational definitions.

Controlling Variables In a well-designed experiment, you need to keep all variables the same except for one. A **variable** is any factor that can change in an experiment. The factor that you change is called the **manipulated variable**. In this experiment, the manipulated variable is the amount of salt added to the water. Other factors, such as the amount of water or the starting temperature, are kept constant.

The factor that changes as a result of the manipulated variable is called the **responding variable**. The responding variable is what you measure or observe to obtain your results. In this experiment, the responding variable is how long the water takes to freeze.

An experiment in which all factors except one are kept constant is called a **controlled experiment.** Most controlled experiments include a test called the control. In this experiment, Container 3 is the control. Because no salt is added to Container 3, you can compare the results from the other containers to it. Any difference in results must be due to the addition of salt alone.

Forming Operational Definitions Another important aspect of a well-designed experiment is having clear operational definitions. An **operational definition** is a statement that describes how a particular variable is to be measured or how a term is to be defined. For example, in this experiment, how will you determine if the water has frozen? You might decide to insert a stick in each container at the start of the experiment. Your operational definition of "frozen" would be the time at which the stick can no longer move.

Experimental Procedure

1. Fill 3 containers with 300 milliliters of cold tap water.

2. Add 10 grams of salt to Container 1; stir. Add 20 grams of salt to Container 2; stir. Add no salt to Container 3.

3. Place the 3 containers in a freezer.

4. Check the containers every 15 minutes. Record your observations.

Interpreting Data

The observations and measurements you make in an experiment are called **data.** At the end of an experiment, you need to analyze the data to look for any patterns or trends. Patterns often become clear if you organize your data in a data table or graph. Then think through what the data reveal. Do they support your hypothesis? Do they point out a flaw in your experiment? Do you need to collect more data?

Drawing Conclusions

A **conclusion** is a statement that sums up what you have learned from an experiment. When you draw a conclusion, you need to decide whether the data you collected support your hypothesis or not. You may need to repeat an experiment several times before you can draw any conclusions from it. Conclusions often lead you to pose new questions and plan new experiments to answer them.

Activity

Is a ball's bounce affected by the height from which it is dropped? Using the steps just described, plan a controlled experiment to investigate this problem.

Skills Handbook ◆ 165

Interpreting Data

Focus Ask: **What kind of data would you collect from the experiment with freezing salt water?** (*Time and state of the water*)

Teach Ask: **What if you forgot to record some data during an investigation?** (*You wouldn't be able to draw valid conclusions because some data are missing.*) Then, ask: **Why are data tables and graphs a good way to organize data?** (*They make it easier to record data accurately, as well as compare and analyze data.*) **What kind of data table and graph might you use for this experiment?** (*A table would have columns for each container with a row for each time interval in which the state of water is recorded. A bar graph would show the time elapsed until water froze for each container.*)

Drawing Conclusions

Focus Help students understand that a conclusion is not necessarily the end of a scientific investigation. A conclusion about one experiment may lead right into another experiment.

Teach Point out that in scientific investigations, a conclusion is a summary and explanation of the results of an experiment. For the Experimental Procedure described on this page, tell students to suppose that they obtained the following results: Container 1 froze in 45 minutes, Container 2 in 80 minutes, and Container 3 in 25 minutes. Ask: **What conclusions can you draw from this experiment?** (*Students might conclude that water takes longer to freeze as more salt is added to it. The hypothesis is supported, and the question of which freezes faster is answered—fresh water.*)

Activity

You might wish to have students work in pairs to plan the controlled experiment. Students should develop a hypothesis, such as, "If I increase the height from which a ball is dropped, then the height of its bounce will increase." They can test the hypothesis by dropping a ball from varying heights (the manipulated variable). All trials should be done with the same kind of ball and on the same surface (constants). For each trial, they should measure the height of the bounce (responding variable). After students have designed the experiment, provide rubber balls, and invite them to carry out the experiment so they can collect and interpret data and draw conclusions.

Technology Design Skills

Students can refer to this part of the Skills Handbook whenever they need to review the process of designing new technologies. You can use the activities here to teach or reinforce the steps in this process.

Identify a Need

Focus Solicit from students any situations in which they have thought that a tool, machine, or other object would be really helpful to them or others. Explain that this is the first step in the design of new products.

Teach Point out that identifying specific needs is very important to the design process. Ask: **If it was specified that the toy boat be wind-powered, how might that affect the design?** (*The boat would likely be designed with sails.*)

Research the Problem

Focus Explain that research focuses the problem so that the design is more specific.

Teach Ask: **What might happen if you didn't research the problem before designing the solution?** (*Answers include developing a design that has already been found to fail, using materials that aren't the best, or designing a solution that already exists.*) **What would you research before designing your toy boat?** (*Students might research designs and materials.*)

Design a Solution

Focus Emphasize the importance of a design team. Ask: **Why are brainstorming sessions important in product design?** (*A group will propose more new ideas than one person.*)

Teach Divide the class into teams to design the toy boat. Instruct them to brainstorm design ideas. Then, ask: **Why do you think engineers evaluate constraints after brainstorming?** (*Evaluating constraints while brainstorming often stops the flow of new ideas.*) **What design constraints do you have for your toy boat?** (*Materials must be readily available and teacher-approved. The boat must be 15 centimeters or less in length and must travel 2 meters in a straight line carrying a load of 20 pennies.*)

Technology Design Skills

Engineers are people who use scientific and technological knowledge to solve practical problems. To design new products, engineers usually follow the process described here, even though they may not follow these steps in the exact order. As you read the steps, think about how you might apply them in technology labs.

Identify a Need

Before engineers begin designing a new product, they must first identify the need they are trying to meet. For example, suppose you are a member of a design team in a company that makes toys. Your team has identified a need: a toy boat that is inexpensive and easy to assemble.

Research the Problem

Engineers often begin by gathering information that will help them with their new design. This research may include finding articles in books, magazines, or on the Internet. It may also include talking to other engineers who have solved similar problems. Engineers often perform experiments related to the product they want to design.

For your toy boat, you could look at toys that are similar to the one you want to design. You might do research on the Internet. You could also test some materials to see whether they will work well in a toy boat.

Drawing for a boat design ▼

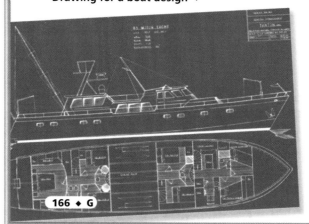

Design a Solution

Research gives engineers information that helps them design a product. When engineers design new products, they usually work in teams.

Generating Ideas Often design teams hold brainstorming meetings in which any team member can contribute ideas. **Brainstorming** is a creative process in which one team member's suggestions often spark ideas in other group members. Brainstorming can lead to new approaches to solving a design problem.

Evaluating Constraints During brainstorming, a design team will often come up with several possible designs. The team must then evaluate each one.

As part of their evaluation, engineers consider constraints. **Constraints** are factors that limit or restrict a product design. Physical characteristics, such as the properties of materials used to make your toy boat, are constraints. Money and time are also constraints. If the materials in a product cost a lot, or if the product takes a long time to make, the design may be impractical.

Making Trade-offs Design teams usually need to make trade-offs. In a **trade-off,** engineers give up one benefit of a proposed design in order to obtain another. In designing your toy boat, you will have to make trade-offs. For example, suppose one material is sturdy but not fully waterproof. Another material is more waterproof, but breakable. You may decide to give up the benefit of sturdiness in order to obtain the benefit of waterproofing.

Build and Evaluate a Prototype

Once the team has chosen a design plan, the engineers build a prototype of the product. A **prototype** is a working model used to test a design. Engineers evaluate the prototype to see whether it works well, is easy to operate, is safe to use, and holds up to repeated use.

Think of your toy boat. What would the prototype be like? Of what materials would it be made? How would you test it?

Troubleshoot and Redesign

Few prototypes work perfectly, which is why they need to be tested. Once a design team has tested a prototype, the members analyze the results and identify any problems. The team then tries to **troubleshoot,** or fix the design problems. For example, if your toy boat leaks or wobbles, the boat should be redesigned to eliminate those problems.

Communicate the Solution

A team needs to communicate the final design to the people who will manufacture and use the product. To do this, teams may use sketches, detailed drawings, computer simulations, and word descriptions.

Activity

You can use the technology design process to design and build a toy boat.

Research and Investigate

1. Visit the library or go online to research toy boats.

2. Investigate how a toy boat can be powered, including wind, rubber bands, or baking soda and vinegar.

3. Brainstorm materials, shapes, and steering for your boat.

Design and Build

4. Based on your research, design a toy boat that
   • is made of readily available materials
   • is no larger than 15 cm long and 10 cm wide

   • includes a power system, a rudder, and an area for cargo
   • travels 2 meters in a straight line carrying a load of 20 pennies

5. Sketch your design and write a step-by-step plan for building your boat. After your teacher approves your plan, build your boat.

Evaluate and Redesign

6. Test your boat, evaluate the results, and troubleshoot any problems.

7. Based on your evaluation, redesign your toy boat so it performs better.

Skills Handbook ◆ 167

Build and Evaluate a Prototype

Focus Explain that building a prototype enables engineers to test design ideas.

Teach Relate building and testing a prototype to conducting an experiment. Explain that engineers set up controlled experiments to test the prototype. Ask: **Why do you think engineers set up controlled experiments?** (*From the data, they can determine which component of the design is working and which is failing.*) **How would you test your prototype of the toy boat**? (*Answers will vary depending on the toy boat's propulsion system.*)

Troubleshoot and Redesign

Focus Make sure students know what it means to troubleshoot. If necessary, give an example. One example is a stapler that isn't working. In that case, you would check to see if it is out of staples or if the staples are jammed. Then you would fix the problem and try stapling again. If it still didn't work, you might check the position of staples and try again.

Teach Explain that engineers often are not surprised if the prototype doesn't work. Ask: **Why isn't it a failure if the prototype doesn't work?** (*Engineers learn from the problems and make changes to address the problems. This process makes the design better.*) Emphasize that prototypes are completely tested before the product is made in the factory.

Communicate the Solution

Focus Inquire whether students have ever read the instruction manual that comes with a new toy or electronic device.

Teach Emphasize the importance of good communication in the design process. Ask: **What might happen if engineers did not communicate their design ideas clearly?** (*The product might not be manufactured correctly or used properly.*)

Activity

The design possibilities are endless. Students might use small plastic containers, wood, foil, or plastic drinking cups for the boat. Materials may also include toothpicks, straws, or small wooden dowels. Brainstorm with students the different ways in which a toy boat can be propelled. The boats may be any shape, but must be no longer than 15 centimeters.

As student groups follow the steps in the design process, have them record their sources, brainstorming ideas, and prototype design in a logbook. Also give them time to troubleshoot and redesign their boats. When students turn in their boats, they should include assembly directions with a diagram, as well as instructions for use.

Creating Data Tables and Graphs

Students can refer to this part of the Skills Handbook whenever they need to review the skills required to create data tables and graphs. You can use the activities provided here to teach or reinforce these skills.

Data Tables

Focus Emphasize the importance of organizing data. Ask: **What might happen if you didn't use a data table for an experiment?** (*Possible answers include that data might not be collected or they might be forgotten.*)

Teach Have students create a data table to show how much time they spend on different activities during one week. Suggest that students first list the main activities they do every week. Then they should determine the amount of time they spend on each activity each day. Remind students to give the data table a title. A sample data table is shown below.

Bar Graphs

Focus Have students compare and contrast the data table and the bar graph on this page. Ask: **Why would you make a bar graph if the data are already organized in a table?** (*The bar graph organizes the data in a visual way that makes them easier to interpret.*)

Teach Students can use the data from the data table they created to make a bar graph that shows the amount of time they spend on different activities during a week. The vertical axis should be divided into units of time, such as hours. Remind students to label both axes and give their graph a title. A sample bar graph is shown below.

Creating Data Tables and Graphs

How can you make sense of the data in a science experiment? The first step is to organize the data to help you understand them. Data tables and graphs are helpful tools for organizing data.

Data Tables

You have gathered your materials and set up your experiment. But before you start, you need to plan a way to record what happens during the experiment. By creating a data table, you can record your observations and measurements in an orderly way.

Suppose, for example, that a scientist conducted an experiment to find out how many Calories people of different body masses burn while doing various activities. The data table shows the results.

Notice in this data table that the manipulated variable (body mass) is the heading of one column. The responding variable (for

Calories Burned in 30 Minutes

Body Mass	Experiment 1: Bicycling	Experiment 2: Playing Basketball	Experiment 3: Watching Television
30 kg	60 Calories	120 Calories	21 Calories
40 kg	77 Calories	164 Calories	27 Calories
50 kg	95 Calories	206 Calories	33 Calories
60 kg	114 Calories	248 Calories	38 Calories

Experiment 1, the number of Calories burned while bicycling) is the heading of the next column. Additional columns were added for related experiments.

Bar Graphs

To compare how many Calories a person burns doing various activities, you could create a bar graph. A bar graph is used to display data in a number of separate, or distinct, categories. In this example, bicycling, playing basketball, and watching television are the three categories.

To create a bar graph, follow these steps.

1. On graph paper, draw a horizontal, or *x*-, axis and a vertical, or *y*-, axis.

2. Write the names of the categories to be graphed along the horizontal axis. Include an overall label for the axis as well.

3. Label the vertical axis with the name of the responding variable. Include units of measurement. Then create a scale along the axis by marking off equally spaced numbers that cover the range of the data collected.

4. For each category, draw a solid bar using the scale on the vertical axis to determine the height. Make all the bars the same width.

5. Add a title that describes the graph.

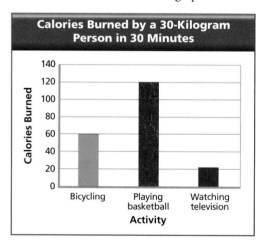

Calories Burned by a 30-Kilogram Person in 30 Minutes

Time Spent on Different Activities in a Week

	Going to Classes	Eating Meals	Playing Soccer	Watching Television
Monday	6	2	2	0.5
Tuesday	6	1.5	1.5	1.5
Wednesday	6	2	1	2
Thursday	6	2	2	1.5
Friday	6	2	2	0.5
Saturday	0	2.5	2.5	1
Sunday	0	3	1	2

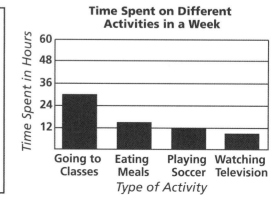

Time Spent on Different Activities in a Week

Line Graphs

To see whether a relationship exists between body mass and the number of Calories burned while bicycling, you could create a line graph. A line graph is used to display data that show how one variable (the responding variable) changes in response to another variable (the manipulated variable). You can use a line graph when your manipulated variable is **continuous,** that is, when there are other points between the ones that you tested. In this example, body mass is a continuous variable because there are other body masses between 30 and 40 kilograms (for example, 31 kilograms). Time is another example of a continuous variable.

Line graphs are powerful tools because they allow you to estimate values for conditions that you did not test in the experiment. For example, you can use the line graph to estimate that a 35-kilogram person would burn 68 Calories while bicycling.

To create a line graph, follow these steps.

1. On graph paper, draw a horizontal, or *x-*, axis and a vertical, or *y-*, axis.

2. Label the horizontal axis with the name of the manipulated variable. Label the vertical axis with the name of the responding variable. Include units of measurement.

3. Create a scale on each axis by marking off equally spaced numbers that cover the range of the data collected.

4. Plot a point on the graph for each piece of data. In the line graph above, the dotted lines show how to plot the first data point (30 kilograms and 60 Calories). Follow an imaginary vertical line extending up from the horizontal axis at the 30-kilogram mark. Then follow an imaginary horizontal line extending across from the vertical axis at the 60-Calorie mark. Plot the point where the two lines intersect.

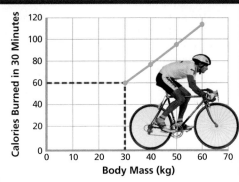

Effect of Body Mass on Calories Burned While Bicycling

5. Connect the plotted points with a solid line. (In some cases, it may be more appropriate to draw a line that shows the general trend of the plotted points. In those cases, some of the points may fall above or below the line. Also, not all graphs are linear. It may be more appropriate to draw a curve to connect the points.)

6. Add a title that identifies the variables or relationship in the graph.

Activity

Create line graphs to display the data from Experiment 2 and Experiment 3 in the data table.

Activity

You read in the newspaper that a total of 4 centimeters of rain fell in your area in June, 2.5 centimeters fell in July, and 1.5 centimeters fell in August. What type of graph would you use to display these data? Use graph paper to create the graph.

Line Graphs

Focus Ask: **Would a bar graph show the relationship between body mass and the number of Calories burned in 30 minutes?** (*No. Bar graphs can only show data in distinct categories.*) Explain that line graphs are used to show how one variable changes in response to another variable.

Teach Walk students through the steps involved in creating a line graph using the example illustrated on the page. For example, ask: **What is the label on the horizontal axis? On the vertical axis?** (*Body Mass (kg); Calories Burned in 30 Minutes*) **What scale is used on each axis?** (*10 kg on the x-axis and 20 Calories on the y-axis*) **What does the second data point represent?** (*77 Calories burned for a body mass of 40 kg*) **What trend or pattern does the graph show?** (*The number of Calories burned in 30 minutes of cycling increases with body mass.*)

Activity

Students should make a different graph for each experiment. Each graph should have a different *x*-axis scale that is appropriate for the data. See sample graphs below.

Activity

Students should conclude that a bar graph would be best for displaying the data.

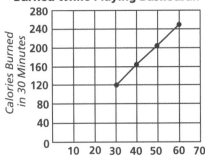

Effect of Body Mass on Calories Burned While Playing Basketball

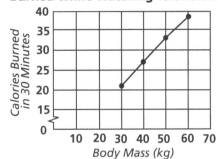

Effect of Body Mass on Calories Burned While Watching Television

Circle Graphs

Focus Emphasize that a circle graph must include 100 percent of the categories for the topic being graphed. For example, ask: **Could the data in the bar graph titled "Calories Burned by a 30-Kilogram Person in Various Activities" (on the previous page) be shown in a circle graph? Why or why not?** *(No. It does not include all the possible ways a 30-kilogram person can burn Calories.)*

Teach Walk students through the steps for making a circle graph. If necessary, help them with the compass and the protractor. Use the protractor to illustrate that a circle has 360 degrees. Make sure students understand the mathematical calculations involved in making a circle graph.

Activity

You might have students work in pairs to complete the activity. Students' circle graphs should look like the graph below.

Ways Students Get to School

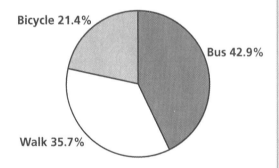

Circle Graphs

Like bar graphs, circle graphs can be used to display data in a number of separate categories. Unlike bar graphs, however, circle graphs can only be used when you have data for *all* the categories that make up a given topic. A circle graph is sometimes called a pie chart. The pie represents the entire topic, while the slices represent the individual categories. The size of a slice indicates what percentage of the whole a particular category makes up.

The data table below shows the results of a survey in which 24 teenagers were asked to identify their favorite sport. The data were then used to create the circle graph at the right.

Favorite Sports

Sport	Students
Soccer	8
Basketball	6
Bicycling	6
Swimming	4

To create a circle graph, follow these steps.

1. Use a compass to draw a circle. Mark the center with a point. Then draw a line from the center point to the top of the circle.

2. Determine the size of each "slice" by setting up a proportion where *x* equals the number of degrees in a slice. (*Note:* A circle contains 360 degrees.) For example, to find the number of degrees in the "soccer" slice, set up the following proportion:

$$\frac{\text{Students who prefer soccer}}{\text{Total number of students}} = \frac{x}{\text{Total number of degrees in a circle}}$$

$$\frac{8}{24} = \frac{x}{360}$$

Cross-multiply and solve for x.

$$24x = 8 \times 360$$
$$x = 120$$

The "soccer" slice should contain 120 degrees.

Sports That Teens Prefer

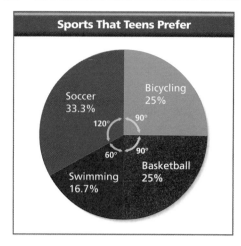

3. Use a protractor to measure the angle of the first slice, using the line you drew to the top of the circle as the 0° line. Draw a line from the center of the circle to the edge for the angle you measured.

4. Continue around the circle by measuring the size of each slice with the protractor. Start measuring from the edge of the previous slice so the wedges do not overlap. When you are done, the entire circle should be filled in.

5. Determine the percentage of the whole circle that each slice represents. To do this, divide the number of degrees in a slice by the total number of degrees in a circle (360), and multiply by 100%. For the "soccer" slice, you can find the percentage as follows:

$$\frac{120}{360} \times 100\% = 33.3\%$$

6. Use a different color for each slice. Label each slice with the category and with the percentage of the whole it represents.

7. Add a title to the circle graph.

Activity

In a class of 28 students, 12 students take the bus to school, 10 students walk, and 6 students ride their bicycles. Create a circle graph to display these data.

Math Review

Scientists use math to organize, analyze, and present data.
This appendix will help you review some basic math skills.

Mean, Median, and Mode

The **mean** is the average, or the sum of the data divided by the number of data items. The middle number in a set of ordered data is called the **median**. The **mode** is the number that appears most often in a set of data.

> **Example**
>
> A scientist counted the number of distinct songs sung by seven different male birds and collected the data shown below.
>
> | Male Bird Songs | | | | | | |
> |---|---|---|---|---|---|---|
> | Bird | A | B | C | D | E | F | G |
> | Number of Songs | 36 | 29 | 40 | 35 | 28 | 36 | 27 |
>
> To determine the mean number of songs, add the total number of songs and divide by the number of data items—in this case, the number of male birds.
>
> $$\text{Mean} = \frac{231}{7} = 33 \text{ songs}$$
>
> To find the median number of songs, arrange the data in numerical order and find the number in the middle of the series.
>
> **27 28 29 35 36 36 40**
>
> The number in the middle is 35, so the median number of songs is 35.
>
> The mode is the value that appears most frequently. In the data, 36 appears twice, while each other item appears only once. Therefore, 36 songs is the mode.

> **Practice**
>
> Find out how many minutes it takes each student in your class to get to school. Then find the mean, median, and mode for the data.

Probability

Probability is the chance that an event will occur. Probability can be expressed as a ratio, a fraction, or a percentage. For example, when you flip a coin, the probability that the coin will land heads up is 1 in 2, or $\frac{1}{2}$, or 50 percent.

The probability that an event will happen can be expressed in the following formula.

$$P(\text{event}) = \frac{\text{Number of times the event can occur}}{\text{Total number of possible events}}$$

> **Example**
>
> A paper bag contains 25 blue marbles, 5 green marbles, 5 orange marbles, and 15 yellow marbles. If you close your eyes and pick a marble from the bag, what is the probability that it will be yellow?
>
> $$P(\text{yellow marbles}) = \frac{15 \text{ yellow marbles}}{50 \text{ marbles total}}$$
>
> $$P = \frac{15}{50}, \text{ or } \frac{3}{10}, \text{ or } 30\%$$

> **Practice**
>
> Each side of a cube has a letter on it. Two sides have *A*, three sides have *B*, and one side has *C*. If you roll the cube, what is the probability that *A* will land on top?

Math Review

Students can refer to this part of the Skills Handbook whenever they need to review some basic math skills. You can use the activities provided here to teach or reinforce these skills.

Mean, Median, and Mode

Focus Remind students that data from an experiment might consist of hundreds or thousands of numbers. Unless analyzed, the numbers likely will not be helpful.

Teach Work through the process of determining mean, median, and mode using the example in the book. Make sure students realize that these three numbers do not always equal each other. Point out that taken together, these three numbers give more information about the data than just one of the numbers alone.

> **Practice**
>
> Answers will vary based on class data. The mean should equal the total number of minutes divided by the number of students. The median should equal the number in the middle after arranging the data in numerical order. The mode should equal the number of minutes that is given most frequently.

Probability

Focus Show students a coin and ask: **What is the chance that I will get tails when I flip the coin?** (*Some students might know that there is a 1 in 2, or 50 percent, chance of getting tails.*)

Teach Set up a bag of marbles like the one in the example. Allow students to practice determining the probabilities of picking marbles of different colors. Then, encourage them to actually pick marbles and compare their actual results with those results predicted by probability.

> **Practice**
>
> $$P(A) = 2 \text{ sides with } \frac{A}{6} \text{ sides total}$$
> $$P = \frac{2}{6}, \text{ or } \frac{1}{3}, \text{ or } 33\%$$

Area

Focus Ask: **Who knows what area is?** (*Area is equal to the number of square units needed to cover a certain shape or object.*) On the board, write the formulas for the area of a rectangle and a circle.

Teach Give students various objects of different shapes. Have them measure each object and determine its area based on the measurements. Point out that the units of the answer are squared because they are multiplied together. If students are interested, you might also explain that π is equal to the ratio of the circumference of a circle to its diameter. For circles of all sizes, π is approximately equal to the number 3.14, or $\frac{22}{7}$.

Practice

The area of the circle is equal to
$21 \text{ m} \times 21 \text{ m} \times \frac{22}{7}$, or $1{,}386 \text{ m}^2$.

Circumference

Focus Draw a circle on the board. Then trace the outline with your finger and explain that this is the circumference of the circle, or the distance around it.

Teach Show students that the radius is equal to the distance from the center of the circle to any point on it. Point out that the diameter of a circle is equal to two times the radius. Give students paper circles of various sizes, and have them calculate the circumference of each.

Practice

The circumference is equal to $2 \times 28 \text{ m} \times \frac{22}{7}$, or 176 m.

Volume

Focus Fill a beaker with 100 milliliters of water. Ask: **What is the volume of water?** (*100 milliliters*) Explain that volume is the amount of space that something takes up. Then point out that one milliliter is equal to one cubic centimeter (cm^3).

Teach Write on the board the formulas for calculating the volumes of a rectangle and a cylinder. Point out that volume is equal to the area of an object multiplied by its height. Then measure the beaker to show students the relationship between liquid volume (100 milliliters) and the number of cubic units it contains (100 cubic centimeters).

Area

The **area** of a surface is the number of square units that cover it. The front cover of your textbook has an area of about 600 cm^2.

Area of a Rectangle and a Square To find the area of a rectangle, multiply its length times its width. The formula for the area of a rectangle is

$$A = \ell \times w, \text{ or } A = \ell w$$

Since all four sides of a square have the same length, the area of a square is the length of one side multiplied by itself, or squared.

$$A = s \times s, \text{ or } A = s^2$$

Example

A scientist is studying the plants in a field that measures 75 m × 45 m. What is the area of the field?

$$A = \ell \times w$$
$$A = 75 \text{ m} \times 45 \text{ m}$$
$$A = 3{,}375 \text{ m}^2$$

Area of a Circle The formula for the area of a circle is

$$A = \pi \times r \times r, \text{ or } A = \pi r^2$$

The length of the radius is represented by r, and the value of π is approximately $\frac{22}{7}$.

Example

Find the area of a circle with a radius of 14 cm.

$$A = \pi r^2$$
$$A = 14 \times 14 \times \frac{22}{7}$$
$$A = 616 \text{ cm}^2$$

Practice

Find the area of a circle that has a radius of 21 m.

Circumference

The distance around a circle is called the circumference. The formula for finding the circumference of a circle is

$$C = 2 \times \pi \times r, \text{ or } C = 2\pi r$$

Example

The radius of a circle is 35 cm. What is its circumference?

$$C = 2\pi r$$
$$C = 2 \times 35 \times \frac{22}{7}$$
$$C = 220 \text{ cm}$$

Practice

What is the circumference of a circle with a radius of 28 m?

Volume

The volume of an object is the number of cubic units it contains. The volume of a wastebasket, for example, might be about 26,000 cm^3.

Volume of a Rectangular Object To find the volume of a rectangular object, multiply the object's length times its width times its height.

$$V = \ell \times w \times h, \text{ or } V = \ell w h$$

Example

Find the volume of a box with length 24 cm, width 12 cm, and height 9 cm.

$$V = \ell w h$$
$$V = 24 \text{ cm} \times 12 \text{ cm} \times 9 \text{ cm}$$
$$V = 2{,}592 \text{ cm}^3$$

Practice

What is the volume of a rectangular object with length 17 cm, width 11 cm, and height 6 cm?

Practice

The volume of the rectangular object is equal to 17 cm × 11 cm × 6 cm, or 1,122 cm^3.

Fractions

A **fraction** is a way to express a part of a whole. In the fraction $\frac{4}{7}$, 4 is the numerator and 7 is the denominator.

Adding and Subtracting Fractions To add or subtract two or more fractions that have a common denominator, first add or subtract the numerators. Then write the sum or difference over the common denominator.

   To find the sum or difference of fractions with different denominators, first find the least common multiple of the denominators. This is known as the least common denominator. Then convert each fraction to equivalent fractions with the least common denominator. Add or subtract the numerators. Then write the sum or difference over the common denominator.

> **Example**
> $$\frac{5}{6} - \frac{3}{4} = \frac{10}{12} - \frac{9}{12} = \frac{10-9}{12} = \frac{1}{12}$$

Multiplying Fractions To multiply two fractions, first multiply the two numerators, then multiply the two denominators.

> **Example**
> $$\frac{5}{6} \times \frac{2}{3} = \frac{5 \times 2}{6 \times 3} = \frac{10}{18} = \frac{5}{9}$$

Dividing Fractions Dividing by a fraction is the same as multiplying by its reciprocal. Reciprocals are numbers whose numerators and denominators have been switched. To divide one fraction by another, first invert the fraction you are dividing by—in other words, turn it upside down. Then multiply the two fractions.

> **Example**
> $$\frac{2}{5} \div \frac{7}{8} = \frac{2}{5} \times \frac{8}{7} = \frac{2 \times 8}{5 \times 7} = \frac{16}{35}$$

> **Practice**
> Solve the following: $\frac{3}{7} \div \frac{4}{5}$.

Decimals

Fractions whose denominators are 10, 100, or some other power of 10 are often expressed as decimals. For example, the fraction $\frac{9}{10}$ can be expressed as the decimal 0.9, and the fraction $\frac{7}{100}$ can be written as 0.07.

Adding and Subtracting With Decimals To add or subtract decimals, line up the decimal points before you carry out the operation.

> **Example**
> $$\begin{array}{r} 27.4 \\ + \ 6.19 \\ \hline 33.59 \end{array} \qquad \begin{array}{r} 278.635 \\ - \ 191.4 \\ \hline 87.235 \end{array}$$

Multiplying With Decimals When you multiply two numbers with decimals, the number of decimal places in the product is equal to the total number of decimal places in each number being multiplied.

> **Example**
> $$\begin{array}{r} 46.2 \ \text{(one decimal place)} \\ \times \ 2.37 \ \text{(two decimal places)} \\ \hline 109.494 \ \text{(three decimal places)} \end{array}$$

Dividing With Decimals To divide a decimal by a whole number, put the decimal point in the quotient above the decimal point in the dividend.

> **Example**
> $$15.5 \div 5$$
> $$\begin{array}{r} 3.1 \\ 5\overline{)15.5} \end{array}$$

To divide a decimal by a decimal, you need to rewrite the divisor as a whole number. Do this by multiplying both the divisor and dividend by the same multiple of 10.

> **Example**
> $$1.68 \div 4.2 = 16.8 \div 42$$
> $$\begin{array}{r} 0.4 \\ 42\overline{)16.8} \end{array}$$

> **Practice**
> Multiply 6.21 by 8.5.

Fractions

Focus Draw a circle on the board, and divide it into eight equal sections. Shade in one of the sections, and explain that one out of eight, or one eighth, of the sections is shaded. Also use the circle to show that four eighths is the same as one half.

Teach Write the fraction $\frac{3}{4}$ on the board. Ask: **What is the numerator?** *(Three)* **What is the denominator?** *(Four)* Emphasize that when adding and subtracting fractions, the denominators of the two fractions must be the same. If necessary, review how to find the least common denominator. Remind students that when multiplying and dividing, the denominators do not have to be the same.

> **Practice**
> $$\frac{3}{7} \div \frac{4}{5} = \frac{3}{7} \times \frac{5}{4} = \frac{15}{28}$$

Decimals

Focus Write the number *129.835* on the board. Ask: **What number is in the ones position?** *(9)* **The tenths position?** *(8)* **The hundredths position?** *(3)* Make sure students know that 0.8 is equal to $\frac{8}{10}$ and 0.03 is equal to $\frac{3}{100}$.

Teach Use the examples in the book to review addition, subtraction, multiplication, and division with decimals. Make up a worksheet of similar problems to give students additional practice. Also show students how a fraction is converted to a decimal by dividing the numerator by the denominator. For example, $\frac{1}{2}$ is equal to 0.5.

> **Practice**
> $6.21 \times 8.5 = 52.785$

Ratio and Proportion

Focus Differentiate a ratio from a fraction. Remind students that a fraction tells how many parts of the whole. In contrast, a ratio compares two different numbers. For example, $\frac{12}{22}$, or $\frac{6}{11}$, of a class are girls. But the ratio of boys to girls in the class is 10 to 12, or $\frac{5}{6}$.

Teach Use the example in the book to explain how to use a proportion to find an unknown quantity. Provide students with additional practice problems, if needed.

> **Practice**

$6 \times 49 = 7x$
$294 = 7x$
$294 \div 7 = x$
$x = 42$

Percentage

Focus On the board, write $50\% = \frac{50}{100}$. Explain that a percentage is a ratio that compares a number to 100.

Teach Point out that when calculating percentages, you are usually using numbers other than 100. In this case, you set up a proportion. Go over the example in the book. Emphasize that the number representing the total goes on the bottom of the ratio, as does the 100%.

> **Practice**

Students should set up the proportion

$\frac{42 \text{ marbles}}{300 \text{ marbles}} = \frac{x\%}{100\%}$

$42 \times 100 = 300x$

$4200 = 300x$

$4200 \div 300 = 14\%$

Ratio and Proportion

A **ratio** compares two numbers by division. For example, suppose a scientist counts 800 wolves and 1,200 moose on an island. The ratio of wolves to moose can be written as a fraction, $\frac{800}{1,200}$, which can be reduced to $\frac{2}{3}$. The same ratio can also be expressed as 2 to 3 or 2 : 3.

A **proportion** is a mathematical sentence saying that two ratios are equivalent. For example, a proportion could state that $\frac{800 \text{ wolves}}{1,200 \text{ moose}} = \frac{2 \text{ wolves}}{3 \text{ moose}}$. You can sometimes set up a proportion to determine or estimate an unknown quantity. For example, suppose a scientist counts 25 beetles in an area of 10 square meters. The scientist wants to estimate the number of beetles in 100 square meters.

> **Example**
>
> 1. Express the relationship between beetles and area as a ratio: $\frac{25}{10}$, simplified to $\frac{5}{2}$.
> 2. Set up a proportion, with x representing the number of beetles. The proportion can be stated as $\frac{5}{2} = \frac{x}{100}$.
> 3. Begin by cross-multiplying. In other words, multiply each fraction's numerator by the other fraction's denominator.
>
> $5 \times 100 = 2 \times x$, or $500 = 2x$
>
> 4. To find the value of x, divide both sides by 2. The result is 250, or 250 beetles in 100 square meters.

> **Practice**
>
> Find the value of x in the following proportion: $\frac{6}{7} = \frac{x}{49}$.

Percentage

A **percentage** is a ratio that compares a number to 100. For example, there are 37 granite rocks in a collection that consists of 100 rocks. The ratio $\frac{37}{100}$ can be written as 37%. Granite rocks make up 37% of the rock collection.

You can calculate percentages of numbers other than 100 by setting up a proportion.

> **Example**
>
> Rain falls on 9 days out of 30 in June. What percentage of the days in June were rainy?
>
> $\frac{9 \text{ days}}{30 \text{ days}} = \frac{d\%}{100\%}$
>
> To find the value of d, begin by cross-multiplying, as for any proportion:
>
> $9 \times 100 = 30 \times d$ $d = \frac{900}{30}$ $d = 30$

> **Practice**
>
> There are 300 marbles in a jar, and 42 of those marbles are blue. What percentage of the marbles is blue?

Significant Figures

The **precision** of a measurement depends on the instrument you use to take the measurement. For example, if the smallest unit on the ruler is millimeters, then the most precise measurement you can make will be in millimeters.

The sum or difference of measurements can only be as precise as the least precise measurement being added or subtracted. Round your answer so that it has the same number of digits after the decimal as the least precise measurement. Round up if the last digit is 5 or more, and round down if the last digit is 4 or less.

Example

Subtract a temperature of 5.2°C from the temperature 75.46°C.

75.46 − 5.2 = 70.26

5.2 has the fewest digits after the decimal, so it is the least precise measurement. Since the last digit of the answer is 6, round up to 3. The most precise difference between the measurements is 70.3°C.

Practice

Add 26.4 m to 8.37 m. Round your answer according to the precision of the measurements.

Significant figures are the number of nonzero digits in a measurement. Zeroes between nonzero digits are also significant. For example, the measurements 12,500 L, 0.125 cm, and 2.05 kg all have three significant figures. When you multiply and divide measurements, the one with the fewest significant figures determines the number of significant figures in your answer.

Example

Multiply 110 g by 5.75 g.

110 × 5.75 = 632.5

Because 110 has only two significant figures, round the answer to 630 g.

Scientific Notation

A **factor** is a number that divides into another number with no remainder. In the example, the number 3 is used as a factor four times.

An **exponent** tells how many times a number is used as a factor. For example, $3 \times 3 \times 3 \times 3$ can be written as 3^4. The exponent 4 indicates that the number 3 is used as a factor four times. Another way of expressing this is to say that 81 is equal to 3 to the fourth power.

Example

$$3^4 = 3 \times 3 \times 3 \times 3 = 81$$

Scientific notation uses exponents and powers of ten to write very large or very small numbers in shorter form. When you write a number in scientific notation, you write the number as two factors. The first factor is any number between 1 and 10. The second factor is a power of 10, such as 10^3 or 10^6.

Example

The average distance between the planet Mercury and the sun is 58,000,000 km. To write the first factor in scientific notation, insert a decimal point in the original number so that you have a number between 1 and 10. In the case of 58,000,000, the number is 5.8.

To determine the power of 10, count the number of places that the decimal point moved. In this case, it moved 7 places.

58,000,000 km = 5.8 × 10^7 km

Practice

Express 6,590,000 in scientific notation.

Significant Figures

Focus Measure the length of a paper clip using two different rulers. Use one ruler that is less precise than the other. Compare the two measurements. Ask: **Which measurement is more precise?** (*The ruler with the smallest units will give the more precise measurement.*)

Teach Give students the opportunity to take measurements of an object using tools with different precision. Encourage students to add and subtract their measurements, making sure that they round the answers to reflect the precision of the instruments. Go over the example for significant digits. Check for understanding by asking: **How many significant digits are in the number 324,000?** (*Three*) **In the number 5, 901?** (*Four*) **In the number 0.706?** (*Three*) If students need additional practice, create a worksheet with problems in multiplying and dividing numbers with various significant digits.

Practice

26.4 m + 8.37 m = 34.77 m
This answer should be rounded to 34.8 m because the least precise measurement has only one digit after the decimal. This number is rounded up to 8 because the last digit is more than 5.

Scientific Notation

Focus Write a very large number on the board, such as 100 million, using all the zeros. Then, write the number using scientific notation. Ask: **Why do you think scientists prefer to write very large numbers using scientific notation?** (*Possible answers include that it is easier to do calculations, convert units, and make comparisons with other numbers.*)

Teach Go over the examples, and ask: **In the second example, which numbers are the factors?** (*5.8 and 10^7*) **Which number is the exponent?** (*7*) Explain that very small numbers have a negative exponent because the decimal point is moved to the right to produce the first factor. For example, 0.00000628 is equal to 6.28×10^{-6}.

Practice

$$6,590,000 = 6.59 \times 10^6$$

Reading Comprehension Skills

Students can refer to this part of the Skills Handbook whenever they need to review a reading skill. You can use the activities provided here to teach or reinforce these skills.

All in One **Teaching Resources**

• Target Reading Skills Handbook

Using Prior Knowledge

Focus Explain to students that using prior knowledge helps connect what they already know to what they are about to read.

Teach Point out that prior knowledge might not be accurate because memories have faded or perspectives have changed. Encourage students to ask questions to resolve discrepancies between their prior knowledge and what they have learned.

Asking Questions

Focus Demonstrate to students how to change a text heading into a question to help them anticipate the concepts, facts, and events they will read about.

Teach Encourage students to use this reading skill for the next section they read. Instruct them to turn the text headings into questions. Also challenge students to write at least four *what, how, why, who, when,* or *where* questions. Then, have students evaluate the skill. Ask: **Did asking questions about the text help you focus on the reading and remember what you read?** *(Answers will vary, but encourage honesty.)* If this reading skill didn't help, challenge them to assess why not.

Previewing Visuals

Focus Explain to students that looking at the visuals before reading will help them activate prior knowledge and predict what they are about to read.

Teach Assign a section for students to preview the visuals. First, instruct them to write a sentence describing what the section will be about. Then, encourage them to write one or two questions for each visual to give purpose to their reading. Also have them list any prior knowledge about the subject.

Reading Comprehension Skills

Each section in your textbook introduces a Target Reading Skill. You will improve your reading comprehension by using the Target Reading Skills described below.

Using Prior Knowledge

Your prior knowledge is what you already know before you begin to read about a topic. Building on what you already know gives you a head start on learning new information. Before you begin a new assignment, think about what you know. You might look at the headings and the visuals to spark your memory. You can list what you know. Then, as you read, consider questions like these.

• How does what you learn relate to what you know?

• How did something you already know help you learn something new?

• Did your original ideas agree with what you have just learned?

Asking Questions

Asking yourself questions is an excellent way to focus on and remember new information in your textbook. For example, you can turn the text headings into questions. Then your questions can guide you to identify the important information as you read. Look at these examples:

Heading: Using Seismographic Data

Question: How are seismographic data used?

Heading: Kinds of Faults

Question: What are the kinds of faults?

You do not have to limit your questions to text headings. Ask questions about anything that you need to clarify or that will help you understand the content. *What* and *how* are probably the most common question words, but you may also ask *why, who, when,* or *where* questions.

Previewing Visuals

Visuals are photographs, graphs, tables, diagrams, and illustrations. Visuals contain important information. Before you read, look at visuals and their labels and captions. This preview will help you prepare for what you will be reading.

Often you will be asked what you want to learn about a visual. For example, after you look at the normal fault diagram below, you might ask: What is the movement along a normal fault? Questions about visuals give you a purpose for reading—to answer your questions.

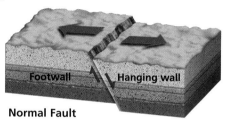

Normal Fault

Outlining

An outline shows the relationship between main ideas and supporting ideas. An outline has a formal structure. You write the main ideas, called topics, next to Roman numerals. The supporting ideas, called subtopics, are written under the main ideas and labeled A, B, C, and so on. An outline looks like this:

Technology and Society
I. Technology through history
II. The impact of technology on society
A.
B.

Outlining

Focus Explain that using an outline format helps organize information by main topic, subtopic, and details.

Teach Choose a section in the book, and demonstrate how to make an outline for it. Make sure students understand the structure of the outline by asking: **Is this a topic or a subtopic? Where does this information go in the outline? Would I write this heading next to a Roman numeral or a capital letter?** *(Answers depend on the section being outlined.)* Also show them how to indent and add details to the outline using numerals and lowercase letters.

Identifying Main Ideas

When you are reading science material, it is important to try to understand the ideas and concepts that are in a passage. Each paragraph has a lot of information and detail. Good readers try to identify the most important—or biggest—idea in every paragraph or section. That's the main idea. The other information in the paragraph supports or further explains the main idea.

Sometimes main ideas are stated directly. In this book, some main ideas are identified for you as key concepts. These are printed in boldface type. However, you must identify other main ideas yourself. In order to do this, you must identify all the ideas within a paragraph or section. Then ask yourself which idea is big enough to include all the other ideas.

Comparing and Contrasting

When you compare and contrast, you examine the similarities and differences between things. You can compare and contrast in a Venn diagram or in a table.

Venn Diagram A Venn diagram consists of two overlapping circles. In the space where the circles overlap, you write the characteristics that the two items have in common. In one of the circles outside the area of overlap, you write the differing features or characteristics of one of the items. In the other circle outside the area of overlap, you write the differing characteristics of the other item.

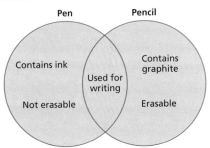

Table

Table In a compare/contrast table, you list the characteristics or features to be compared across the top of the table. Then list the items to be compared in the left column. Complete the table by filling in information about each characteristic or feature.

Blood Vessel	Function	Structure of Wall
Artery	Carries blood away from heart	
Capillary		
Vein		

Identifying Supporting Evidence

A hypothesis is a possible explanation for observations made by scientists or an answer to a scientific question. Scientists must carry out investigations and gather evidence that either supports or disproves the hypothesis.

Identifying the supporting evidence for a hypothesis or theory can help you understand the hypothesis or theory. Evidence consists of facts—information whose accuracy can be confirmed by testing or observation.

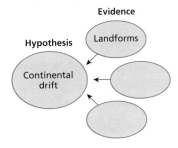

Identifying Main Ideas

Focus Explain that identifying main ideas and details helps sort the facts from the information into groups. Each group can have a main topic, subtopics, and details.

Teach Tell students that paragraphs are often written so that the main idea is in the first or second sentence, or in the last sentence. Assign students a page in the book. Instruct them to write the main idea for each paragraph on that page. If students have difficulty finding the main idea, suggest that they list all of the ideas given in the paragraph, and then choose the idea that is big enough to include all the others.

Comparing and Contrasting

Focus Explain that comparing and contrasting information shows how concepts, facts, and events are similar or different. The results of the comparison can have importance.

Teach Point out that Venn diagrams work best when comparing two things. To compare more than two things, students should use a compare/contrast table. Have students make a Venn diagram or compare/contrast table using two or more different sports or other activities, such as playing musical instruments. Emphasize that students should select characteristics that highlight the similarities and differences in the activities.

Identifying Supporting Evidence

Focus Explain to students that identifying the supporting evidence will help them to understand the relationship between the facts and the hypothesis.

Teach Remind students that a hypothesis is neither right nor wrong, but it is either supported or not supported by the evidence from testing or observation. If evidence is found that does not support a hypothesis, the hypothesis can be changed to accommodate the new evidence, or it can be dropped.

Sequencing

Focus Tell students that organizing information from beginning to end will help them understand a step-by-step process.

Teach Encourage students to create a flowchart to show the things they did this morning to get ready for school. Remind students that a flowchart should show the correct order in which events occur. *(A typical flowchart might include: got up → took a shower → got dressed → ate breakfast → brushed teeth → gathered books and homework → put on jacket.)*

Then explain that a cycle diagram shows a sequence of events that is continuous. Point out the cycle diagram that shows how the weather changes with the seasons of the year. Ask: **Why is a cycle diagram used instead of a flowchart to show the sequence of the seasons?** *(A cycle diagram shows that the sequence is continuous, not just a series of events.)* Challenge students to make a sequence diagram for a section of the text. Have them explain why they chose either a cycle diagram or a flowchart. Remind them to include at least four steps in the sequence.

Relating Cause and Effect

Focus Explain to students that cause is the reason for what happens. The effect is what happens in response to the cause. Relating cause and effect helps students relate the reason for what happens to what happens as a result.

Teach Emphasize that not all events that occur together have a cause-and-effect relationship. For example, tell students that you went to the grocery store and your car stalled. Ask: **Is there a cause-and-effect relationship in this situation? Explain.** *(No. Going to the grocery store could not cause a car to stall. There must be another cause to make the car stall.)*

Sequencing

A sequence is the order in which a series of events occurs. A flowchart or a cycle diagram can help you visualize a sequence.

Flowchart To make a flowchart, write a brief description of each step or event in a box. Place the boxes in order, with the first event at the top of the page. Then draw an arrow to connect each step or event to the next.

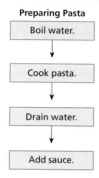

Preparing Pasta

Boil water.
↓
Cook pasta.
↓
Drain water.
↓
Add sauce.

Cycle Diagram A cycle diagram shows a sequence that is continuous, or cyclical. A continuous sequence does not have an end because when the final event is over, the first event begins again. To create a cycle diagram, write the starting event in a box placed at the top of a page in the center. Then, moving in a clockwise direction, write each event in a box in its proper sequence. Draw arrows that connect each event to the one that occurs next.

Seasons of the Year

Winter → Spring → Summer → Fall → Winter

Relating Cause and Effect

Science involves many cause-and-effect relationships. A cause makes something happen. An effect is what happens. When you recognize that one event causes another, you are relating cause and effect.

Words like *cause, because, effect, affect,* and *result* often signal a cause or an effect. Sometimes an effect can have more than one cause, or a cause can produce several effects.

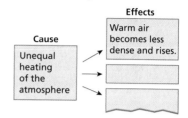

Cause
Unequal heating of the atmosphere

Effects
Warm air becomes less dense and rises.

Concept Mapping

Concept maps are useful tools for organizing information on any topic. A concept map begins with a main idea or core concept and shows how the idea can be subdivided into related subconcepts or smaller ideas.

You construct a concept map by placing concepts (usually nouns) in ovals and connecting them with linking words (usually verbs). The biggest concept or idea is placed in an oval at the top of the map. Related concepts are arranged in ovals below the big idea. The linking words connect the ovals.

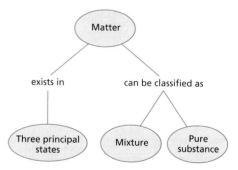

Matter
exists in — Three principal states
can be classified as — Mixture, Pure substance

Concept Mapping

Focus Elicit from students how a map shows the relationship of one geographic area to another. Connect this idea to how a concept map shows the relationship between terms and concepts.

Teach Challenge students to make a concept map with at least three levels of concepts to organize information about types of transportation. All students should start with the phrase *Types of transportation* at the top of the concept map. After that point, their concepts may vary. *(For example, some students might place* private transportation *and* public transportation *at the next level, while other students might choose* human-powered *and* gas-powered.)* Make sure students connect the concepts with linking words.

Building Vocabulary

Knowing the meaning of these prefixes, suffixes, and roots will help you understand the meaning of words you do not recognize.

Word Origins Many science words come to English from other languages, such as Greek and Latin. By learning the meaning of a few common Greek and Latin roots, you can determine the meaning of unfamiliar science words.

Prefixes A prefix is a word part that is added at the beginning of a root or base word to change its meaning.

Suffixes A suffix is a word part that is added at the end of a root word to change the meaning.

Greek and Latin Roots

Greek Roots	Meaning	Example
ast-	star	astronaut
geo-	Earth	geology
metron-	measure	kilometer
opt-	eye	optician
photo-	light	photograph
scop-	see	microscope
therm-	heat	thermostat

Latin Roots	Meaning	Example
aqua-	water	aquarium
aud-	hear	auditorium
duc-, duct-	lead	conduct
flect-	bend	reflect
fract-, frag-	break	fracture
ject-	throw	reject
luc-	light	lucid
spec-	see	inspect

Prefixes and Suffixes

Prefix	Meaning	Example
com-, con-	with	communicate, concert
de-	from; down	decay
di-	two	divide
ex-, exo-	out	exhaust
in-, im-	in, into; not	inject, impossible
re-	again; back	reflect, recall
trans-	across	transfer

Suffix	Meaning	Example
-al	relating to	natural
-er, -or	one who	teacher, doctor
-ist	one who practices	scientist
-ity	state of	equality
-ology	study of	biology
-tion, -sion	state or quality of	reaction, tension

Building Vocabulary

Reading in a content area presents challenges different from those encountered when reading fiction. Science texts often have more new vocabulary and more unfamiliar concepts that place greater emphasis on inferential reasoning. Students who can apply vocabulary strategies will be more successful in reading and understanding a science textbook. Challenge students to use Greek and Latin word origins and the meanings of prefixes and suffixes to learn the Key Terms in each section.

Word Origins

Focus Explain that word origins describe the older, foreign words that many modern English words have come from. Many science words come from Greek and Latin.

Teach Tell students that most dictionaries give the word origin just before the definition. Choose a section that has a Key Term with a Greek or Latin word origin. Encourage students to learn the meaning of the root word. Ask: **How does knowing the word origin help you remember the meaning of the Key Term?** (*Answers will vary, but the meaning of the Latin or Greek root should provide a clue to the definition of the Key Term.*) Ask: **What other words do you know that come from the same word origin?** (*Students may mention other words related to the Key Term.*) Challenge students to use word origins to figure out the meanings of unfamiliar words as they read. Students should confirm their definitions as necessary by checking a dictionary.

Prefixes

Focus Tell students that learning the meaning of common prefixes can help them determine the meaning of words they don't recognize. They will also increase their vocabulary.

Teach Remind students that a prefix is a word part that is added at the beginning of a root word to change its meaning. List some of the familiar prefixes and meanings, such as *de-* and *re-*, on the chalkboard. Ask: **What words do you know that use these same prefixes?** (*Students should list at least two words for each prefix.*) Ask: **How does the prefix affect the meaning of the root word?** (*Students should explain how it changes the meaning.*) Challenge students to learn the meaning of common prefixes and to use the skill to increase their vocabulary.

Suffixes

Focus Explain to students that learning the meanings of common suffixes and recognizing them in words are two effective strategies for learning word meanings and building vocabulary.

Teach Remind students that a suffix is added to the end of a word to change its meaning. In addition, students can use suffixes to discover the part of speech of an unfamiliar word. On the chalkboard, draw a four-column chart. Label the columns Noun, Verb, Adjective, and Adverb. Choose a Key Term that has a familiar base word, such as *tension*. Ask: **What are the noun, verb, adjective, and adverb forms of this word?** (*Students should give all possible answers, which may include only two forms of the word.*) Ask: **What endings signal that the word is a noun, adjective, or adverb?** (*Students should list the suffixes.*) Challenge students to learn the meanings of suffixes and to use them to decode new words.

- Complete student edition
- Video and audio
- Simulations and activities
- Section and chapter activities

Laboratory Safety

Laboratory safety is an essential element of a successful science class. Students need to understand exactly what is safe and unsafe behavior and what the rationale is behind each safety rule.

All in One Teaching Resources

- Laboratory Safety Teacher Notes
- Laboratory Safety Rules
- Laboratory Safety Symbols
- Laboratory Safety Contract

General Precautions

- Post safety rules in the classroom, and review them regularly with students before beginning every science activity.
- Familiarize yourself with the safety procedures for each activity before introducing it to your students.
- For open-ended activities like Chapter Projects, have students submit their procedures or design plans in writing and check them for safety considerations.
- Always act as an exemplary role model by displaying safe behavior.
- Know how to use safety equipment, such as fire extinguishers and fire blankets, and always have it accessible.
- Have students practice leaving the classroom quickly and orderly to prepare them for emergencies.
- Explain to students how to use the intercom or other available means of communication to get help during an emergency.
- Never leave students unattended while they are engaged in science activities.
- Provide enough space for students to safely carry out science activities.
- Instruct students to report all accidents and injuries to you immediately.

Safety Symbols

These symbols warn of possible dangers in the laboratory and remind you to work carefully.

 Safety Goggles Wear safety goggles to protect your eyes in any activity involving chemicals, flames or heating, or glassware.

 Lab Apron Wear a laboratory apron to protect your skin and clothing from damage.

 Breakage Handle breakable materials, such as glassware, with care. Do not touch broken glassware.

 Heat-Resistant Gloves Use an oven mitt or other hand protection when handling hot materials such as hot plates or hot glassware.

 Plastic Gloves Wear disposable plastic gloves when working with harmful chemicals and organisms. Keep your hands away from your face, and dispose of the gloves according to your teacher's instructions.

 Heating Use a clamp or tongs to pick up hot glassware. Do not touch hot objects with your bare hands.

 Flames Before you work with flames, tie back loose hair and clothing. Follow instructions from your teacher about lighting and extinguishing flames.

 No Flames When using flammable materials, make sure there are no flames, sparks, or other exposed heat sources present.

 Corrosive Chemical Avoid getting acid or other corrosive chemicals on your skin or clothing or in your eyes. Do not inhale the vapors. Wash your hands after the activity.

 Poison Do not let any poisonous chemical come into contact with your skin, and do not inhale its vapors. Wash your hands when you are finished with the activity.

 Fumes Work in a ventilated area when harmful vapors may be involved. Avoid inhaling vapors directly. Only test an odor when directed to do so by your teacher, and use a wafting motion to direct the vapor toward your nose.

 Sharp Object Scissors, scalpels, knives, needles, pins, and tacks can cut your skin. Always direct a sharp edge or point away from yourself and others.

 Animal Safety Treat live or preserved animals or animal parts with care to avoid harming the animals or yourself. Wash your hands when you are finished with the activity.

 Plant Safety Handle plants only as directed by your teacher. If you are allergic to certain plants, tell your teacher; do not do an activity involving those plants. Avoid touching harmful plants such as poison ivy. Wash your hands when you are finished with the activity.

 Electric Shock To avoid electric shock, never use electrical equipment around water, or when the equipment is wet or your hands are wet. Be sure cords are untangled and cannot trip anyone. Unplug equipment not in use.

 Physical Safety When an experiment involves physical activity, avoid injuring yourself or others. Alert your teacher if there is any reason you should not participate.

 Disposal Dispose of chemicals and other laboratory materials safely. Follow the instructions from your teacher.

 Hand Washing Wash your hands thoroughly when finished with the activity. Use antibacterial soap and warm water. Rinse well.

⚠ **General Safety Awareness** When this symbol appears, follow the instructions provided. When you are asked to develop your own procedure in a lab, have your teacher approve your plan before you go further.

End-of-Experiment Rules

- Always have students use warm water and soap for washing their hands.

Heating and Fire Safety

- No flammable substances should be in use around hot plates, light bulbs, or open flames.
- Test tubes should be heated only in water baths.

- Students should be permitted to strike matches to light candles or burners *only* with strict supervision. When possible, you should light the flames, especially when working with younger students.
- Be sure to have proper ventilation when fumes are produced during a procedure.
- All electrical equipment used in the lab should have GFI (Ground Fault Interrupter) switches.

Science Safety Rules

General Precautions

Follow all instructions. Never perform activities without the approval and supervision of your teacher. Do not engage in horseplay. Never eat or drink in the laboratory. Keep work areas clean and uncluttered.

Dress Code

Wear safety goggles whenever you work with chemicals, glassware, heat sources such as burners, or any substance that might get into your eyes. If you wear contact lenses, notify your teacher.

Wear a lab apron or coat whenever you work with corrosive chemicals or substances that can stain. Wear disposable plastic gloves when working with organisms and harmful chemicals. Tie back long hair. Remove or tie back any article of clothing or jewelry that can hang down and touch chemicals, flames, or equipment. Roll up long sleeves. Never wear open shoes or sandals.

First Aid

Report all accidents, injuries, or fires to your teacher, no matter how minor. Be aware of the location of the first-aid kit, emergency equipment such as the fire extinguisher and fire blanket, and the nearest telephone. Know whom to contact in an emergency.

Heating and Fire Safety

Keep all combustible materials away from flames. When heating a substance in a test tube, make sure that the mouth of the tube is not pointed at you or anyone else. Never heat a liquid in a closed container. Use an oven mitt to pick up a container that has been heated.

Using Chemicals Safely

Never put your face near the mouth of a container that holds chemicals. Never touch, taste, or smell a chemical unless your teacher tells you to.

Use only those chemicals needed in the activity. Keep all containers closed when chemicals are not being used. Pour all chemicals over the sink or a container, not over your work surface. Dispose of excess chemicals as instructed by your teacher.

Be extra careful when working with acids or bases. When mixing an acid and water, always pour the water into the container first and then add the acid to the water. Never pour water into an acid. Wash chemical spills and splashes immediately with plenty of water.

Using Glassware Safely

If glassware is broken or chipped, notify your teacher immediately. Never handle broken or chipped glass with your bare hands.

Never force glass tubing or thermometers into a rubber stopper or rubber tubing. Have your teacher insert the glass tubing or thermometer if required for an activity.

Using Sharp Instruments

Handle sharp instruments with extreme care. Never cut material toward you; cut away from you.

Animal and Plant Safety

Never perform experiments that cause pain, discomfort, or harm to animals. Only handle animals if absolutely necessary. If you know that you are allergic to certain plants, molds, or animals, tell your teacher before doing an activity in which these are used. Wash your hands thoroughly after any activity involving animals, animal parts, plants, plant parts, or soil.

During field work, wear long pants, long sleeves, socks, and closed shoes. Avoid poisonous plants and fungi as well as plants with thorns.

End-of-Experiment Rules

Unplug all electrical equipment. Clean up your work area. Dispose of waste materials as instructed by your teacher. Wash your hands after every experiment.

Appendix A ◆ 181

Handling Organisms Safely

- In an activity where students are directed to taste something, be sure to store the material in clean, *nonscience* containers. Distribute the material to students in *new* plastic or paper dispensables, which should be discarded after the tasting. Tasting or eating should never be done in a lab classroom.

- When growing bacterial cultures, use only disposable petri dishes. After streaking, the dishes should be sealed and not opened again by students. After the lab, students should return the unopened dishes to you.

- Two methods are recommended for the safe disposal of bacterial cultures. *First method:* Autoclave the petri dishes and discard them without opening. *Second method:* If no autoclave is available, carefully open the dishes (never have a student do this), pour full-strength bleach into the dishes, and let them stand for a day. Then pour the bleach from the petri dishes down a drain, and flush the drain with lots of water. Tape the petri dishes back together, and place them in a sealed plastic bag. Wrap the plastic bag with a brown paper bag or newspaper, and tape securely. Throw the sealed package in the trash. Thoroughly disinfect the work area with bleach.

- To grow mold, use a new, sealable plastic bag that is two to three times larger than the material to be placed inside. Seal the bag and tape it shut. After the bag is sealed, students should not open it. To dispose of the bag and mold culture, make a small cut near an edge of the bag, and cook the bag in a microwave oven on a high setting for at least one minute. Discard the bag according to local ordinance, usually in the trash.

- Students should wear disposable nitrile, latex, or food-handling gloves when handling live animals or nonliving specimens.

Using Glassware Safely

- Use plastic containers, graduated cylinders, and beakers whenever possible. If using glass, students should wear safety goggles.
- Use only nonmercury thermometers with anti-roll protectors.

Using Chemicals Safely

- When students use both chemicals and microscopes in one activity, microscopes should be in a separate part of the room from the chemicals so that when students remove their goggles to use the microscopes, their eyes are not at risk.

UNITED STATES
Physical

	International boundary
	State boundary
⊛ Washington, D.C.	National capital
★ Atlanta	State capital
• Detroit	Major city

ELEVATION

Meters		Feet
Over 3000		Over 10,000
1500 to 3000		5,000 to 10,000
600 to 1500		2,000 to 5,000
300 to 600		1,000 to 2,000
150 to 300		500 to 1,000
0 to 150		0 to 500
Below sea level		Below sea level

WATER DEPTH

Less than 200		Less than 600
Greater than 200		Greater than 600

0   100   200   300 Miles

0 100 200 300 Kilometers

Complete legend on page 7

A

abrasion The grinding away of rock by other rock particles carried in water, ice, or wind. (pp. 41, 87)
abrasión Desgaste de la roca por otras partículas de roca llevadas por el agua, el viento o el hielo.

absolute age The age of a rock given as the number of years since the rock formed. (p. 117)
edad absoluta Edad de una roca basada en el número de años desde que se formó la roca.

alluvial fan A wide, sloping deposit of sediment formed where a stream leaves a mountain range. (p. 77)
abanico aluvial Depósito ancho de sedimento en declive, que se forma donde un arroyo sale de una cordillera.

amphibian A vertebrate that lives part of its life on land and part of its life in water. (p. 136)
anfibio Vertebrado que vive parte de su vida en la tierra y parte en el agua.

atom The smallest particle of an element. (p. 124)
átomo Partícula más pequeña de un elemento.

B

beach Wave-washed sediment along a coast. (p. 99)
playa Sedimento depositado por las olas a lo largo de una costa.

bedrock The solid layer of rock beneath the soil. (p. 48)
lecho rocoso Capa sólida de roca debajo del suelo.

C

carbon film A type of fossil consisting of an extremely thin coating of carbon on rock. (p. 112)
película de carbono Tipo de fósil que consiste en una capa de carbono extremadamente fina que recubre la roca.

solid cast A fossil that is a solid copy of an organism's shape, formed when minerals seep into a mold. (p. 111)
vaciado sólido Fósil que es una copia sólida de la forma de un organismo, creado cuando los minerales penetran en un molde.

chemical weathering The process that breaks down rock through chemical changes. (p. 42)
desgaste químico Proceso que erosiona la roca mediante cambios químicos.

comet A ball of ice and dust that orbits the sun. (p. 132)
cometa Bola de hielo y polvo que orbita el Sol.

conservation plowing Soil conservation method in which the dead stalks from the previous year's crop are left in the ground to hold the soil in place. (p. 59)
arada de conservación Método de conservación del suelo en el cual los tallos muertos de la cosecha del año anterior se dejan en la tierra para que sujeten el suelo en su lugar.

continental drift The slow movement of the continents over Earth's surface caused by forces inside Earth. (p. 132)
deriva continental Movimiento lento de los continentes sobre la superficie de la Tierra causado por las fuerzas dentro de la Tierra.

continental glacier A glacier that covers much of a continent or large island. (p. 92)
glaciar continental Glaciar que cubre gran parte de un continente o una isla grande.

contour interval The difference in elevation from one contour line to the next. (p. 27)
intervalo entre curvas de nivel Diferencia de elevación de una curva de nivel a otra.

contour line A line on a topographic map that connects points of equal elevation. (p. 27)
curva de nivel Línea en un mapa topográfico que conecta puntos de igual elevación.

contour plowing Plowing fields along the curves of a slope to prevent soil loss. (p. 59)
arada en contorno Arar los campos siguiendo las curvas de una pendiente para evitar que el suelo se suelte.

crop rotation The planting of different crops in a field each year to maintain the soil's fertility. (p. 59)
rotación de cultivos Plantación de cultivos diferentes en un campo cada año para mantener la fertilidad del suelo.

decomposer Soil organism that breaks down the remains of organisms and digests them. (p. 53)
descomponedor Organismo del suelo que desintegra los restos de organismos y los digiere.

deflation Wind erosion that removes surface materials. (p. 102)
deflación Erosión por viento que se lleva materiales superficiales.

degree A unit used to measure distances around a circle. One degree equals 1/360 of a full circle. (p. 13)
grado Unidad usada para medir distancias alrededor de un círculo. Un grado es igual a 1/360 de un círculo completo.

delta A landform made of sediment that is deposited where a river flows into an ocean or lake. (p. 77)
delta Accidente geográfico formado por sedimentos que se depositan en la desembocadura de un río a un océano o lago.

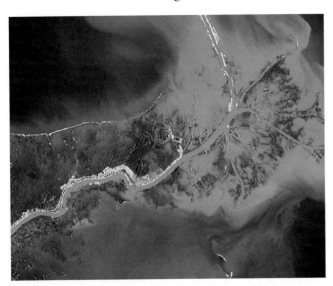

deposition Process in which sediment is laid down in new locations. (p. 67)
sedimentación Proceso por el cual se asientan sedimentos en sitios nuevos.

digitizing Converting information to numbers for use by a computer. (p. 21)
digitalizar Convertir información a números para que pueda ser usada por una computadora.

Dust Bowl The area of the Great Plains where wind erosion caused soil loss during the 1930s. (p. 58)
Cuenca del polvo Área de las Grandes Llanuras donde la erosión por el viento causó la pérdida de suelo durante la década de 1930.

element A type of matter in which all the atoms are the same. (p. 124)
elemento Tipo de materia en la cual todos los átomos son iguales.

elevation Height above sea level. (p. 7)
elevación Altura sobre el nivel del mar.

energy The ability to do work or cause change. (p. 86)
energía Capacidad para realizar trabajo o producir cambios.

equator An imaginary line that circles Earth halfway between the North and South poles. (p. 14)
ecuador Línea imaginaria que rodea la Tierra por el centro, entre los polos Norte y Sur.

era One of the three long units of geologic time between the Precambrian and the present. (p. 129)
era Cada una de las tres unidades largas del tiempo geológico entre el Precámbrico y el presente.

erosion The process by which water, ice, wind, or gravity moves weathered rock and soil. (p. 39, 66)
erosión Proceso por el cual el agua, el hielo, el viento o la gravedad desplazan rocas desgastadas y suelo.

evolution The process by which all the different kinds of living things have changed over time. (p. 116)
evolución Proceso por el cual los diferentes tipos de seres vivos han cambiado con el tiempo.

extinct Describes a type of organism that no longer exists anywhere on Earth. (p. 116)
extinto Describe un tipo de organismo que ya no existe en la Tierra.

extrusion An igneous rock layer formed when lava flows onto Earth's surface and hardens. (p. 119)
extrusión Capa de roca ígnea formada cuando la lava fluye hacia la superficie de la Tierra y se endurece.

fault A break or crack in Earth's lithosphere along which the rocks move. (p. 119)
falla Fisura o grieta en la litosfera de la Tierra a lo largo de la cual se mueven las rocas.

fertility A measure of how well soil supports plant growth. (p. 49)
fertilidad Medida de lo apropiado de un suelo para mantener el crecimiento de las plantas.

flood plain Wide valley through which a river flows. (p. 75)
llanura de aluvión Valle ancho por el cual fluye un río.

fossil The preserved remains or traces of living things. (p. 110)
fósil Restos preservados o huellas de seres vivos.

friction The force that opposes the motion of one surface as it moves across another surface. (p. 89)
fricción La fuerza que se opone al movimiento de una superficie con la que está en contacto.

 G

geologic time scale A record of the geologic events and life forms in Earth's history. (p. 127)
escala geocronológica Registro de los sucesos geológicos y de las formas de vida en la historia de la Tierra.

glacier A large mass of moving ice and snow on land. (p. 92)
glaciar Gran masa de hielo y nieve que se mantiene en movimiento sobre la tierra.

Global Positioning System A method of finding latitude and longitude using a network of satellites. (p. 23)
sistema de posicionamiento global Método para hallar la latitud y longitud usando una red de satélites.

globe A sphere that represents Earth's entire surface. (p. 12)
globo terráqueo Esfera que representa toda la superficie de la Tierra.

gravity A force that moves rocks and other materials downhill. (p. 67)
gravedad Fuerza que mueve rocas y otros materiales cuesta abajo.

groundwater Water that fills the cracks and spaces in underground soil and rock layers. (p. 80)
aguas freáticas Aguas que llenan las grietas y huecos de las capas subterráneas de tierra y roca.

gully A large channel in soil formed by erosion. (p. 74)
barranco Canal grande en el suelo, formado por la erosión.

 H

half-life The time it takes for half of the atoms of a radioactive element to decay. (p. 124)
vida media Tiempo que demoran en desintegrarse la mitad de los átomos de un elemento radiactivo.

headland A part of the shore that sticks out into the ocean. (p. 97)
promontorio Parte de la costa que se interna en el mar.

hemisphere One half of the sphere that makes up Earth's surface. (p. 14)
hemisferio La mitad de la esfera que forma la superficie de la Tierra.

humus Dark-colored organic material in soil. (p. 49)
humus Material orgánico de color oscuro en el suelo.

 I

ice age Times in the past when continental glaciers covered large parts of Earth's surface. (p. 92)
glaciación Épocas del pasado en las que glaciares continentales cubrieron grandes extensiones de la superficie terrestre.

ice wedging Process that splits rock when water seeps into cracks, then freezes and expands. (p. 41)
efecto cuña de hielo Proceso que parte la roca cuando el agua penetra en las grietas, y luego se congela y expande.

index contours On a topographic map, a heavier contour line that is labeled with elevation of that contour line in round units. (p. 27)
curva de nivel índice En un mapa topográfico, una curva de nivel más gruesa que lleva rotulada la elevación de esa curva de nivel en unidades redondeadas.

index fossil Fossils of widely distributed organisms that lived during only one short period. (p. 120)
fósil indicador Fósiles de organismos ampliamente dispersos que vivieron durante un período corto.

intrusion An igneous rock layer formed when magma hardens beneath Earth's surface. (p. 119)
intrusión Capa de roca ígnea formada cuando el magma se endurece bajo la superficie de la Tierra.

invertebrate An animal without a backbone. (p. 135)
invertebrado Animal sin columna vertebral.

karst topography A region in which a layer of limestone close to the surface creates deep valleys, caverns and sinkholes. (p. 80)
topografía kárstica Región en la que una capa de piedra caliza cercana a la superficie forma valles profundos, grutas y dolinas.

kettle A small depression that forms when a chunk of ice is left in glacial till. (p. 94)
marmita Pequeña depresión que se forma cuando queda un trozo de hielo en la tillita.

key A list of the symbols used on a map. (p. 12)
clave Lista de símbolos usados en un mapa.

kinetic energy The energy an object has due to its motion. (p. 86)
energía cinética Energía que tiene un objeto por el hecho de estar en movimiento.

landform A feature of topography formed by the processes that shape Earth's surface. (p. 7)
accidente geográfico Característica de la topografía creada por los procesos de formación de la superficie terrestre.

landform region A large area of land where the topography is similar. (p. 10)
región con accidentes geográficos Gran extensión de tierra con topografía similar.

latitude The distance in degrees north or south of the equator. (p. 16)
latitud Distancia en grados al norte o al sur del ecuador.

law of superposition The geologic principle that states that in horizontal layers of sedimentary rock, each layer is older than the layer above it and younger than the layer below it. (p. 118)
ley de la superposición Principio geológico que enuncia que en las capas horizontales de la roca sedimentaria, cada capa es más vieja que la capa superior y más joven que la capa inferior.

litter The loose layer of dead plant leaves and stems on the surface of the soil. (p. 52)
mantillo Capa suelta de hojas y tallos de plantas muertas en la superficie del suelo.

load The amount of sediment that a river or stream carries. (p. 87)
carga La cantidad de sedimento que lleva un río o arroyo.

loam Rich, fertile soil that is made up of about equal parts of clay, sand, and silt. (p. 49)
limo arcilloso arenoso Suelo rico y fértil que está formado por partes casi iguales de arcilla, arena y limo.

loess A wind-formed deposit made of fine particles of clay and silt. (p. 103)
loes Depósito de partículas finas de arcilla y limo arrastradas por el viento.

longitude The distance in degrees east or west of the prime meridian. (p. 16)
longitud Distancia en grados al este o al oeste del primer meridiano.

longshore drift The movement of water and sediment down a beach caused by waves coming in to shore at an angle. (p. 99)
deriva litoral Movimiento de agua y sedimentos paralelo a una playa debido a la llegada de olas inclinadas respecto a la costa.

mammal A warm-blooded vertebrate that feeds its young milk. (p. 142)
mamífero Vertebrado de sangre caliente que alimenta con leche a sus crías.

map A flat model of all or part of Earth's surface as seen from above. (p. 12)
mapa Modelo plano de toda la superficie de la Tierra o parte de ella tal y como se ve desde arriba.

map projection A framework of lines that helps to show landmasses on a flat surface. (p. 18)
proyección cartográfica Sistema de líneas que ayuda a mostrar volúmenes de tierra en una superficie plana.

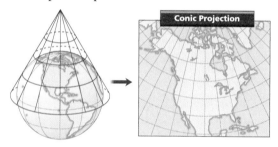

Conic Projection

mass extinction When many types of living things become extinct at the same time. (p. 137)
extinción en masa Cuando muchos tipos de seres vivos se extinguen al mismo tiempo.

mass movement Any one of several processes by which gravity moves sediment downhill. (p. 67)
movimiento de masas Cualquiera de varios procesos por los cuales la gravedad desplaza sedimentos cuesta abajo.

meander A looplike bend in the course of a river. (p. 76)
meandro Curva muy pronunciada en el curso de un río.

mechanical weathering The type of weathering in which rock is physically broken into smaller pieces. (p. 40)
desgaste mecánico Tipo de desgaste en el cual una roca se rompe físicamente en trozos más pequeños.

mold A fossil formed when an organism buried in sediment dissolves, leaving a hollow area. (p. 111)
molde Fósil que se forma cuando un organismo enterrado en sedimento se disuelve y deja un área hueca.

moraine A ridge formed by the till deposited at the edge of a glacier. (p. 94)
morrena Montículo formado por la tillita depositada en el borde de un glaciar.

mountain A landform with high elevation and high relief. (p. 9)
montaña Accidente geográfico con una elevación alta y un relieve alto.

mountain range A series of mountains that have the same general shape and structure. (p. 9)
cordillera Serie de montañas que tienen la misma forma y estructura generales.

natural resource Anything in the environment that humans use. (p. 57)
recurso natural Cualquier cosa de la naturaleza que usan los humanos.

oxbow lake A meander cut off from a river. (p. 76)
meandro abandonado Meandro que ha quedado aislado de un río.

oxidation A chemical change in which a substance combines with oxygen, as when iron oxidizes, forming rust. (p. 43)
oxidación Cambio químico en el cual una sustancia se combina con el oxígeno, como cuando el hierro se oxida y se forma herrumbre.

paleontologist A scientist who studies fossils to learn about organisms that lived long ago. (p. 114)
paleontólogo Científico que estudia fósiles para aprender acerca de los organismos que vivieron hace mucho tiempo.

period One of the units of geologic time into which geologists divide eras. (p. 129)
período Una de las unidades del tiempo geológico dentro de las cuales los geólogos dividen las eras.

permeable Characteristic of a material that is full of tiny, connected air spaces that water can seep through. (p. 44)
permeable Característica de un material que está lleno de diminutos espacios de aire conectados entre sí, por los que puede penetrar el agua.

petrified fossil A fossil in which minerals replace all or part of an organism. (p. 112)
fósil petrificado Fósil en el cual los minerales reemplazan todo el organismo o parte de él.

pixels The tiny dots in a satellite image. (p. 22)
píxeles Puntos diminutos en una imagen de satélite.

plain A landform made up of flat or gently rolling land with low relief. (p. 8)
llanura Accidente geográfico que consiste en un terreno plano o ligeramente ondulado con un relieve bajo.

plateau A landform that has high elevation and a more or less level surface. (p. 9)
meseta Accidente geográfico que tiene una elevación alta y cuya superficie está más o menos nivelada.

plucking The process by which a glacier picks up rocks as it flows over the land. (p. 93)
arranque glaciar Proceso por el cual un glaciar arranca rocas al fluir sobre la tierra.

potential energy Energy that is stored and available to be used later. (p. 86)
energía potencial Energía que se encuentra almacenada y puede utilizarse posteriormente.

prime meridian The line that makes a half circle from the North Pole to the South Pole and that passes through Greenwich, England. (p. 15)
primer meridiano Línea que forma medio círculo desde el Polo Norte al Polo Sur y que pasa por Greenwich, Inglaterra.

 R

radioactive decay The breakdown of a radioactive element, releasing particles and energy. (p. 124)
desintegración radiactiva Descomposición de un elemento radiactivo que libera partículas y energía.

relative age The age of a rock compared to the ages of rock layers. (p. 117)
edad relativa Edad de una roca comparada con la edad de las capas de roca.

relief The difference in elevation between the highest and lowest parts of an area. (p. 7)
relieve Diferencia en la elevación entre las partes más altas y más bajas en un área.

reptile A vertebrate with scaly skin that lays eggs with tough, leathery shells. (p. 136)
reptil Vertebrado con piel de escamas que pone huevos de cascarón duro y correoso.

rill A tiny groove in soil made by flowing water. (p. 74)
arroyuelo Pequeño surco en el suelo que deja el agua al fluir.

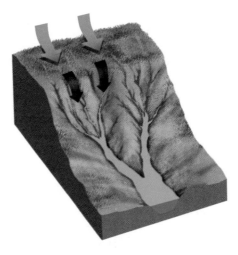

runoff Water that flows over the ground surface rather than soaking into the ground. (p. 73)
escorrentía Agua que fluye sobre la superficie del suelo en lugar de ser absorbida por éste.

 S

sand dune A deposit of wind-blown sand. (p. 101)
duna de arena Depósito de arena arrastrada por el viento.

satellite images Pictures of the land surface based on computer data collected from satellites. (p. 22)
imágenes satelitales Fotografías de la superficie terrestre basadas en información computarizada reunida por satélites.

English and Spanish Glossary

scale Used to compare distance on a map or globe to distance on Earth's surface. (p. 12)
escala Se usa para comparar la distancia en un mapa o globo terráqueo con la distancia en la superficie de la Tierra.

scientific theory A well-tested concept that explains a wide range of observations. (p. 116)
teoría científica Concepto bien comprobado que explica un amplia gama de observaciones.

sediment Earth materials deposited by erosion. (p. 67)
sedimento Materiales terrestres depositados por la erosión.

sedimentary rock The type of rock that is made of hardened sediment. (p. 110)
roca sedimentaria Tipo de roca formada de sedimento endurecido.

sod A thick mass of grass roots and soil. (p. 56)
tepe Masa gruesa de raíces de hierbas y suelo.

soil The loose, weathered material on Earth's surface in which plants can grow. (p. 48)
suelo Material suelto y desgastado sobre la superficie de la Tierra en donde crecen las plantas.

soil conservation The management of soil to prevent its destruction (p. 59)
conservación del suelo Cuidado del suelo para prevenir su destrucción.

soil horizon The layer of soil that differs in color and texture from the layers above or below it. (p. 50)
horizonte de suelo Capa de suelo que se diferencia en color y textura de las capas que tiene encima o debajo.

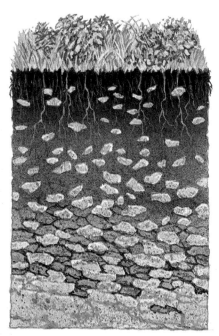

spit A beach formed by longshore drift that projects like a finger out into the water. (p. 100)
banco de arena Playa formada por la deriva litoral y que se interna como un dedo dentro del agua.

stalactite A calcite deposit that hangs from the roof of a cave. (p. 80)
estalactita Depósito de calcita que cuelga del techo de una gruta.

stalagmite A cone-shaped calcite deposite that builds up from the floor of a cave. (p. 80)
estalagmita Depósito cónico de calcita que se forma en el piso de una gruta

stream A channel through which water is continually flowing downhill. (p. 74)
arroyo Canal por el cual fluye continuamente agua cuesta abajo.

subsoil The layer of soil beneath the topsoil that contains mostly clay and other minerals. (p. 50)
subsuelo Capa del suelo bajo el suelo superior que contiene principalmente arcilla y otros minerales.

surveying The process of gathering data for a map by using instruments and the principles of geometry to determine distance and elevations. (p. 21)
agrimensura Proceso de reunir información para un mapa usando instrumentos y los principios de geometría para determinar distancias y elevaciones.

symbol On a map, pictures used by mapmakers to stand for features on Earth's surface. (p. 12)
símbolos En un mapa, los dibujos que usan los cartógrafos para representar características de la superficie de la Tierra.

T

till The sediments deposited directly by a glacier. (p. 94)
tillita Sedimentos depositados directamente por un glaciar.

topographic map A map that shows the surface features of an area. (p. 27)
mapa topográfico Mapa que muestra los accidentes geográficos de la superficie terrestre de un área.

topography The shape of the land determined by elevation, relief, and landforms. (p. 6)
topografía Forma del terreno determinada por la elevación, el relieve y los accidentes geográficos.

topsoil Mixture of humus, clay, and other minerals that forms the crumbly, topmost layer of soil. (p, 50)
suelo superior Mezcla de humus, arcilla y otros minerales que forman la capa superior y suelta del suelo.

trace fossil A type of fossil that provides evidence of the activities of ancient organisms. (p. 112)
vestigios fósiles Tipo de fósil que da evidencia de las actividades de los organismos antiguos.

tributary A stream that flows into a larger stream. (p. 74)
afluente Arroyo que desemboca en una corriente de agua más grande.

turbulence A type of movement of water in which, rather than moving downstream, the water moves every which way. (p. 89)
turbulencia Tipo de movimiento del agua en el que, en vez de moverse corriente abajo, el agua se mueve en todas direcciones.

U

unconformity A place where an old, eroded rock surface is in contact with a newer rock layer. (p. 120)
discordancia Lugar donde una superficie rocosa erosionada y vieja está en contacto con una capa de rocas más nueva.

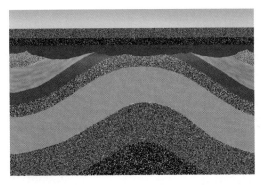

uniformitarianism The geologic principle that the same geologic processes that operate today operated in the past to change Earth's surface. (p. 39)
uniformismo Principio geológico que enuncia que los mismos procesos geológicos que cambian la superficie de la Tierra en la actualidad, ocurrían en el pasado.

V

valley glacier A long, narrow glacier that forms when snow and ice build up in a mountain valley. (p. 92)
glaciar de valle Glaciar largo y angosto que se forma por acumulación de hielo y nieve en un valle de montaña.

vertebrate An animal with a backbone. (p. 135)
vertebrado Animal con columna vertebral.

W

weathering The chemical and physical processes that break down rock at Earth's surface. (p. 39)
desgaste Procesos químicos y físicos que rompen las rocas de la superficie de la Tierra.

Index

Page numbers for key terms are printed in **boldface** type.
Page numbers for illustrations, maps, and charts are printed in *italics*.

Index

Page numbers for key terms are printed in **boldface** type.
Page numbers for illustrations, maps, and charts are printed in *italics*.

Acknowledgments

Acknowledgment for page 153: Excerpt from "The Hymn to Hapy" from volume 1 of *Ancient Egyptian Literature*, by Miriam Lichtheim. Copyright ©1973–1980 Regents of the University of California. Reprinted by permission of the University of California Press.

Staff Credits

Diane Alimena, Michele Angelucci, Scott Andrews, Jennifer Angel, Laura Baselice, Carolyn Belanger, Barbara A. Bertell, Suzanne Biron, Peggy Bliss, Stephanie Bradley, James Brady, Anne M. Bray, Sarah M. Carroll, Kerry Cashman, Jonathan Cheney, Joshua D. Clapper, Lisa J. Clark, Bob Craton, Patricia Cully, Patricia M. Dambry, Kathy Dempsey, Leanne Esterly, Emily Ellen, Thomas Ferreira, Jonathan Fisher, Patricia Fromkin, Paul Gagnon, Kathy Gavilanes, Holly Gordon, Robert Graham, Ellen Granter, Diane Grossman, Barbara Hollingdale, Linda Johnson, Anne Jones, John Judge, Kevin Keane, Kelly Kelliher, Toby Klang, Sue Langan, Russ Lappa, Carolyn Lock, Rebecca Loveys, Constance J. McCarty, Carolyn B. McGuire, Ranida Touranont McNeally, Anne McLaughlin, Eve Melnechuk, Natania Mlawer, Janet Morris, Karyl Murray, Francine Neumann, Baljit Nijjar, Marie Opera, Jill Ort, Kim Ortell, Joan Paley, Dorothy Preston, Maureen Raymond, Laura Ross, Rashid Ross, Siri Schwartzman, Melissa Shustyk, Laurel Smith, Emily Soltanoff, Jennifer A. Teece, Elizabeth Torjussen, Amanda M. Watters, Merce Wilczek, Amy Winchester, Char Lyn Yeakley. **Additional Credits:** Tara Alamilla, Louise Gachet, Allen Gold, Andrea Golden, Terence Hegarty, Etta Jacobs, Meg Montgomery, Stephanie Rogers, Kim Schmidt, Adam Teller, Joan Tobin.

Illustration

Morgan Cain & Associates: 49, 52, 53, 68, 69, 90, 102, 107, 124, 126; **Kerry Cashman:** 35, 44; **John Edwards and Associates:** 14t, 16, 17t, 27, 44, 87, 88, 93r, 95, 111, 132, 133; **GeoSystems Global Corporation:** 7b, 10, 55, 58, 77, 92; **Kevin Jones Associates:** 8, 9, 40, 41, 67, 74, 93b, 98, 99, 103, 106, 114, 115; **Martucci Design:** 28; **Richard McMahon, with J/B Woolsey Associates:** 128, 138, 139, 140, 141; **Karen Minot:** 73; **Matthew Pippin:** 51, 78, 79, 94, 95; **J/B Woolsey Associates:** 62, 116, 118, 121, 122; **XNR Productions:** 12, 13, 17b, 18, 19, 29, 80. **All charts and graphs by Matt Mayerchak.**

Photography

Photo Research Paula Wehde
Cover Image top, Jeff Drewitz/DRK Photo; **bottom,** Gavriel Jecan/Corbis. **Page vi t,** Howard Grey/Getty Images, Inc.; **vi b,** Tom Bean; **vii,** Richard Haynes; **viii,** Richard Haynes; **x t,** Dave King/Dorling Kindersley; **x b,** Courtesy of Karen Chin; **1all,** Courtesy of Karen Chin; **2tl,** Douglas Henderson; **2tr,** Courtesy of Karen Chin; **2b,** Courtesy of Karen Chin; **3,** Courtesy of Karen Chin.

Chapter 1
Pages 4–5, Image courtesy of NASA Landsat Project Science Office and USGS EROS Data Center; **5r,** Richard Haynes; **6,** National Museum of American History/Smithsonian Institution; **8,** Tom Bean; **9l,** David Muench; **9r,** Tom Bean; **11,** Russ Lappa; **13,** Jim Wark/Airphoto; **14l,** The Granger Collection; **14m,** Bodleian Library, Oxford, U.K.; **14r,** Royal Geographical Society, London, UK/Bridgeman Art Library; **15l,** British Library, London/Bridgeman Art Library, London/Superstock, Inc.; **15m,** The Granger Collection; **15r,** The Granger Collection; **20,** Richard Haynes; **21t,** Russ Lappa; **21b,** Geographix; **22l,** Library of Congress; **22r,** U.S. Geological Survey; **24t,** © Boeing, all rights reserved; **24b,** Forest Johnson/Masterfile Corporation; **24–25,** Index Stock Imagery; **25,** Richard Haynes; **26t,** Richard Haynes; **26b,** Mitch Wojnarowicz/The Image Works; **27l,** Elliot Cohen/Janelco; **28,** U.S. Geological Survey; **30,** Robert Rathe/Stock Boston; **31,** Richard Haynes; **32,** British Library, London/Bridgeman Art Library, London/Superstock, Inc.; **34,** U.S. Geological Survey.

Chapter 2
Pages 36–37, Frozen Images/The Image Works; **37r,** Richard Haynes; **38,** Richard Haynes; **39t,** Jerry D. Greer; **39b,** Ron Watts/Corbis; **40t,** Susan Rayfield/Photo Researchers, Inc.; **40m,** Breck P. Kent/Animals Animals/Earth Scenes; **40b,** E.R. Degginger/Photo Researchers, Inc.; **41l,** John Sohlden/Visuals Unlimited; **41r,** Jim Steinberg/Animals Animals/Earth Scenes; **43,** Mike Mazzaschi/Stock Boston; **45all,** T.C. Meierding; **47,** Richard Haynes; **48t,** Richard Haynes; **48–49b,** Tom Bean; **54,** J.M. Labat/Jacana/Photo Researchers, Inc.; **55,** Richard Haynes; **56t,** Richard Haynes; **56b,** Tom Bean; **57t,** Corbis; **57b,** Grant Heilman Photography, Inc.; **58,** AP/Wide World Photos; **59,** Larry Lefever/Grant Heilman Photography, Inc.; **60,** David Muench.

Chapter 3
Pages 64–65, Ron Watts/Corbis; **65r,** Richard Haynes; **66,** AP/Wide World Photos; **68l,** Martin Miller/Visuals Unlimited; **68r,** Thomas G. Rampton/Grant Heilman Photography, Inc.; **69,** Steven Holt/Stockpix.com; **70,** Richard Haynes; **71,** Richard Haynes; **72–73,** Walter Bibikow/The Viesti Collection; **74,** Jim Wark/Airphoto; **75,** Dorling Kindersley; **76,** Tom Bean; **77t,** Martin Miller; **77b,** NASA/SADO/Tom Stack & Associates, Inc.; **81,** Dorling Kindersley; **81inset,** Laurence Parent; **82,** Russ Lappa; **83,** Richard Haynes; **84–85b,** David Sailors/Corbis; **85t,** Alex Wong/Getty Images, Inc.; **86t,** Richard Haynes; **86b,** Eliot Cohen; **87,** Michael Quinton/Minden Pictures; **89,** Corbis; **91t,** Richard Haynes; **91b,** Marc Muench/Muench Photography, Inc.; **92,** Dorling Kindersley; **96t,** Richard Haynes; **96b,** Corbis; **97,** Dick Roberts/Visuals Unlimited; **100,** F. Stuart Westmoreland/Photo Researchers, Inc.; **101t,** Richard Haynes; **101b,** Jess Stock/Getty Images, Inc.; **102,** Tom Bean.

Chapter 4
Pages 108–109, Dave G. Houser/Corbis; **109r,** Richard Haynes; **110,** Sinclair Stammers/Photo Researchers, Inc.; **111,** Dorling Kindersley; **112l,** Francois Gohier/Photo Researchers, Inc.; **112m,** Runk/Schoenberger/Grant Heilman Photography, Inc.; **112r,** Breck P. Kent; **113l,** Park Street/PhotoEdit; **113m,** Michelle Bridwell/PhotoEdit; **113r,** Howard Grey/Stone/Getty Images, Inc.; **114t,** Peabody Museum of Natural History; **114b,** Ken Lucas/Visuals Unlimited; **115,** T. Wiewandt/DRK Photo; **116,** Frans Lanting/Minden Pictures; **117t,** Richard Haynes; **117b,** Zephyr Picture/Index Stock Imagery/PictureQuest; **118,** Jeff Greenberg/Photo Researchers, Inc.; **119all,** PH Photo; **121,** Photo Researchers, Inc.; **123t,** Richard Haynes; **123bl,** Dr. Dennis Kunkel/Visuals Unlimited; **123br,** Michael Fogden/DRK Photo; **129,** The Natural History Museum, London; **131,** Mark Garlick/Science Photo Library/Photo Researchers, Inc.; **134t,** Breck P. Kent; **134m,** Runk/Schoenberger/Grant Heilman Photography, Inc.; **134b,** Auscape International; **135l,** John Sibbick; **136t,** Chip Clark/Smithsonian Institution; **136b,** © The Field Museum, Neg.#CSGEO 75400c.; **142,** Dorling Kindersley; **143tl,** Jane Burton/Bruce Coleman, Inc.; **143tr,** David M. Dennis/Tom Stack & Associates, Inc.; **143b,** D. Van Ravenswaay/Photo Researchers, Inc.; **144,** © 2002 Mark Hallett, all rights reserved; **145,** Photo Researchers, Inc.; **146,** Richard Haynes. **152t,** Robert Caputo/Stock Boston; **152b,** David Sanger Photography; **153t,** Brian Braker/Photo Researchers, Inc.; **153b,** British Museum/The Image Works; **154,** Groenendyk/Photo Researchers, Inc.; **155,** Corbis; **156,** Robert Caputo/Stock Boston; **157t,** Charlie Waite/Getty Images Inc.; **157b,** Robert Caputo/Stock Boston; **158,** David Ball/The Picture Cube/Index Stock Imagery, Inc.; **159t,** Richard Haynes; **159b,** Erich Lessing/Art Resource; **160,** Tony Freeman/PhotoEdit; **161t,** Russ Lappa; **161m,** Richard Haynes; **161b,** Russ Lappa; **162,** Richard Haynes; **164,** Richard Haynes; **166,** Morton Beebe/Corbis; **167,** Richard Haynes; **169t,** Dorling Kinderlsey; **169b,** Richard Haynes; **171,** Imagestop/Phototake; **174,** Richard Haynes; **181,** Richard Haynes; **184,** U.S. Geological Survey; **185,** NASA/SADO/Tom Stack & Associates, Inc.; **190,** Laurence Parent; **191,** Park Street/PhotoEdit.